Machine Design Fundamentals

A Mechanical Designers' Workbook

D1478118

Other Books in
The McGraw-Hill Mechanical Designers' Workbook Series

Machine Design Fundamentals

A Mechanical Designers' Workbook

Editors in Chief

Joseph E. Shigley

Professor Emeritus
The University of Michigan
Ann Arbor, Michigan

Charles R. Mischke

Professor of Mechanical Engineering
Iowa State University
Ames, Iowa

McGraw-Hill Publishing Company

New York   St. Louis   San Francisco   Auckland   Bogotá
Caracas   Hamburg   Lisbon   London   Madrid   Mexico
Milan   Montreal   New Delhi   Oklahoma City
Paris   San Juan   São Paulo   Singapore
Sydney   Tokyo   Toronto

Library of Congress Cataloging-in-Publication Data

Main entry under title:

Standard handbook of machine design.

    Includes index.
    1. Machinery—Design—Handbooks, manuals, etc.
I. Shigley, Joseph Edward. II. Mischke, Charles R.
TJ230.S8235   1986   621.8′15   85-17079
ISBN 0-07-056892-8
ISBN 0-07-056922-3 (workbook)

1234567890 KGP/KGP 8965432109

ISBN 0-07-056922-3

The material in this volume has been published previously in *Standard Handbook of Machine Design* by Joseph E. Shigley and Charles R. Mischke. Copy-
right © 1986 by McGraw-Hill, Inc. All rights reserved.

*The editors for this book were Robert Hauserman and Scott Amerman,
and the production supervisor was Dianne Walber. It was set
in Times Roman by Techna Type.*

Printed and bound by The Kingsport Press.

*For more information about other McGraw-Hill materials,
call 1-800-MCGRAW in the United States. In other
countries, call your nearest McGraw-Hill office.*

In Loving Memory of
Opal Shigley

CONTENTS

CONTRIBUTORS

Jerry Lee Hall, *Professor of Mechanical Engineering,* Iowa State University, Ames, Iowa

Edward B. Haugen, *Associate Professor Emeritus,* The University of Arizona, Tucson, Arizona

R. Bruce Hopkins, The Hopkins Engineering Co., Cedar Falls, Iowa

Ray C. Johnson, *Higgins Professor of Mechanical Engineering,* Worcester Polytechnic Institute, Worcester, Massachusetts

Charles R. Mischke, *Professor of Mechanical Engineering,* Iowa State University, Ames, Iowa

Leo C. Peters, *Professor of Mechanical Engineering,* Iowa State University, Ames, Iowa

PREFACE

There is no shortage of good textbooks treating the subject of machine design and related topics of study. But the beginning designer quickly learns that there is a great deal more to successful design than is presented in textbooks or taught in technical schools or colleges. A handbook connects formal education and the practice of design engineering by including the general knowledge required by every machine designer.

Much of the practicing designer's daily informational needs are satisfied in various pamphlets or brochures such as are published by the various standards organizations as well as manufacturers of various components used in design. Other sources include research papers, design magazines, and corporate publications concerned with specific products. More often than not, however, a visit to a design library or to a file cabinet will reveal that a specific publication is on loan, lost, or out of date. A handbook is intended to serve such needs quickly and immediately by giving the designer authoritative, up-to-date, understandable, and informative answers to the hundreds of such questions that arise every day in the work of a designer.

The *Standard Handbook of Machine Design** was written for working designers, and its place is on their desks, not on their bookshelves, for it contains a great many formulas, tables, charts, and graphs, many in condensed form. These are intended to give quick answers to the many questions that seem to arise constantly.

The *Mechanical Designers' Workbook* series consists of eight volumes, each containing a group of related topics selected from the *Standard Handbook of Machine Design.* Limiting each workbook to a single subject area of machine design makes it possible to create a thin, convenient volume bound in such a manner as to open flat and provide an opportunity to enter notes, references, graphs, equations, standard corporate practices, and other useful data. In fact, each chapter in every workbook contains gridded pages located in critical sections for this specific purpose. This flat-opening workbook is easier to use on the designer's work space and will save much wear and tear on the source handbook.

This workbook is devoted to fundamentals utilized by any practicing mechanical designer. Chapter 1 reminds the designer of the basic considerations. Checklists are displayed which can be augmented as necessary using the worksheets. Communication through drawings is reviewed with examples. Legal considerations are identified. Standards are categorized, sources identified, and a large number of references displayed.

Chapter 2 treats statistical considerations in design and the interpretation of data. Reliability is defined. Descriptive statistics, functions of random variables, and reliability estimations are discussed.

*By Joseph E. Shigley and Charles R. Mischke, Coeditors-in-Chief, McGraw-Hill Publishing Company, New York, 1986.

Chapter 3 considers measurement and inference. Measuring systems are described, as is resolution and response. Selected measuring-system components are treated with examples. Sources of error in measurements are identified. Also treated are analysis of data, confidence limits, and propagation of error.

Chapter 4 treats numerical methods in a brief and understandable way. Common effective numerical methods for curve-fitting, interpolation, and rootfinding are explained.

Chapter 5 summarizes computational considerations in design, identifies that which computers and humans can do, and suggests a division of labor capitalizing on the *forte* of each. Guidance is given on how to implement an algorithmic approach to design, as well as illuminating the roles of the specification set, decision set, adequacy assessment, and figure of merit. An optimization algorithm is described. The *C*omputer-*A*ugmented *D*esign *E*ngineering *T*echnique (CADET) is outlined; computer requirements, documentation, error messaging, monitors, testing, and augmentation procedures for adding to an existing capability are cited.

Most of the artwork was competently prepared and supervised by Mr. Gary Roys of Madrid, Iowa, to whom the editors are indebted.

Care has been exercised to avoid error. The editors will appreciate being informed of errors discovered, so that they may be eliminated in subsequent printings.

JOSEPH E. SHIGLEY
CHARLES R. MISCHKE

chapter 1
INTRODUCTION

LEO C. PETERS, Ph.D., P.E.
Professor of Mechanical Engineering
Iowa State University
Ames, Iowa

R. BRUCE HOPKINS, Ph.D., P.E.
The Hopkins Engineering Co., P.C.
Cedar Falls, Iowa

1-1 THE DESIGNER AND THE DESIGNER'S PROBLEMS

1-1-1 Design and the Designer

Design and engineering, although sometimes viewed as distinct, are two facets of the same profession. Krick [1-1] states that engineering is a profession concerned primarily with the application of a certain body of knowledge, set of skills, and point of view in the creation of devices, structures, and processes used to transform resources to forms which satisfy the needs of society.

Design is the activity in which engineers accomplish the preceding task, usually by responding to a design imperative for the required task. The design imperative is the result of a problem definition and has the following general form [1-2]: "Design (subject to certain problem-solving constraints) a component, system or process that will perform a specified task (subject to certain solution constraints) optimally."

The end result of the engineering design process is a specification set from which a machine, process, or system may be built and operated to meet the original need. The designer's task is then to create this specification set for the manufacture, assembly, testing, installation, operation, repair, and use of a solution to a problem. Although primarily decision making and problem solving, the task is a complex activity requiring special knowledge and abilities. A designer cannot effectively operate in a vacuum, but must know, or be able to discover, information affecting the design, such as the state of the art, the custom of the industry, governmental regulations, standards, good engineering practice, user expectations, legal considerations (such as product liability), and legal design requirements.

In addition, an effective designer possesses the ability to make decisions; to innovate solutions to engineering problems; to exhibit knowledge of other technologies and the economics involved; to judge, promote, negotiate, and trade off; and finally, to sell an acceptable problem solution which meets the imposed constraints.

The designer must also be an effective communicator, not only with design supervisors and peers, but also with the public, as represented by federal, state, and local governments, the courts, and the news media.

Most of the time design proceeds by evolution rather than revolution. Thus many of the requirements may have already been met by contributions of others, and most of the time the engineer has to work on only a small portion of the design, requiring only some of the requisites previously identified.

1-1-2 Design Criteria

Although the general criteria used by a designer are many, the following list addresses almost all concerns:

- Function
- Safety
- Reliability
- Cost
- Manufacturability
- Marketability

The inclusion of safety and reliability at or near the level of importance of function is a recent development due to governmental regulation, expansion in the numbers of standards created, and development of product liability law, all occurring in the late 1960s and early 1970s.

Although cost is explicitly fourth on the list, its consideration permeates all the criteria just listed and is part of all design decisions.

As taught and practiced in the past, design criteria emphasized function, cost, manufacturability, and marketability. Reliability was generally included as a part of functional considerations. If product safety was included, it was somewhere in the function-cost considerations.

Design critiques were accomplished at in-house policy committee meetings or their equivalent with design engineers, a production representative, a materials representative, and possibly those representing marketing and service.

In the current design climate, the traditional design criteria are still valid; however, the additional constraints of governmental regulations, standards, and society's desire for safety, as exemplified in product liability litigation, have to be included in the design process. In addition, engineers must now be prepared to have their designs evaluated by nondesigners or nontechnical people. This evaluation will not be in the inner confines of a design department by peers or supervisors, as in the past, but may be in a courtroom by a jury of nontechnical people and attorneys who have an ulterior motive in their approach or in the public arena.

Since such a design evaluation is generally a result of an incident which caused damage or injury, to mitigate the nontechnical evaluation, current design procedures should emphasize the following factors in addition to traditional design criteria:

1. *Safety* This is associated with all modes of the product usage. In providing for safety, the priorities in design are first, if at all possible, to design the hazards out of the product. If this cannot be done, then shielding and guarding should be provided so that operators and bystanders cannot be exposed to the hazard. Otherwise, if a risk-benefit analysis shows that production and sale of the machine are still justified (and only as a last resort), effective warning should be given against the hazard present. Even though warnings are the least expensive and easiest way to handle hazards in the design process, there has never been a warning that physically prevented an accident in progress. Warnings require human action or intervention. If warnings are required, excellent reference sources are publications of the National Safety Council in Chicago and a notebook entitled *Machinery Product Safety Signs and Labels* [1-78].

2. *Failure analysis* If failure cannot be prevented, it is necessary that it be foreseen and its consequences controlled.

3. *Documentation* Associated with the evolution of the design, documentation is developed so that it can satisfy the involved nontechnical public as to the rationale behind the design and the decisions and trade-offs that were made.

The designer is in a new mode which places safety on the same level of importance in design considerations as the function or the ability of the design to perform as intended.

Arguments may be made that cost considerations are the most important. This is true only if the cost of the design includes the costs of anticipated litigation. These costs include product liability insurance premiums; direct out-of-pocket costs in investigation and defending claims; and indirect costs in the loss of otherwise productive time used in reviewing the design involved, in finding information for interrogatories, in being deposed, and in developing defense testimony and exhibits. If a lawsuit is lost, the amount of the verdict and the probable increase in product liability insurance premiums must also be included.

No longer can product liability be considered after the design is on the market and the first lawsuit is filed. Product liability considerations must be an integral part of the entire design process throughout the function, safety, cost, manufacturing, and marketing phases.

Additional criteria, considerations, and procedures should be included in programs to address specifically the product safety, failure, or malfunction problems which have contributed significantly to the existing product liability situation. Some of the important considerations and procedures are

1. Development and utilization of a design review system specifically emphasizing failure analysis, safety considerations, and compliance with standards and governmental regulations
2. Development of a list of modes of operation and examination of the product utilization in each mode
3. Identification of the environments of usage for the product, including expected uses, foreseeable misuses, and intended uses
4. Utilization of specific design theories emphasizing failure or malfunction analysis and safety considerations in each mode of operation

Design reviews have been used extensively for improving product performance, reducing cost, and improving manufacturability. In the current product liability climate, it is very important to include, and document in the review, specific failure analysis and safety emphases as well as to check compliance with standards and governmental regulations.

An important consideration in the design review process is to have it conducted by personnel who were not involved in the original design work, so that a fresh, disinterested, competent outlook and approach can be applied in the review.

1-1-3 Influences on the Designer

While attempting to meet the general criteria discussed earlier, the designer's work and the results are affected by both internal and external influences. The external influences, shown in Fig. 1-1, reflect the desires of society as represented by econom-

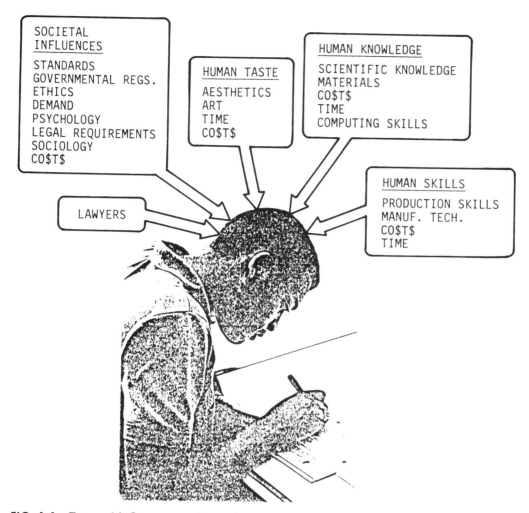

FIG. 1-1 External influences on the engineering designer.

ics, governmental regulations, standards, legal requirements, and ethics, as well as the items shown as human taste.

The other broad area of external influences reflects what is known and available for use in a design problem. The designer is limited by human knowledge, human skills, and again, economics as to what can be made.

Another important external influence on the designer and the design is legal in nature. The designer is directly influenced by the in-house legal staff or outside attorney retained for legal advice on patents, product liability, and other legal matters and also is affected by product liability suits against the product being designed or similar products.

Internal influences also affect the design. Figure 1-2 identifies some of these. They are a result of the designer's environment while maturing, education, life experiences, moral and ethical codes, personality, and personal needs. These personal or internal influences help shape the engineer's philosophy of design as well as the approach and execution. Individual designs will vary depending on the most important local influences at any given time.

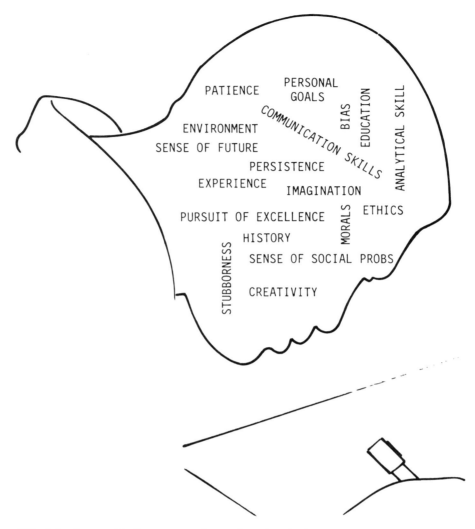

FIG. 1-2 Internal influences on the engineering designer.

1-1-4 Design Procedure

The general procedure for design is widely available in the literature (see Refs. [1-3] to [1-12]). The following procedure is representative of those found in the literature and is discussed extensively by Hill [1-3]:

1. Identification of need
2. Problem statement or definition of goal
3. Research
4. Development of specifications
5. Generation of ideas
6. Creation of concepts based on the ideas
7. Analysis of alternative concepts

8. Prototype and laboratory testing
9. Selection and specification of best concept
10. Production
11. Marketing
12. Usage (maintenance and repair)

The flowchart in Fig. 1-3 (taken from Ref. [1-13]) illustrates the design process. Note that although not all feedback paths are shown, each step in the process can result in arresting progress and reverting to a prior step, emphasizing that product design is an iterative process.

Much of the design work done is in a small part of one of the feedback or feed-forward portions of the chart and thus is evolutionary. Rarely will an individual designer start at the beginning of the chart with a clean sheet of paper and go through the entire process.

For those designers who do start at the beginning, the checklist in Table 1-1 is an example of one that may be used to organize the information required to define the design problem and aid in establishing design goals. An example list of information for a design specification based on the checklist in Table 1-1 is given in Table 1-2.

After defining the problem and setting the goals for the new design, as much search effort should be made as is feasible to gather all the information possible that applies to the design. This effort includes information on other competitive products or products of a similar nature, governmental regulations and codes, standards, field reports on failure and operation, recall, safety and accident reports, information from lawsuits, plus all the traditional technical information provided in design education (see Ref. [1-14]).

Some of these information sources have attained importance only recently. One example is governmental regulations which have been promulgated since the late 1960s and early 1970s with a major stated purpose of increasing safety both in the workplace (Occupational Safety and Health Act) and elsewhere (Consumer Product Safety Act). Litigation has also provided additional emphasis on including safety

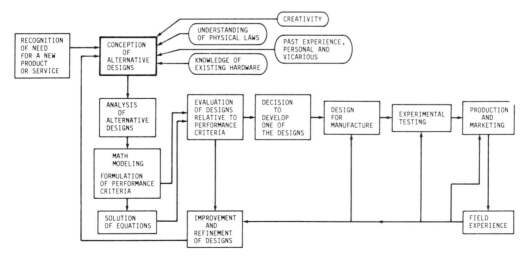

FIG. 1-3 A flowchart for the design process. *(Adapted from Ref. [1-13]. Used by permission of Charles E. Merrill Publishing Co.)*

Notes ▪ Drawings ▪ Ideas

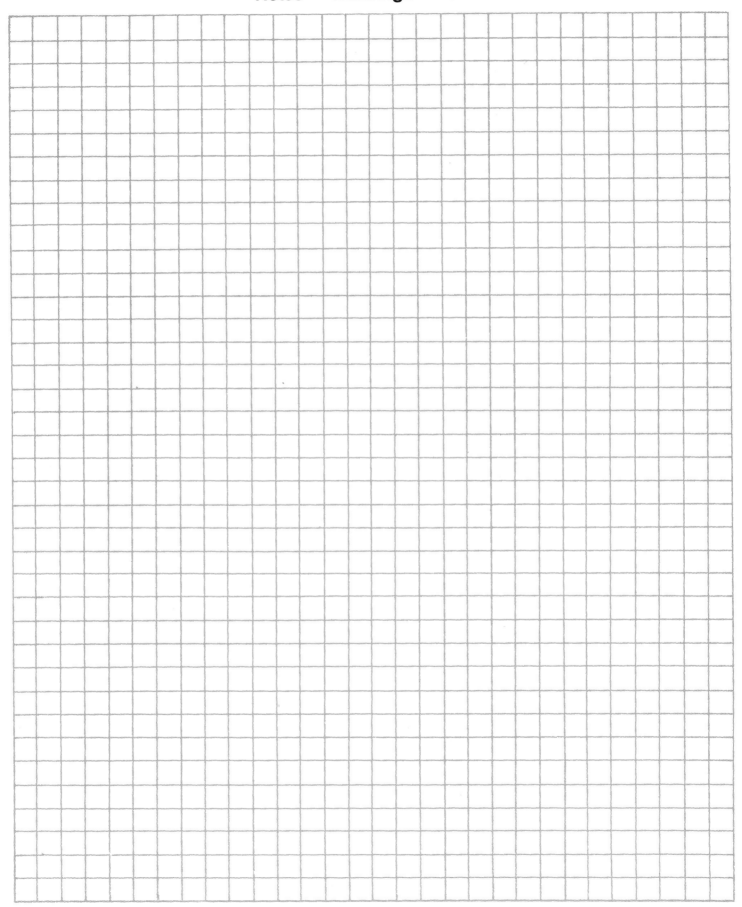

TABLE 1-1 Design Checklist

---

1. Function:

   A simple statement of the objective

2. Detailed functional requirements:

   Required performance stated numerically

3. Operating constraints:

Power supplies	Life
Operating procedures	Reliability
Maintenance procedures	Other operating constraints

4. Manufacturing constraints:

Manufacturing processes available	Labor available
Development facilities available	Delivery program
Permissible manufacturing cost	Number required
Other manufacturing constraints	

5. Environment:

Ambient temperature	Installation limitations
Ambient pressure	Expected operators
Climate	Effect on other parts of the parent system
Acceleration	Vibration
Contaminants	Other environmental factors

6. Other constraints:

Applicable governmental regulations	Applicable standards
Legal requirements—patents	Possible litigation

SOURCE: Adapted from Leech [1-14].

considerations in design. Even so, the question of how safe a product has to be is very complex and ultimately can be answered only in the courts.

Including safety considerations in the design of a product requires knowledge of the types of hazards that can occur and the application of good design principles to the product involved. One of the appropriate considerations for including safety in design is to recognize that the product will ultimately fail. If this is done, then the product can be designed such that the location and mode of failure are planned and the failure and consequences can be predicted, accommodated, and controlled.

Hazards can be classified as human-caused or non-human-caused. The listings in Tables 1-3 and 1-4 are not meant to be complete or all-inclusive, but they do provide a guide for designers to know, appreciate, and include in any project. To reduce the effect of these hazards in designing a product, the designer should consider the possible modes of usage; the users, operators, or bystanders; the environment or use; and the functions or requirements of expected use.

The word *expected,* instead of *intended,* is used intentionally because society, through the courts, expects the designer and manufacturer to know and provide for *expected* usage. This will be discussed in more detail in Sec. 1-5.

Table 1-5 lists some modes of usage to include in design deliberations. Considerations for each of the modes of usage are presented in Tables 1-6 and 1-7. Naturally, not all products require consideration of all the items listed in Tables 1-3 to 1-7, and some will require even more. Further information on procedure and other aspects of a designer's tasks can be found in the references cited at the end of this chapter.

TABLE 1-2 Example of Information Provided on a Design Specification Form

1. Product or job identification number
2. Modification or change number and date
3. Function: In basic terms, what is the function to be performed by the item when designed?
4. Application: Include the system requiring this application.
5. Origin: When, how, and by whom was the requirement made?
6. Customer's specification: Identify the customer's specification and note whether it is in writing or was oral. If oral, who made it, who in your organization received it, and when was this done?
7. General related specifications: Identify all general specifications, definitions, standards, or other useful documents and information that contribute to the design specifications.
8. Safety: Identify standard and special safety precautions or requirements to be included in design considerations, manufacture, marketing, or usage.
9. Governmental regulations and standards applicable: Identify and list.
10. Environment: Identify and list the environmental specifications required using the items included under "Environment" in Table 1-1 as guidelines.
11. Number required and delivery schedule.
12. Desired cost or price information
13. Functional requirements:

    Life | Performance requirements with acceptable tolerance limits

    Reliability | Servicing, maintenance, or repair restrictions
    Unacceptable modes of failure | Any other functional requirements
14. Additional relevant information:

    Limitations of manufacturing facilities
    Special procedural requirements
    Any other relevant information
15. Action required: For example, preparation of proposal, preparation of detail drawings, manufacture of prototypes, or manufacture of full production quantity.

SOURCE: Adapted from Leech [1-14].

TABLE 1-3 Hazards of Human Origin

Ignorance	Smoking
Overqualification	Physical limitations
Boredom, loafing, daydreaming	Sickness
Negligence, carelessness, indifference	Exhaustion
Supervisory direction	Emotional distress
Overproduction	Disorientation
Poor judgment	Personal conflicts
Horseplay	Vandalism
Improper or insufficient training	Physical skills
Alcohol, drugs	Shortcuts

TABLE 1-4 Hazards of Nonhuman Origin

Weight	Visibility	Cold
Flammability	Pinch and crush points	Pressure and suction
Speed (high or low)	Noise	Emissions (particulates/gaseous)
Temperature	Light, strobe effect, intensity	Explosions, implosions
Toxicity (poison)	Electric shock	Vibrations
Sharp edges	Radiation	Stored energy
Rotating parts	Chemical burn	High-frequency radiowaves
Reciprocating parts	Sudden actions	Slick surfaces
Shrapnel (flying objects)	Height	Surface finish
Stability, mounting	Heat	Flames or sparks

TABLE 1-5 Modes of Product Usage

Intended operation or use	Commercial and industrial use	Repair
Unintended operation or use	Assembly	Cleaning
Expected operation or use	Setup	Packaging
Misuse	Installation	Storage
Abuse	Testing/certification	Shipping/transportation
Emergency use	Maintenance/service	Starting/stopping
Changing modes of operation	Isolation	Disposal
Salvaging	Recreational use	Inspection
Repair	Servicing	Modification

TABLE 1-6 Considerations during Each Mode of Usage†

Life expectancy	Observation of operation	Weight and size
Duration of length of use	Materials for cleaning	Speed of operation
Complexity	Materials handling devices	Pay/compensation plan
Operator position/station	Frequency of repair	Insertion/removal of
Nonoperator position/station	Test fixtures, ancillary	workpiece
Labeling	equipment	Failure of workpiece
Misuse	Controls and human	Temperature of operation
Material used	factors	Noise of operation
Operator education/skill	Operator comfort	Emissions (particulate/
Operator mental/physical	Ratings and loadings	gaseous)
condition	Guarding and shielding	Stability
Environment or surrounding	Warnings (audible, visual)	Social restrictions
condition	Types of failure	Weather
Type of tool required	Consequences of failure	Local specific operating
Reliability	Ventilation	procedure
Waste materials	Cost	Leakage
Operating instructions	Service instructions	Light/lighting
Machine action	Power source/loss	Instructions, maintenance
Accessories/attachments	Appurtenant parts	Effects of usage/wear
Aesthetics	Government regulation	Maintenance/repair/service
		Standards

†There is no significance to the order in the table; various products and situations will establish the relative importance in specific cases.

Notes ▪ Drawings ▪ Ideas

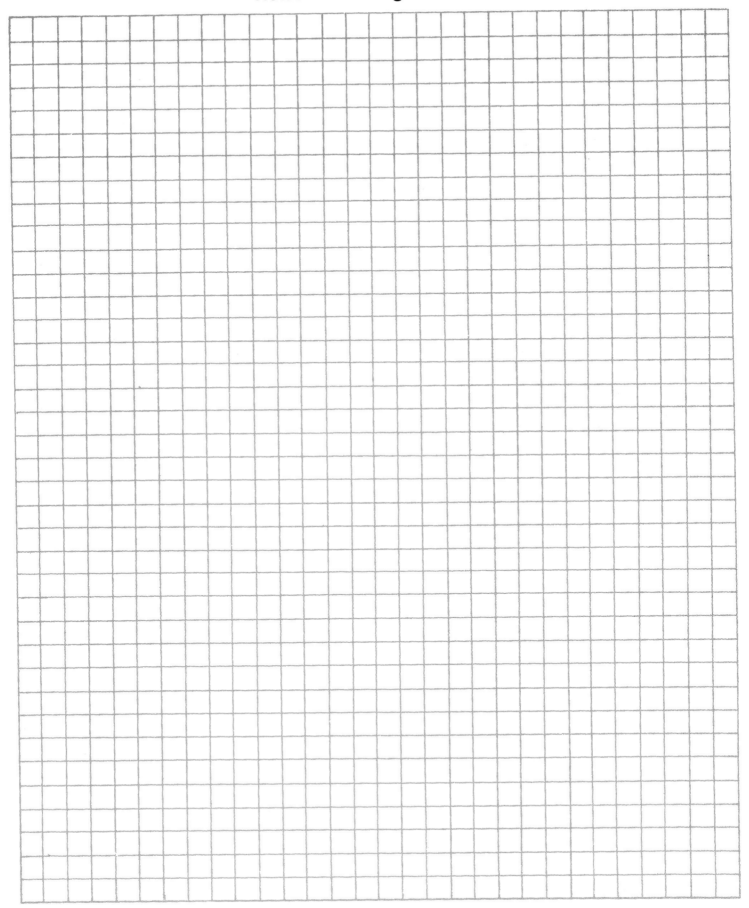

TABLE 1-7 Specific Design Concepts and Philosophies

K.I.S.S.†	Foreign material sensing/ elimination	Deadman switches
Fail safe		Shield and guard interlocks
Design hazards out	Prevention of modification	Avoid the use of set screws and friction locking devices
Positive lockouts	Isolation of operators from point of machine operation	
Warnings		
Emergency shutoffs		Use self-closing lids/hatches/ closures
Prevention of inadvertent actuation	Controls user-friendly	
	Provide proper safety equipment	Consider two-handed operation for each operator
Prevention of unauthorized actuation		
	Provide overload/overspeed alarms	
Shielding and guarding		Use load readouts when possible
Proper materials for operation	Training programs	
	High feasible factor of safety	Control failure mode so consequences are predictable
Accessibility for adjustments/service		
	Redundant systems	
	Proper use of components	

†Keep it simple, stupid!

1-2 DECISIONS AND THEIR IDENTIFICATION

1-2-1 General

Decision making is a key part of the design process in which the designer tries to provide a solution to a problem faced by a customer. The customer is interested primarily in performance (including safety), time (how soon the solution will be available and how long it will last), and cost (including price, maintenance cost, and today, litigation and insurance costs).

The designer, in order to meet the requirements of the customer, generally uses as design criteria function, safety, economy, manufacturability, and marketability. To achieve these criteria the designer may use as a problem statement the design imperative as presented in Mischke (see Sec. 1-1 or Ref. [1-2]) and then make basic product decisions of the types listed in Table 1-8. From this point on, the decisions required to establish the solution to the design problem appear to be without bound. A second level of more detailed decisions then needs to be reached. Examples are shown in Table 1-9.

Neither Table 1-8 nor Table 1-9 is represented as being complete, all-inclusive, or in any order of priority, since priority is established on a job-by-job basis.

TABLE 1-8 Basic Product Decisions to Be Made by the Designer†

Anticipated market	Expected maintenance	Controls
Component elements	Types of loadings	Materials
Fabrication methods	Target costs	Expected life
Evolutionary design or original design	Energy source(s)	Permissible stresses
		Permissible distortions

†No significance is to be attached to order or extent.
SOURCE: J. P. Vidosic, *Elements of Design Engineering,* The Ronald Press Company, New York, 1969.

TABLE 1-9 Second-Level Decision to Be Made by the Designer†

Strength of each element	Reliability of each element	Maintenance required
Allowable distortion	Style	Noise allowable
Governing regulations	Governing standards	Governing codes
Control requirements	Surface finish	Corrosion anticipated
Friction anticipated	Lubrication required	Wear anticipated
Geometry	Tolerances	

†No significance is to be attached to order or extent.

1-2-2 Approach to Problem Solving

To make decisions effectively, a rational problem-solving approach is required. The first step in problem solving is to provide a statement defining the problem to be solved. The essential ingredients as stated and discussed in Dieter [1-15] are

- A need statement
- Goals, aims, objectives
- Constraints and allowable trade-offs
- Definitions of terms or conditions
- Criteria for evaluating the design

All these ingredients require evaluation of safety, potential litigation, and environmental impact. Establishing each of these ingredients includes decision making from the start of the design process.

1-2-3 The Decision Maker and Decision Making

Decision makers are concerned with the consequences of their decisions for both their employers and society, as well as for their own egos and professional reputations. By themselves, these concerns may cause faulty decision making.

The decision maker may operate in one of the following ways (Janis and Mann [1-15a] as discussed by Dieter [1-15]):

- Decide to continue with current actions and ignore information about risk of losses.
- Uncritically adopt the most strongly recommended course of action.
- Evade conflict by putting off the decision, passing it off to someone else.
- Search frantically for an immediate solution.
- Search painstakingly for relevant information, digest it in an unbiased way, and evaluate it carefully before making a decision.

Unfortunately, only the last way leads to a good, effective decision, and it may be compromised by time constraints.

The basic ingredients for a good, effective decision are listed in Table 1-10, along with substitutions that may have to be made in practice. The use of these items [1-15b] is discussed at length in Dieter [1-15].

TABLE 1-10 Basic Decision-Making Ingredients

Ingredient	Surrogate
Fact	Information
Knowledge	Advice
Experience	Ad hoc experimentation
Analysis	Intuition
Judgment	None

SOURCE: D. Fuller, *Machine Design,* July 22, 1976, pp. 64–68.

An action of some type is implied after a decision is made and may be classified as a *must* action, a *should* action, a *want* action, or an *actual* action.

A *must* action is one that has to be done and differentiates between acceptability and unacceptability. A *should* action is what ought to be done and is the expected standard of performance for meeting objectives. A *should* action is compared with an *actual* action, or what is occurring at the time the decision is being made. A *want* action does not have to be implemented but may be negotiated as reflecting desires rather than requirements (discussed in Dieter [1-15]).

The steps in [1-15b] for making a good decision are summarized by Dieter [1-15] as follows:

1. Establish the objectives of the decision to be made.

2. Classify objectives by importance, identifying *musts, shoulds,* and *wants.*

3. Develop alternate actions.

4. Evaluate alternatives for meeting the objectives.

5. Choose the alternative having the most promising potential for achieving the objectives as the tentative decision.

6. Explore future consequences of tentative decision for adverse effects.

7. Control effects of final decision by taking appropriate action while monitoring both the implementation of the final decision and the consequences of the implementation.

1-2-4 Decision Theory

The following discussion is adapted from and extensively quotes Dieter [1-15], who in turn cites extensive references in the area of decision theory.

Decision theory is based on utility theory, which develops values, and probability theory, which makes use of knowledge and expectations available. A decision-making model contains the basic elements listed in Table 1-11. Decision-making models are usually classified on the basis of the state of the knowledge available as listed in Table 1-12.

In applying decision theory, a method of determining the *utility* of a solution must be established. The *utility* of a solution is defined as being a characteristic of the proposed solution that relates to a value in use or a goal of the solution that has meaning in the marketplace. Utility can be cost, price, weight, speed of performance, statistical reliability (probability of failure), factor of safety, or other like attributes.

Notes · Drawings · Ideas

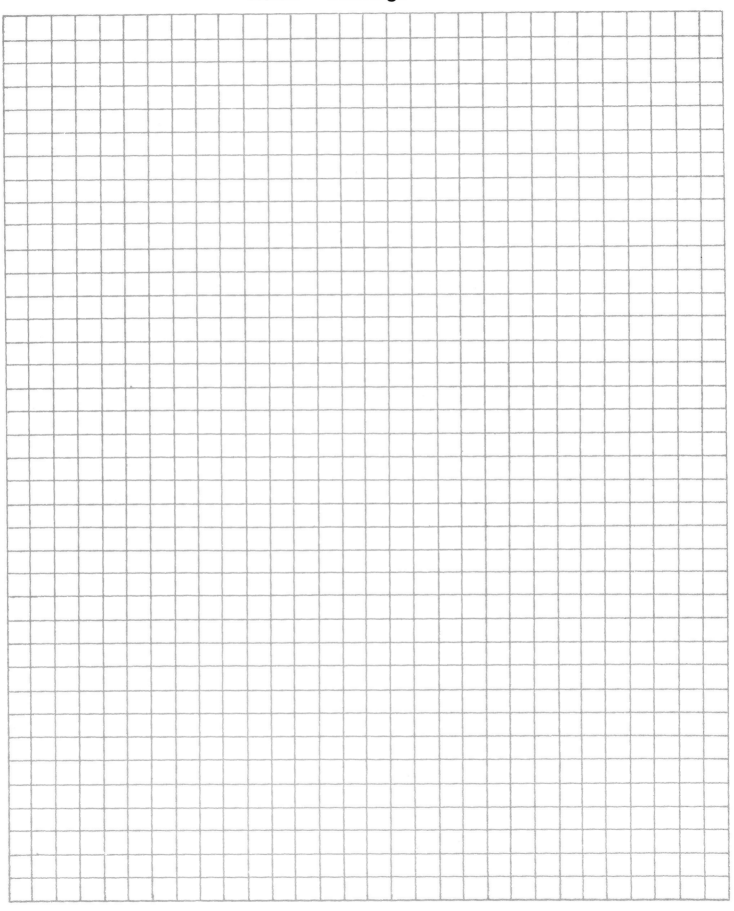

TABLE 1-11 Elements of a Decision-Making Model

1. Alternative courses of action
2. States of nature: The environment of operation of the decision model. The designer has very little, if any, control over this element.
3. Outcome: The result of a combination of an action and a state of nature.
4. Objective: The statement of what the decision maker wishes to achieve.
5. Utility: The satisfaction of value associated with each outcome.
6. State of knowledge: Certainty associated with states of nature, usually given in terms of probabilities.

SOURCE: Adapted from Dieter [1-15].

Another name for utility is *merit,* which is also discussed in Sec. 1-3-4 and is extensively presented in Ref. [1-2].

The occurrence of specific states of nature, such as those expressed as materials properties, part geometries, loadings, odors, aesthetics or taste, may be expressed deterministically, probabilistically, or not at all. If the desired state-of-nature variable can be quantified deterministically, then the utility or merit of a given course of action (problem solution) may be determined and compared to the values of utility or merit for other solutions, allowing the decision maker to choose the better solution for each comparison and, ultimately, the best solution.

If the variables are known only probabilistically, either as a probability distribution or as a mean and variance, statistical expectation techniques as described in Haugen [1-16] or propagation of uncertainty techniques as described in Beers [1-17] have to be used to determine the statistical expectation of the value of the utility for a given course of action (solution). Decisions are then made on the basis of comparisons of expected values of utility or merit. Utility is discussed additionally in Dieter [1-15].

Decision making under risk and decision making under uncertainty are two extremes where, respectively, one does or one does not know the probabilities involved to determine the expected value of utility. Realistically, one can usually estimate the probabilities that affect the outcome, but often without much confidence.

The Bayesian theory of decision making uses the best estimate of the values of utility involved and then bases the decision on the outcome with the maximum expected utility. If probabilities are unknown or cannot be estimated, a weighting function may be established using factors developed from experience or opinion to aid in estimating the utility value for various solutions.

Decision matrices may be used to assist in making decisions where the design

TABLE 1-12 Classification of Decision-Making Models with Respect to State of Knowledge

1. Decision under certainty: Each action results in a known outcome that will occur with a probability of 1.
2. Decision under risk: Each state of nature has an assigned probability of occurrence.
3. Decision under uncertainty: Each action can result in two or more outcomes, but the probabilities for the states of nature are unknown.
4. Decision under conflict: States of nature are replaced by courses of action, determined by an opponent who is trying to maximize his or her objectives function; this is also known as *game theory.*

SOURCE: Adapted from Dieter [1-15].

Notes ▪ Drawings ▪ Ideas

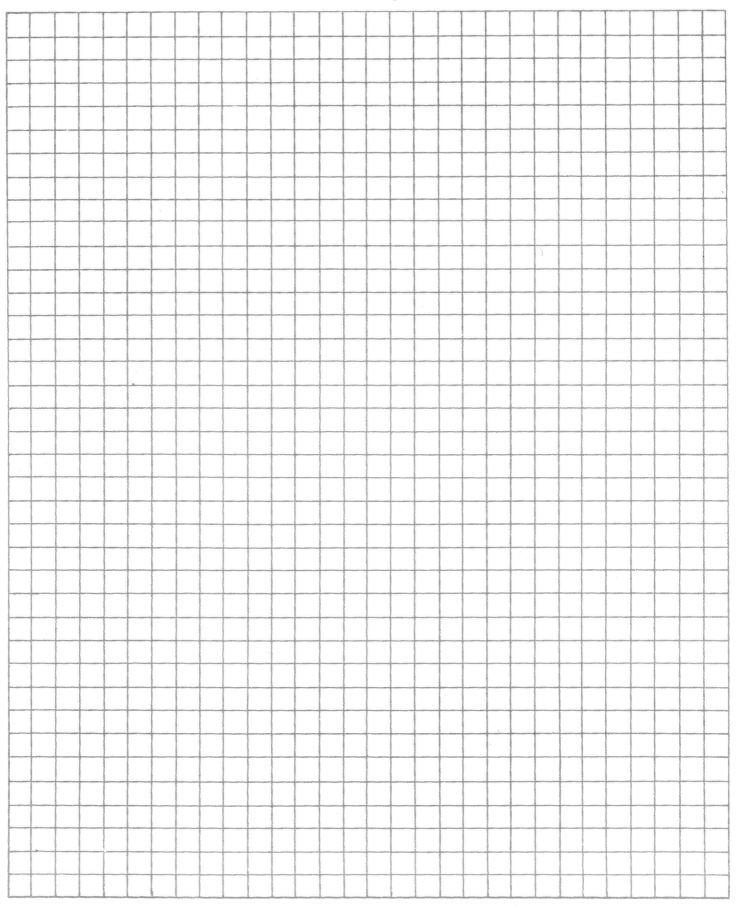

goals establish several measures of utility to be evaluated simultaneously for proposed solutions. An example might be a situation where low cost, small weight, and high strength are all important. Dieter [1-15] discusses creation of decision matrices, also known as *payoff matrices* or *loss tables,* and provides several examples of their use in decision making. If a utility function can be created for these cases, optimization theory (as discussed in Ref. [1-12]) may be applied through available digital computer techniques to maximize utility (or merit) functions of many variables to aid in determining the best course of action (solution).

Sometimes the utility of a given course of action cannot be quantified. Examples are the beauty or aesthetics of a given solution, the bouquet of a wine, or other characteristics that are evaluated subjectively and are presented as matters of opinion. One way of proceeding is to establish arbitrary numerical scales ranging from unac- This technique, which appears to be an adaptation of fault-tree analysis, where utility rate the beauty, fragrance, odor, or whatever the utility is judged to be. These ratings may then be evaluated to assist in making the appropriate decision based on the subjective utility.

Another useful technique for exhibiting the results of a decision matrix for the case where decisions must be made in succession into the future is the *decision tree.* This technique, which appears to be an adaption of fault-tree analysis, where utility is taken to be probability of failure, is described in an example in Dieter [1-15] and as fault-tree analysis in Scerbo and Pritchard [1-18], which also references as sources Larson [1-19], Hammer [1-20], and others. More discussion of decisions, their identification, and decision theory can be found in Wilson [1-7], Dixon [1-5], and Starr [1-10].

1-3   ADEQUACY ASSESSMENT

An *adequacy assessment* is any procedure which ensures that a design is functional, safe, reliable, competitive, manufacturable, and marketable. Usually, in the formative stages, matters of marketability, manufacturability, and competitiveness are addressed and built in, and the principal attention is focused on sustaining function, safety, and reliability. This is why quantitative concepts such as factor of safety and reliability are prominent in examining a completed design.

1-3-1   General

The designer's task is to provide a documented set of specifications for the manufacture, assembly, testing, installation, operation, repair, and use of a solution to a problem. This task may be started by considering several solution concepts, selecting one to pursue, and then generating schemes for meeting the requirements. Usually there are many iterative steps throughout such a process. At each step, decisions must be made as to which concept or detailed specification should be pursued further. This section identifies tools and other considerations necessary to assess adequacy and presents methods of rationally providing and combining information so that informed decisions can be made.

1-3-2   Criteria for Adequacy Assessment

Effective adequacy assessment requires a knowledge of all persons and organizations involved in any way with the product and an understanding of what is important to

TABLE 1-13 Considerations and the Cast of Characters Involved with Design Adequacy Assessment

Important considerations	Criteria	Those involved
Personal reputation	Maintainability	The designer
Keeping one's job	Serviceability	Design peers
Function	Marketability	Design supervisors
Cost	Aesthetics	Users and operators
Safety	Factor of safety	Maintenance and service personnel
Size	Manufacturability	The courts
Reliability	Standards	Governmental bodies
Factor of safety	Public expectations	The public
Government regulations		

those involved. Table 1-13 lists factors to be considered and the cast of people involved in engineering adequacy assessment. The order of priority in engineering practice depends on the specific case considered.

The roles in adequacy assessment of the courts, governmental bodies, and to some extent the public as well as the criteria of governmental regulations, standards, and public expectations are addressed in some detail in Secs. 1-5 and 1-6.

1-3-3 Suitability-Feasibility-Acceptability Method

The suitability-feasibility-acceptability (SFA) method of evaluation (as presented in Ref. [1-2]) may be used to evaluate several proposed solutions or compare the desirability of various courses of action. The method is based on determining, in turn, the suitability, feasibility, and acceptability of the proposed solution using the following procedure and then evaluating the results:

Step 1. Develop a problem statement that is as complete as possible.

Step 2. Specify a solution as completely as possible.

Step 3. Answer the question: Is this solution suitable? In other words, with no other considerations included, does the proposed solution solve the problem?

Step 4. Answer the question: Is this solution feasible? In other words, can this solution be implemented with the personnel available, the time available, and the knowledge available without any other considerations included?

Step 5. Finally, answer the question: Is the proposed solution acceptable? In other words, are the expected results of the proposed solution worth the probable consequences to all concerned?

The results of the SFA test can only be as good as the effort and information put into the test. Done casually with inadequate information, the results will vary. Done with care and skill, it can be very effective in assessing the adequacy of proposed problem solutions.

An example of the application of the SFA test (adapted from Ref. [1-2]) is presented below:

Step 1 (Problem Statement). Metal cans as originally designed require a special tool (can opener) to open. This was true in general, but was especially burdensome to people using beverage cans away from a kitchen or immediate source of a can opener. A method was needed to provide metal beverage cans that could be opened without a can opener or other tool.

Step 2 (Solution). Design a can for beverages that will meet all the requirements of the original cans and, in addition, will have the top manufactured so that a ring is attached to a flap of metal that is part of the top, but is scored so that a person pulling on the ring can pull the flap out of the top of the can, thus opening the can without a tool.

Step 3. Is this solution suitable; i.e., will it solve the stated problem? The answer is yes. For the described solution, the can may be opened generally by the user's fingers without any special tool.

Step 4. Is this solution feasible; i.e., can it be done using available personnel, finances, facilities, time, and knowledge? The answer is yes. The state of manufacturing techniques and materials is such that the design could be produced. The additional cost appears to be reasonable. Thus this solution is feasible.

Step 5. Is the proposed solution acceptable to all concerned? The initial decision was that the solution was acceptable to the designer, the manufacturer, the marketing organizations, and to the consumer, so it was put into production.

However, as later events revealed, the consequences of having the ring and flap removable from the can were not generally acceptable to the public because of the consequences of the discarded flaps and rings, so a new design retaining the flap to the can, evolved.

1-3-4 Figure of Merit or Weighting Function Method

The *figure of merit* (FOM), also known as the *merit function* or weighting function, is applicable in problems where the important parameters can be related through a function that can be evaluated to find the "best" or "highest merit" solution to a problem. This approach differs from the SFA approach in that the SFA approach is based on more subjective factors.

The FOM lends itself well to attaining or approximating the optimal solution sought by the design imperative discussed in Sec. 1-1. Customarily, the merit function is arbitrarily written so that it is maximized in obtaining the best (highest) value of merit.

Comparing the values of the merit variables obtained for the different alternatives examined should consist only of determining which value is the largest. For situations such as the case where minimum weight or minimum cost is desired, customarily the expression for weight or cost is written either as a negative function or as a reciprocal function, thus allowing maximization techniques to be used.

Although any variable can be used as the merit variable (including an arbitrary variable which is the sum of other disparate variables), the most useful equations are written so that the function represents a characteristic of the product used as a criterion by both engineers and the marketplace. Since safety, reliability, cost, and weight are all important characteristics, useful merit variables, for example, could be the weight, cost, design factor, safety factor, reliability, or time. Equations can be either deterministic or probabilistic in nature.

Where such subjective characteristics as taste, beauty, innovation, or smell are the important characteristics, the FOM approach does not work unless some method of quantifying these characteristics is developed that will allow their mathematical representation.

Two examples will be presented to illustrate the technique involved and identify terms used in the figure-of-merit process.

EXAMPLE 1. Design and develop a package for a fragile device that will allow the packaged device to drop through a substantial distance onto concrete without the impact causing the device to fail or break. The package must be of small weight, cost, and size.

Several designs were proposed, built, and tested, and some protected the fragile device adequately. A method was then needed to determine the best of the surviving designs.

A merit function was set up which combined the three design requirements as follows:

$$M = -(A_1 w + A_2 c + A_3 d)$$

where M = merit, the sum of the three terms
w = weight, ounces (oz)
c = cost, cents
d = longest dimension, inches (in)

A_1, A_2, and A_3 are factors selected to weight each of the terms consistent with the importance of the associated variable. The minus sign is used to allow the maximum value of M to be attained when the sum of the three design requirement terms is at a minimum.

The first equation relating merit (which may be a factor of safety, cost, weight, or other desired attribute) to the other variables is known as the *merit function*. It is usually expressed in the form, $M = M(x_1, x_2, \ldots, x_n)$. Regional (inequality) constraints are described limits of values that each of the variables may attain in the given problem. Function (equality) constraints are relationships that exist between variables that appear in the merit function. Both types of constraints are specified as a part of the construction of the merit function.

A detailed discussion and description of the preceding method and terms can be found in Mischke [1-2]. Other discussions of this technique with somewhat different terminology may be found in Wilson [1-7] and Dixon [1-5]. A short example will be set up to illustrate the preceding terms.

EXAMPLE 2. A right-circular cylindrical container is to be made from sheet steel by bending and soldering the seams. Management specifies that it wants the least expensive gallon container that can be made from a given material of a specified thickness. Specify the dimensions for the least expensive container.

Solution. If the bending and soldering are specified, then a fabrication cost per unit length of seam can be estimated. In addition, for a given material of a specific thickness, the material cost is directly proportional to the surface area. A merit function is constructed as follows:

$$M = -(\text{cost of material} + \text{cost of fabrication})$$

If h = height (in) and, d = diameter (in), then

$$M = -\left[\left(\frac{2\pi d^2}{4} + \pi d h\right)k_1 + (2\pi d + h)k_2\right]$$

where k_1 = material cost (dollars/in²) and k_2 = fabrication cost (dollars/inch of seam).

The functional constraint for this problem is the relationship between the volume of the container and the dimensions:

$$V = 1 \text{ gal} = 231 \text{ in}^3 = \frac{\pi d^2 h}{4}$$

where V = volume of container (in^3). The regional constraints are $0 < d$ and $0 < h$, which shows that we are interested only in positive values of d and h.

The next step would be to substitute the functional constraint into the merit function, which reduces the merit function to a function of one variable which may be easily maximized. A robust method such as golden section (see Mischke [1-2]) can be used for optimization.

1-3-5 Design Factor and Factor of Safety

The design factor and the factor of safety are basic tools of the engineer. Both play a role in creating figures of merit, parts and materials specifications, and performance criteria for products being designed. Both may be defined generally as the ratio of the strength or capacity to the load expected, or allowable distortion divided by existing distortion of the object or system in question. Both the design factor and the factor of safety are used to account for uncertainties resulting from manufacturing tolerances, variations in materials properties, variations in loadings, and all other unknown effects that exist when products are put into operation.

The distinction between the design factor and the factor of safety is that the first is the goal at the start of the design process and the latter is what actually exists after the design work is completed and the part or object is manufactured and put into use. The changes occur because of discreteness in sizes of available components or because of compromises that have to be made as a result of materials processing and availability, manufacturing processes, space availability, and changes in loadings and costs.

A simple example would be the design of a rigging system using wire rope to lift loads of 10 tons maximum. The designer could preliminarily specify a design factor of 5, which would be the ratio of the wire rope breaking strength to the expected load, or

$$\text{Design factor} = 5 = \frac{\text{desired breaking strength}}{\text{load}}$$

Using this criterion, a wire rope having a breaking strength of 50 tons would be selected for this application.

The engineer would then evaluate the wire rope selected for use by determining the effect of the environment; the diameters of the sheaves over which the wire rope would be running; the expected loadings, including effects of impact and fatigue; the geometry of the wire rope ends and riggings; and any other factors affecting the wire rope strength to arrive at the final strength, knowing all the application factors. The factor of safety would then be

$$\text{Factor of safety} = \frac{\text{actual breaking strength in application}}{\text{load}}$$

Mischke [1-2], Shigley [1-21], and other machine design books discuss the design factor and the factor of safety extensively, including many more complex examples than the one presented here.

A major danger in the use of both the design factor and the factor of safety is to believe that if either is greater than 1, the product having such a factor is safe. However, the factor of safety has a statistical distribution, and even though the mean value exceeds 1, a fraction of the devices can fail.

Notes ▪ Drawings ▪ Ideas

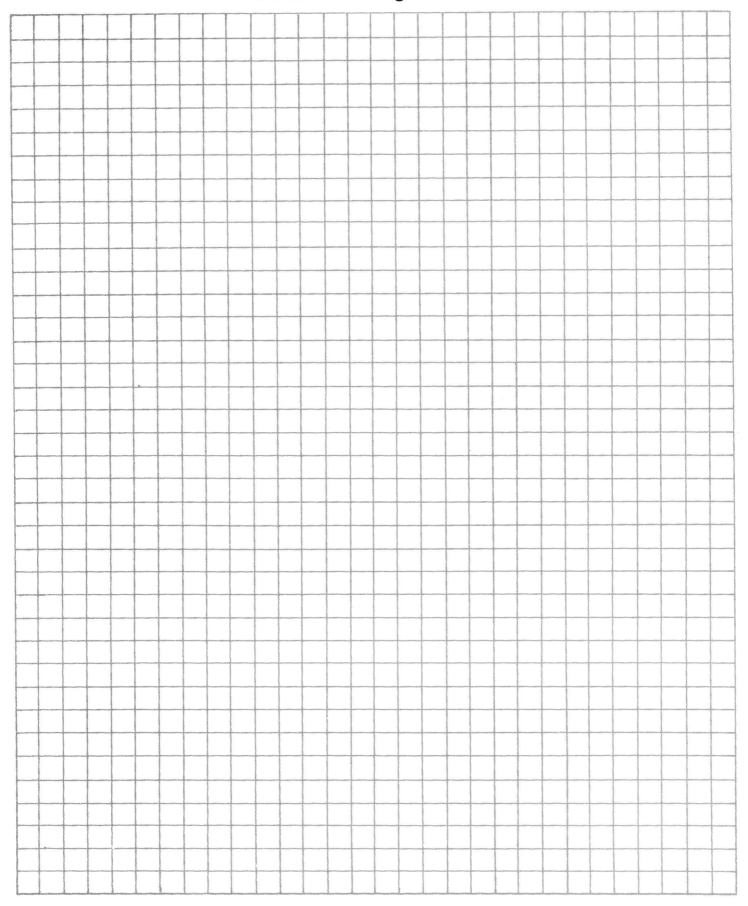

1-3-6 Probabilistic Techniques

Propagation-of-error techniques, as described in Chap. 3 and Beers [1-17], can be used to determine the uncertainty of the value of the factor of safety to allow the designer to better assess the adequacy of the factor of safety finally determined. The techniques of Chap. 2 and Haugen [1-16] work directly with the reliability goal.

Another method of adequacy assessment, presented in Refs. [2-11] and [2-12], uses the load strength and geometry variables combined to form a quantity called the *stimulus parameter* and the material strength for a given design. If the mean values and the standard deviation are known for any two of the variables (i.e., load, geometry, and materials strength), the threshold value of the third variable can be estimated to provide a specified reliability. The actual value present in the design or part can then be compared to the threshold value to see if the part meets the desired reliability criteria and is then adequate for the specifications provided.

1-4 COMMUNICATION OF ENGINEERING INFORMATION

The output of an engineering department consists of specifications for a product or a process. Much of the output is in the form of drawings that convey instructions for the manufacturing of components, the assembly of components into machines, machine installations, and maintenance. Additional information is provided by parts lists and written specifications for assembly and testing of the product.

1-4-1 Drawing Identification

Drawings and machine components are normally identified by number and name, for example, Part no. 123456, Link. Each organization has its own system of numbering drawings. One system assigns numbers in sequence as drawings are prepared. In this system, the digits in the number have no significance; for example, no. 123456 would be followed by numbers 123457, 123458, etc. without regard to the nature of the drawing.

A different system of numbering detail drawings consists of digits that define the shape and nominal dimensions. This eases the task of locating an existing part drawing that may serve the purpose and thus reduces the likelihood of multiple drawings of nearly identical parts.

The generally preferred method of naming parts assigns a name that describes the nature of the part, such as piston, shaft, fender, or wheel assembly. Some organizations add descriptive words following the noun that describes the nature of its part; for example:

Bearing, roller, or bearing, ball

Piston, brake, or piston, engine

Shaft, axle, or shaft, governor

Fender, LH, or fender, RH

Wheel assembly, idler, or wheel assembly, drive

A long name that describes the first usage of a part or that ties the part to a particular model can be inappropriate if other uses are found for that part. A specific ball or roller bearing, for example, might be used for different applications and models.

1-4-2 Standard Components

Components that can be obtained according to commonly accepted standards for dimensions and strength or load capacity are known as *standard parts*. Such components can be used in many different applications, and many organizations assign part numbers from a separate series of numbers to the components. This tends to eliminate multiple part numbers for the same component and reduces the parts inventory. Standard components include such things as antifriction bearings, bolts, nuts, machine screws, cotter pins, rivets, and Woodruff keys.

1-4-3 Mechanical Drawings

Pictorial methods, such as perspective, isometric, and oblique projections, can be useful for visualizing shapes of objects. These methods, however, are very rarely used for working drawings in mechanical engineering. Orthographic projection, in which a view is formed on a plane by projecting perpendicularly from the object to the plane, is used almost exclusively.

In the United States, mechanical drawings are made in what is known as the *third-angle projection*. An example is provided in Fig. 1-4, in which the triangular shape can be considered to be the front view or front elevation. The top view, or plan, appears above the front view and the side view; the side elevation, or end view, appears alongside the front view. In this example, the view of the right-hand side is shown; the left-hand side would be shown to the left of the front view if it were needed.

The first-angle projection is used in many other countries. In that arrangement, the top view appears below the front view, and the view of the left side appears to the right of the front view. Some organizations follow the practice of redoing drawings that are to be sent to different countries in order to eliminate the confusion that results from an unfamiliar drawing arrangement.

Drawings, with the exception of schematics, are made to a convenient scale. The

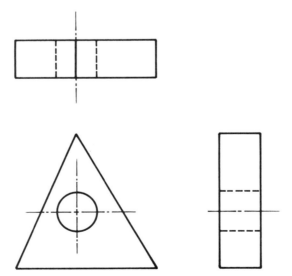

FIG. 1-4 Arrangement of views of an object in third-angle orthographic projection.

choice of scale depends on the size and complexity of the object and fitting it on a standard size of drawing paper. The recommended inch sizes of drawings are, 8.5 $\times$ 11, 11 $\times$ 17, 17 $\times$ 22, 22 $\times$ 34, and 34 $\times$ 44. Then, sizes are multiples of the size of the commercial letterhead in general use, and folded prints will fit in letter-sized envelopes and files.

Drawings should be made to one of the standard scales in common usage. These are full, one-half, one-quarter, and one-eighth size. If a still smaller scale must be used, the mechanical engineer's or architect's rule is appropriate. These rules provide additional scales ranging from 1 in equals 1 ft to $\frac{1}{32}$ in equals 1 ft. The civil engineer's scale with decimal divisions of 20, 30, 40, 50, and 60 parts to the inch is not appropriate for mechanical drawings.

Very small parts or enlarged details of drawings are sometimes drawn larger than full size. Scales such as 2, 4, 5, 10, or 20 times normal size may be appropriate depending on the particular situation.

Several different types of drawings are made, but in numbers produced, the detail drawing (Fig. 1-5) exceeds all other types. A *detail drawing* provides all the instructions for producing a component with a unique set of specifications. The drawing specifies the material, finished dimensions, shape, surface finish, and special processing (such as heat treatment or plating) required. Usually, each component that has a unique set of specifications is a separate drawing. There are numbering systems, however, in which similar components are specified on the same drawing and a table specifies the dimensions that change from item to item. Sometimes the material specification consists of another part to which operations are added. For example, another hole or a plating operation might be added to an existing part. Detail drawings are discussed in considerable detail in the next portion of this section.

An *assembly drawing* specifies the components that are to be joined in a permanent assembly and the procedures required to make the assembly. An example is given in Fig. 1-6. A weldment, for example, will specify the components that are to be welded, the weld locations, and the size of weld beads. The drawing may also specify operations that are to be performed after assembly, such as machining some areas.

Another type of assembly drawing consists of an interference fit followed by subsequent machining. A bushing, for example, may be pressed into the machine bore of the upper end of an engine connecting rod, and the bushing bore may then be machined to a specified dimension.

A *group drawing* (Fig. 1-7) may resemble a layout in that it shows a number of components, in their proper relationship to each other, that are assembled to form a unit. This unit may then be assembled with other units to make a complete machine. The drawing will normally include a parts list that identifies part numbers, part names, and the required number of pieces. A group drawing might be a section through a unit that must be assembled with other equipment to make a complete machine.

A *machine outline drawing* is provided to other engineering departments or to customers who purchase that machine for installation. An example is given in Fig. 1-8. An outline may show the general shape, the location and size of holes for mounting bolts, the shaft diameter, keyseat dimensions, location of the shaft with respect to the mounting holes, and some major dimensions.

Schematic drawings, such as for electrical controls, hydraulic systems, and piping systems, show the major components in symbolic form. An example is given in Fig. 1-9. They also show the manner in which the components are connected together to route the flow of electricity or fluids. Schematic diagrams are sometimes provided for shop use, but more frequently they are used in instruction books or maintenance manuals where the functioning of the system is described.

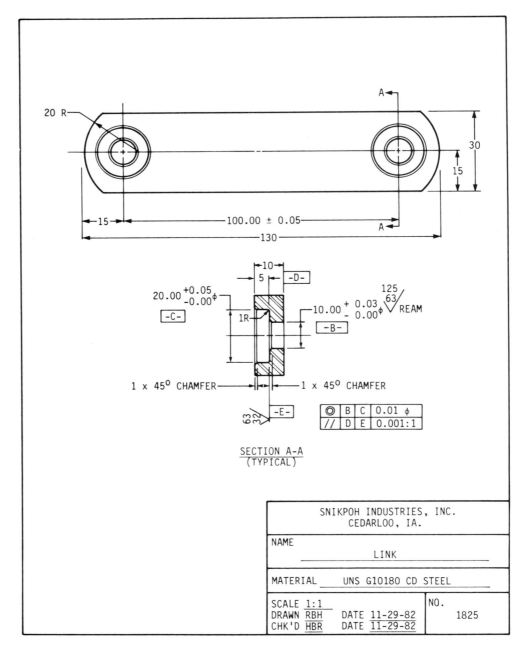

FIG. 1-5   An example of a detail drawing.

1-4-4   Detail Drawings

A complete description of the shape of a part is provided by the views, sections, and specifications on a detail drawing. A simple part, such as a right-circular cylinder, may require only one view. A complex part, such as an engine cylinder block, may require several views and many sections for an adequate description of the geometry. The link in Fig. 1-5 is a basically simple shape with added complexity due to machining. The cut surfaces of sections are indicated by section lining (crosshatching). Stan-

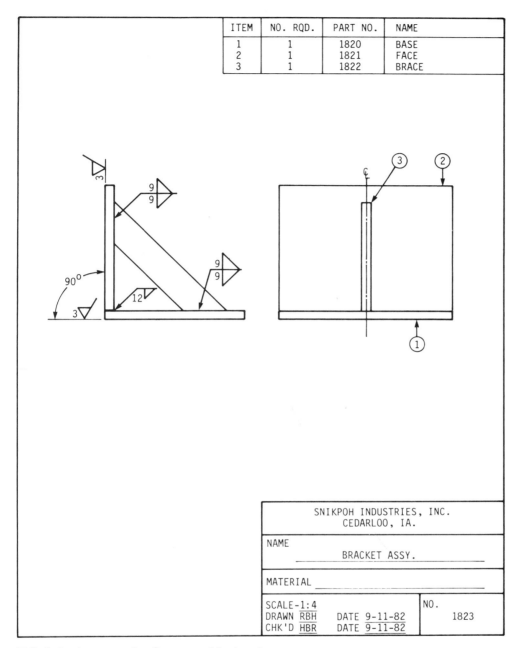

ITEM	NO. RQD.	PART NO.	NAME
1	1	1820	BASE
2	1	1821	FACE
3	1	1822	BRACE

SNIKPOH INDUSTRIES, INC.
CEDARLOO, IA.

NAME
BRACKET ASSY.

MATERIAL

SCALE-1:4
DRAWN RBH   DATE 9-11-82
CHK'D HBR   DATE 9-11-82

NO.
1823

FIG. 1-6   An example of an assembly drawing.

dard symbols (Fig. 1-10)† are available that indicate the type of material sectioned. The use of proper section lining helps the user to understand the drawing with reduced clutter.

DIMENSIONS. There are two reasons for providing dimensions: (1) to specify size and (2) to specify location. Dimensioning for sizes, in many cases, is based on the

†See Sec. 1-6 for a discussion of standards and standards organizations.

ITEM	RQD	PART NO.	NAME
1	1	1826	BODY
2	2	1827	GASKET
3	1	1828	END, CLOSED
4	2	1829	PIN, DOWEL
5	8	1830	NUT, HEX MB-10
6	8	1831	BOLT, HEX HD. M8x65-10.9

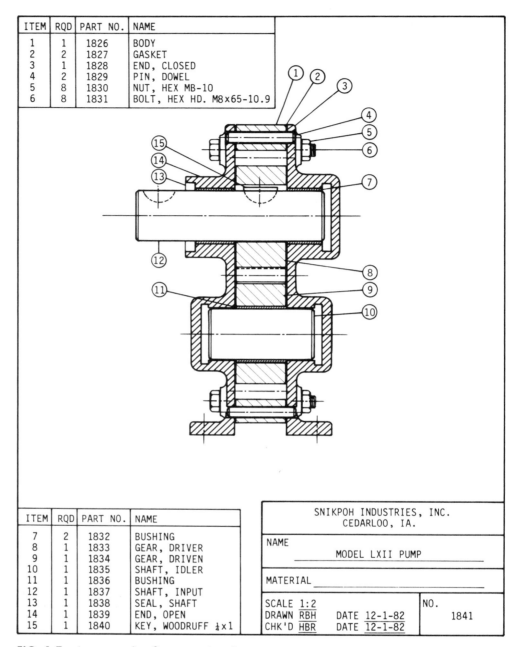

ITEM	RQD	PART NO.	NAME
7	2	1832	BUSHING
8	1	1833	GEAR, DRIVER
9	1	1834	GEAR, DRIVEN
10	1	1835	SHAFT, IDLER
11	1	1836	BUSHING
12	1	1837	SHAFT, INPUT
13	1	1838	SEAL, SHAFT
14	1	1839	END, OPEN
15	1	1840	KEY, WOODRUFF ¼x1

SNIKPOH INDUSTRIES, INC.
CEDARLOO, IA.

NAME
_____MODEL LXII PUMP_____

MATERIAL _____

SCALE 1:2		NO.
DRAWN RBH DATE 12-1-82		1841
CHK'D HBR DATE 12-1-82		

FIG. 1-7   An example of a group drawing.

common geometric solids—cone, cylinder, prism, pyramid, and sphere. The number of dimensions required to specify these shapes varies from 1 for the sphere to 3 for the prism and frustum of a cone. Location dimensions are used to specify the positions of geometric shapes with respect to axes, surfaces, other shapes or other references. A sphere, for example, is located by its center. A cylinder is located by its axis and bases.

For many years, dimensions were stated in terms of inches and common fractions as small as $\frac{1}{64}$ in. The common fractions are cumbersome when adding or subtracting

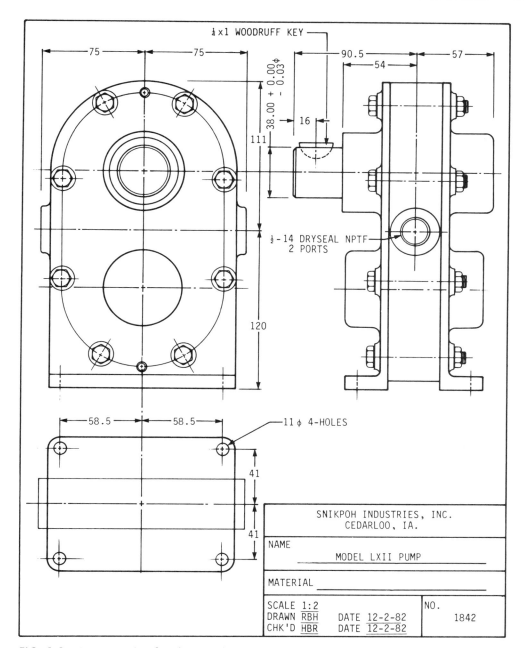

FIG. 1-8 An example of an installation drawing.

dimensions, and decimal fractions are now used extensively. The decimal fractions are usually rounded to two digits following the decimal point unless a close tolerance is to be stated. Thus $\frac{3}{8}$ in, which is precisely equal to 0.375 in, is normally specified by dimension as 0.38 in.

The advent of the International System of Units (SI) has led to detail drawings on which dimensions are specified in metric units, usually millimeters (mm). Thus $\frac{1}{2}$ mm (very nearly equal to 0.020 in) is the smallest dimension ordinarily specified without stating a tolerance. Because machine tools and measuring devices are still

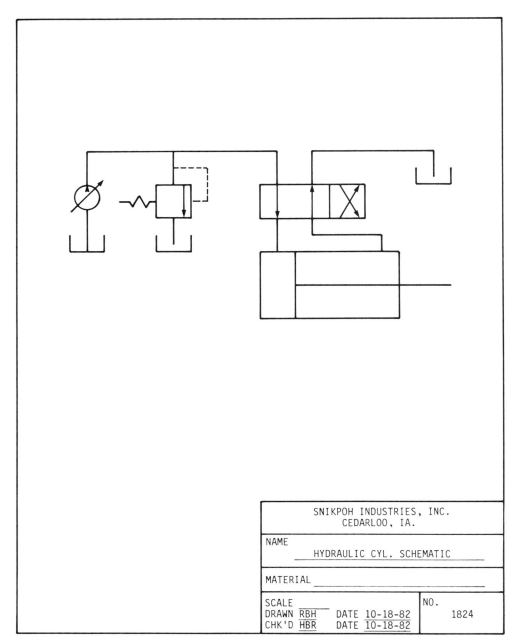

FIG. 1-9 An hydraulic schematic diagram.

graduated in inches, some organizations follow the practice of dual dimensioning. In this system, the dimensions in one system of units are followed by the dimensions in the other in parentheses. Thus a $\frac{1}{2}$-in dimension might be stated as 0.50 (12.7), meaning 0.50 in or 12.7 mm.

It is poor practice to specify a shape or location more than once on a drawing. Not only can the dimensions conflict as originally stated, but the drawing may undergo subsequent changes. In making changes, the duplicate dimensions can be overlooked and the user has the problem of determining the correct dimension.

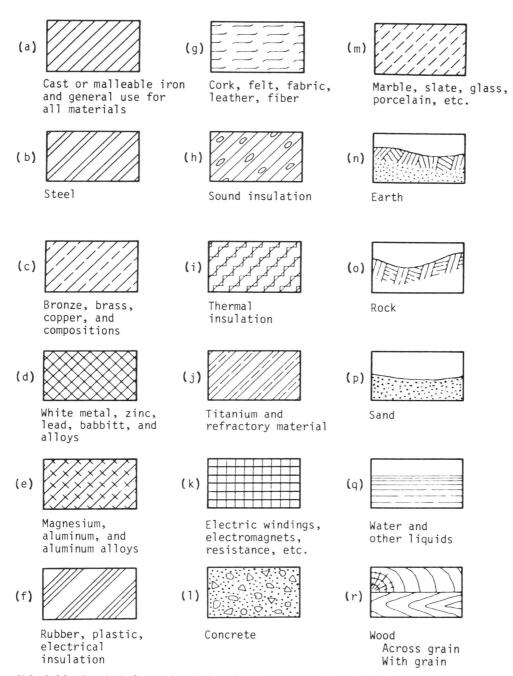

FIG. 1-10 Symbols for section lining. *(ANSI standard Y14.2M-1979.)*

Every dimension has either a stated or implied tolerance associated with it. To avoid costly scrap, follow this rule: In a given direction, a surface should be located by one and only one dimension. To avoid a buildup of tolerances, it is better to locate points from a common datum than to locate each point in turn from the previous point. Standard procedures for specifying dimensions and tolerances are provided in ANSI standard Y14.5-1973.

TOLERANCES. Most organizations have general tolerances that apply to dimensions where an explicit tolerance is not specified on the drawing. In machined dimensions, a general tolerance might be ± 0.02 in or 0.5 mm. Thus a dimension specified as 12 mm may range between 11.5 and 12.5 mm. Other general tolerances may apply to angles, drilled holes, punched holes, linear dimensions on formed metal, castings, forgings, and weld beads and fillets.

Control of dimensions is necessary for interchangeability of close-fitting parts. Consequently, tolerances are specified on critical dimensions that affect small clearances and interference fits. One method of specifying tolerances on a drawing is to state the nominal dimension followed by a permissible variation. Thus a dimension might be specified employing bilateral tolerance as 50.800 ± 0.003 mm. The limit-dimension method is to specify the maximum and minimum dimensions; for example, 50.803/50.797 mm. In this procedure, the first dimension corresponds to minimum removal of material. For a shaft, the display might be 50.803/50.797 mm and for a hole, 50.797/50.803 mm. This method of specifying dimensions and tolerances eliminates the need for each user of the drawing to perform additions and subtractions to obtain the limiting dimensions. Unilateral tolerancing has one tolerance zero, for example, $50.979^{+0.006}_{-0.000}$ mm.

Some organizations specify center-to-center distance on a gear set unilaterally with the positive tolerance nonzero. This is done because an increase in center-to-center distance increases backlash, whereas a decrease reduces backlash. The zero backlash, or tight-meshed, condition cannot be tolerated in the operation of gears unless special precautions are taken.

Standard symbols are available (Fig. 1-11) for use in specifying tolerances on geometric forms, locations, and runout on detail drawings. Information is provided in ANSI standard Y14.5M-1982 on the proper use of these symbols.

Surface Texture. The surface characteristics depend on processing methods used to produce the surface. Surface irregularities can vary over a wide range. Sand casting and hot working of metals, for example, tend to produce highly irregular surfaces. However, the metal-removal processes of grinding, polishing, honing, and lapping can produce surfaces which are very smooth in comparison. The deviations from the nominal surface can be defined in terms of roughness, waviness, lay, and flaws. The finer irregularities of surface which result from the inherent action of the production process is called *roughness*. Roughness may be superimposed on more widely spaced variations from the nominal surface, known as *waviness*. The direction of the pattern of surface irregularities is usually established by the method of material removal and is known as *lay*. *Flaws* are unintentional variations in surface texture, such as cracks, scratches, inclusions, and blow holes. These are usually not involved in the measurement of surface texture.

Surface roughness values that can be obtained by common production methods are provided in SAE standard J449a, "Surface Texture Control." The roughness that can be tolerated depends on the function served by the surface. The roughness of a clearance hole is usually not critical, whereas a surface that moves against another, such as a piston or journal, usually needs to be smooth.

A relationship exists between permissible surface-texture variations and dimensional tolerances. Precise control of dimensions requires precise control of surface texture. Consequently, when a high degree of precision is required in a dimension, it is necessary that the variation in surface roughness and waviness also be small.

Surface texture is specified on drawings through a set of symbols (Fig. 1-12) established by ANSI standard Y14.36-1978. The basic symbol is derived from a 60° letter V which was formerly used to indicate a machined surface. Use of the symbols on a drawing is demonstrated in Fig. 1-13. It is common practice to specify a range for

SYMBOL FOR:	ANSI Y14.5	ISO
STRAIGHTNESS	—	—
FLATNESS	⬭	⬭
CIRCULARITY	○	○
CYLINDRICITY	⬭/	⬭/
PROFILE OF A LINE	⌒	⌒
PROFILE OF A SURFACE	⌓	⌓
ALL-AROUND PROFILE	⊶	NONE
ANGULARITY	∠	∠
PERPENDICULARITY	⊥	⊥
PARALLELISM	//	//
POSITION	⊕	⊕
CONCENTRICITY/COAXIALITY	◎	◎
SYMMETRY	NONE	≡
CIRCULAR RUNOUT	* ↗	↗
TOTAL RUNOUT	* ↗↗	↗↗
AT MAXIMUM MATERIAL CONDITION	Ⓜ	Ⓜ
AT LEAST MATERIAL CONDITION	Ⓛ	NONE
REGARDLESS OF FEATURE SIZE	Ⓢ	NONE
PROJECTED TOLERANCE ZONE	Ⓟ	Ⓟ
DIAMETER	⌀	⌀
BASIC DIMENSION	50	50
REFERENCE DIMENSION	(50)	(50)
DATUM FEATURE	– A –	* 〰 OR * 〰 A
DATUM TARGET	⌀6 A1	⌀6 A1
TARGET POINT	✕	✕

* MAY BE FILLED IN

FIG. 1-11 Symbols for geometric characteristics and tolerances on detail drawings. *(ANSI standard Y14.5M-1982.)*

the surface roughness rather than a single value. In such a case, the maximum roughness is placed above the minimum value. The waviness height and width can be specified above the horizontal line, the distance over which the roughness is measured below the horizontal line, and the direction of lay above the surface.

The use of symbols for material-removal allowance on a weldment is illustrated in Fig. 1-6, and the specifications for a range of surface finishes are given in Fig. 1-5.

MACHINING INFORMATION. Some parts, such as noncircular cams, gears, and involute splines, may require a table of information that is needed for machining and checking the parts. The drawing of a standard spur gear, for example, requires a

Symbol		Meaning
(a)	✓	Basic Surface Texture Symbol. Surface may be produced by any method except when the bar or circle (Figure b or d) is specified.
(b)	▽	Material Removal By Machining Is Required. The horizontal bar indicates that material removal by machining is required to produce the surface and that material must be provided for that purpose.
(c)	3.5 ▽	Material Removal Allowance. The number indicates the amount of stock to be removed by machining in millimeters (or inches). Tolerances may be added to the basic value shown or in a general note.
(d)	⌀	Material Removal Prohibited. The circle in the vee indicates that the surface must be produced by processes such as casting, forging, hot finishing, cold finishing, die casting, powder metallurgy or injection molding without subsequent removal of material.
(e)	✓	Surface Texture Symbol. To be used when any surface characteristics are specified above the horizontal line or the right of the symbol. Surface may be produced by any method except when the bar or circle (Figure b and d) is specified.
(f)		(construction diagram)

In (f): 3x, 1.5x, 60°, 00 00, 3x APPROX., 60°, 3x, 0.00, 1.5x, LETTER HEIGHT = x

FIG. 1-12 Surface-texture symbols and construction. *(ANSI standard, Y14.36-1978.)*

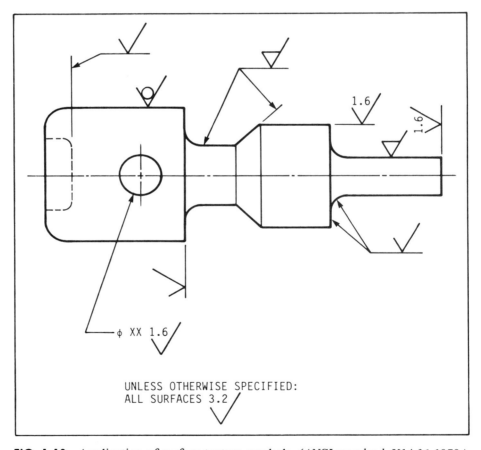

φ XX 1.6 ✓

UNLESS OTHERWISE SPECIFIED:
ALL SURFACES 3.2 ✓

FIG. 1-13 Application of surface-texture symbols. *(ANSI standard, Y14.36-1978.)*

list of the number of teeth, diametral pitch or module, pressure angle, pitch diameter, tooth form, circular tooth thickness, and dimensions for checking the teeth. These data are required for obtaining the proper tools, setting up for the machining, and checking the finished parts.

JOINING INFORMATION. Permanent assembly of components requires instructions for joining and specification of the material for making the connection. These processes include bonding, brazing, riveting, soldering, and welding. The use of symbols to specify welds is illustrated in Fig. 1-6.

The amount of interference in press fits and shrink fits is normally specified through the dimensions and tolerances on the mating parts. Heating or cooling of parts for ease of assembly may be specified on an assembly drawing or in assembly specifications.

MATERIAL SPECIFICATIONS. Designation of the material for a part is essential. Such ambiguous specifications as cast iron, gray iron, or mild steel should not be used. Although there may be a common understanding of the meaning of such terms within the organization, misunderstandings can arise if the drawings are sent outside the firm. The use of the term *cast iron,* for example, might be interpreted as gray iron, white iron, malleable iron, or nodular iron.

Each type of cast iron includes several grades, so castings should be specified by both type and grade of iron. Gray iron castings can be specified according to ASTM standard A48 or SAE standard J431 AUG79, and there are similar standards for malleable iron and nodular iron. When the type and grade of cast iron have been specified, the approximate strength of the metal is known.

The composition of wrought steel bars can be specified through use of the SAE/ANSI numbering system or the newer UNS standard. Steel plate, sheet, and structural shapes are more commonly specified according to ASTM specifications. The surface condition on bars, plate, and sheet can also be specified, such as hot rolled, cold finished, or pickled and oiled. The use of the standard material specification and surface finish, in effect, specifies the minimum material strength and the surface condition.

Some of the larger manufacturers have their own systems of material specifications which may be very similar to the standard systems. Materials are then ordered according to the company's own specification. Such a system prevents surprises due to changes in the standard and also provides a convenient method for specifying special compositions when needed.

HEAT TREATMENT. Processes such as annealing or normalizing may be required prior to machining and are specified on the drawings. Other treatments such as carburizing, induction hardening, or through hardening can be performed after some or all of the machining has been done and must be specified. The results desired (for example, the case depth and surface hardness after carburizing) are a better specification than processing temperatures, times, and quenching media. Especially in the case of induction hardening, it may be necessary to specify both a surface hardness and a hardness at some particular depth below the surface in order to prevent subsurface failures.

SPECIAL PROCESSES. The use of special processes or handling, such as methods of cleaning castings, impregnation of castings to prevent leakage of fluids, degreasing of finished parts, or protection of surfaces, is frequently specified on the drawing. If the painting of internal surfaces or dipping of castings to prevent rusting is to be done, the paint color, paint type, and method of application are usually specified.

Notes · Drawings · Ideas

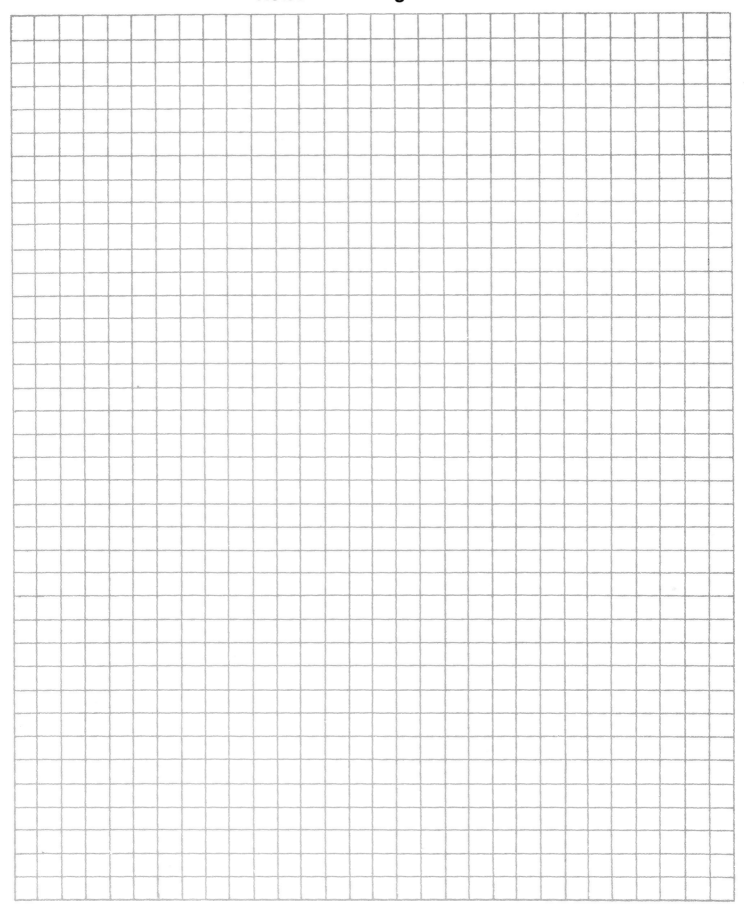

Drawings of parts that are to be plated specify the plating metal and thickness of plating that is to be applied.

Weight limits may also be specified on drawings. Pistons for internal combustion engines, for example, may have provisions for metal removal to obtain the desired weight. The location of material that can be removed and the weight limits are then specified on the drawing. Engine connecting rods may have pads for weight control on each end. The maximum amount of metal that can be removed is then shown and the weight limits at the center of each bearing journal are also specified.

Drawings of rotating parts or assemblies may have specifications for limits on static or dynamic balance. Instructions as to the location and method of metal removal or addition in order to obtain balance are then shown on the drawing.

QUALIFYING TESTS. Drawings of parts of assemblies in which fluid leakage may be detrimental to performance may have a specification for a pressure test to evaluate leakage. A pressure vessel may have a specification for a proof test or a rotating body may have a specification for a spin test to determine that the object will meet performance requirements.

1-4-5 Release of Drawings and Specifications

A formal method of notifying other departments in the organization that drawings and specifications have been prepared is commonly used. This may be accomplished by a decision that lists parts, assemblies, and other necessary specifications for manufacture and assembly. Some organizations use a drawing release form for the same purpose. Regardless of the name by which it is known, the procedure initiates the processes in other departments to obtain tooling, purchase materials, and provide for manufacturing and assembly facilities.

Many drawings undergo changes for such purposes as to correct design or drafting errors, improve the design, or facilitate manufacturing or assembly. If the revised part is interchangeable with the previous version, the same drawing number is retained. If the part is not interchangeable, a new drawing number is assigned. Usually, the changes and the reasons for the changes are given on the decision or drawing change notice.

1-4-6 Deviations

Inevitably, situations arise in which parts do not conform to drawings. In periods of materials shortages, it may become necessary to make a materials substitution. Moreover, manufacturing errors can occur or manufacturing processes may need to be altered quickly for improvement of the part. Such temporary changes can be processed much more quickly through a deviation letter than through the decision process. A *deviation letter* specifies the part number and name, the products affected, the nature of the departure from specifications, the corrective action to be taken, and the records to be kept of the usage of deviant parts.

1-5 LEGAL CONSIDERATIONS IN DESIGN

Legal considerations have always been included in design to some extent, but they came to prominence in 1963 when the concept of strict liability was first enunciated in a court decision [*Greenman* v. *Yuba Power Products, Inc.,* 377 P. 2d 897 (1963)]

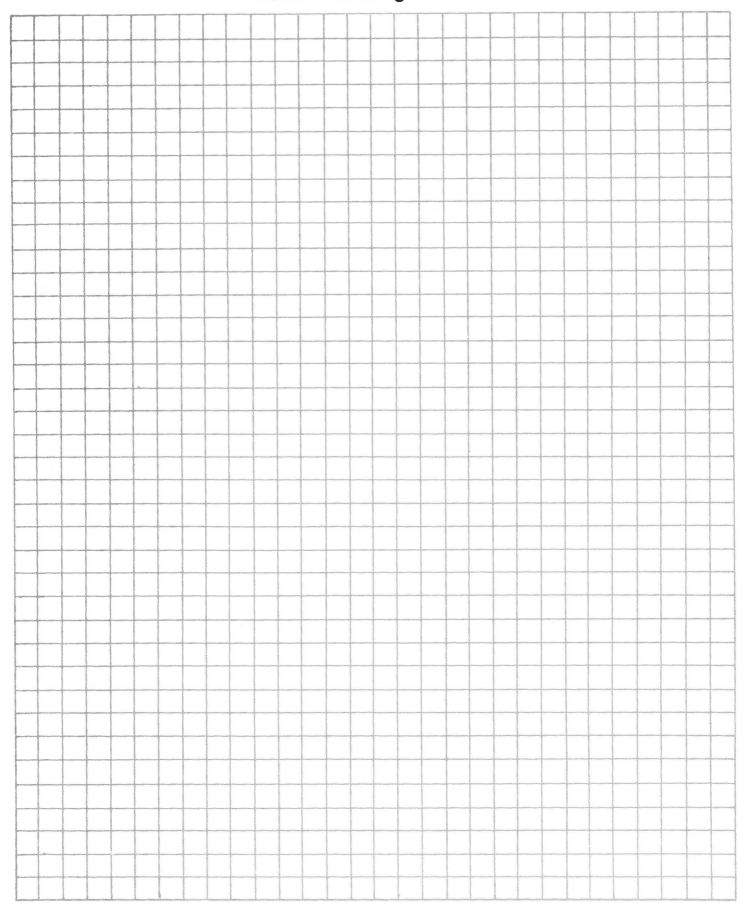

and then was formally established in the Restatement of Torts (2d), Sec. 402A (1965).

In 1970, the National Commission on Product Safety issued a report which included statistics showing that the incidence of product-related injuries was very high. The report concluded that although the user, the environment, and the product were all involved, the best place to reduce the potential for injury was in the design of the products involved. This report, along with a heightened awareness of product-related problems, also contributed to the increase in product liability litigation and further delineation of the legal responsibilities of the designer and manufacturer.

The law addressing the responsibilities and duties of designers and manufacturers changes rapidly; thus details will not be presented here. Instead, the emphasis of the laws as they affect designers, manufacturers, and sellers of products will be discussed.

The law, through the various theories under which lawsuits are filed, addresses contractural representations (express warranty); implied representations of performance and operation (implied warranty); conduct of designers, manufacturers, sellers, and users (negligence); and the characteristics of the product exclusive of the conduct of all involved with the product (strict liability). Litigation affecting machines and their designers is most often filed under negligence or strict liability theories, both of which may allege the presence of a defect. Thus a major concern of designers would be to eliminate or reduce the effect of defects present in products.

A *product defect* is a characteristic of a product that makes it substandard. These characteristics, in a legal sense, lead to conditions under which a product is unreasonably dangerous or hazardous when used in certain expected or foreseeable ways.

The standards applied and the determination of whether a product (as a result of the defined characteristic) is unreasonably dangerous or hazardous is done either by a jury or a judge in court rather than by the action of the designer's peers.

The types of defects encountered may be categorized as manufacturing defects, warning defects, and design defects. *Manufacturing defects* occur when a product is not made to the designer's or manufacturer's own standards, i.e., blueprints, layouts, or specifications. Examples are holes drilled the wrong size or in the wrong place, a different material used than was specified, or welds that do not meet the designer's or manufacturer's specifications.

Warning defects occur when proper warnings are not present at hazardous locations, thus creating a defect. The warnings may be absent, insufficient in extent, unreadable, unclear, or inadequate.

Design defects occur when a product is manufactured to the designer's drawings and specifications and it functions as intended by the designer and the manufacturer but is alleged to be unreasonably hazardous when used in an expected or foreseeable manner.

Since the concept of a defective design was originated in the courts, the definitions and associated tests were legal in nature rather than rooted in engineering. In an attempt to clarify the concept of a design defect, the California Supreme Court, in the case of *Barker* v. *Lull Engineering Co.,* 573 P. 2d. 443 (1978), established two tests to be applied to a product to determine if a design defect existed. If a product does not perform as safely as an ordinary user or consumer would expect when it is used in a reasonably foreseeable manner or if the benefits of a design are not greater than the risks of danger inherent in the use of the product with all things considered, then the product may be found defective.

The *consumer-expectation test* used is based on the idea that consumers expect products to operate reliably and predictably and that if the products fail, the failure will not cause harm. The risk-benefit or risk-utility analysis assumes that all factors involved in designing the product were included and evaluated in arriving at the final design chosen; thus there are no better ways of designing and manufacturing the product to accomplish its intended purposes. When the product design and manufacturing are completed, the hazards that remain have to be evaluated both on the basis of the probability that harm will occur and on all the consequences of that harm, including its seriousness and costs to all involved. Then this evaluation is balanced against the utility or benefits of the product when it is used in a foreseeable manner.

Close examination of consumer expectations and risk-benefit (or utility) considerations show that in many cases conformity to good design practices and procedures, with a heavy emphasis on safety considerations that were well known and utilized prior to the development of product liability litigation, would significantly reduce the occurrence of design defects and the resulting legal actions.

In many states, the final fault is evaluated by the jury or the judge on a comparative basis. Thus if a judgment is rendered against a manufacturer, the percentage of the fault is also established by the jury or the judge. The injured party then recovers only the same percent of the judgment as the percentage of fault not assigned to the injured party.

The law varies from state to state on how long the injured party has after the harm is done to file the suit. This period of time is called the *statute of limitations.* If a lawsuit is not filed within the time specified by the statute of limitations, it cannot be filed at all.

Another period of time, called the *statute of repose,* is in effect in some states. This period of time starts when the product is put in service. When a product is older than the statute of repose specifies, only under certain conditions may a lawsuit be filed.

No specific lengths of time are given in this section because of the variance among states and changes occurring in the various laws involved. For such specific information as the time involved or other laws involved, either a lawyer should be consulted or an updated legal publication such as *Products Liability,* by L. R. Frumer and M. I. Friedman (Matthew Bender, N.Y.) or *American Law of Products Liability,* by R. D. Hursh and H. J. Bailey (2d ed., Lawyers Cooperative Publishing Company, Rochester, N.Y. 1976), should be consulted.

This discussion of legal considerations in design is necessarily brief and general because of the volatility of the law and the overall field. More complete discussions in the law, engineering, and all aspects of the area can be found in other publications such as Weinstein et al. [1-22], Thorpe and Middendorf [1-23], Colangelo and Thornton [1-24], Philo [1-25], Goodman [1-26], and Dieter [1-15].

1-6 STANDARDS, CODES, AND GOVERNMENTAL REGULATIONS IN DESIGN

1-6-1 Definitions and Descriptions

Design constraints, in addition to those provided by the engineer's management and sales organizations and the marketplace, now include standards, codes, and governmental regulations, both domestic and foreign.

A *standard* is defined as a criterion, rule, principle, or description considered by an authority, or by general consent or usage and acceptance, as a basis for comparison or judgment or as an approved model. Standards and specifications are sometimes used interchangeably; however, *standards* refer to generalized situations, whereas *specifications* refer to specialized situations. For example, a standard might refer to mechanical power transmission equipment; a specification might refer to a particular gear drive.

A *code* is a systematic collection of existing laws of a country or of rules and regulations relating to a given subject. Federal, state, or local governments may adopt engineering, design, or safety codes as part of their own laws.

Governmental regulations are the regulations developed as a result of legislation to control some area of activity. Examples are the regulations developed by the Occupational Safety and Health Administration (OSHA). These regulations, in addition to setting up various methods of operation of the areas controlled, refer to standards and codes which are then given the status and weight of laws.

Standards may be classified as mandatory or voluntary, although standards established as voluntary may be made mandatory if they become a part of a code or by themselves are referenced in governmental regulations having the effect of law.

1-6-2 Categorization by Source

Standards may be categorized by source of development as follows:

1. Governmental regulations
2. Governmental standards
3. Consensus standards
4. Technical society, trade association, and industry standards
5. Company standards
6. Standards of good engineering practice
7. Standards of consumer expectations

GOVERNMENTAL REGULATIONS. Governmental regulations function as standards and also create specific standards. Examples are OSHA regulations, CPSC regulations and standards, and the National Highway Traffic Safety Administration Motor Vehicle Safety Standards.

In addition to the regulations and standards developed by these and other governmental agencies, the regulations and standards include, by reference, other standards, such as those of the American National Standards Institute (ANSI), the Society of Automotive Engineers (SAE), and the American Society for Testing and Materials (ASTM), thus giving the referenced standards the same weight as the governmental regulations and standards. Regulations and standards developed or referenced by the government are considered as mandatory standards and have the weight of laws.

GOVERNMENTAL STANDARDS. Another category of governmental standards consists of those which cover items purchased by the U.S. government and its branches. In order for an item to be considered for purchase by the U.S. government, the item must meet Air Force–Navy Aeronautical (AN or AND) standards, military standards (MS), or governmental specifications (GSA), which are standards covering all items not covered in the AN, AND, and MS standards.

CONSENSUS STANDARDS. Consensus standards are standards developed by a group representing all who are interested in the standard. The group is composed of representatives of the manufacturers, sellers, users, and the general or affected public. All items in the standard have to be unanimously agreed to (i.e., a consensus must be reached) before the standard is published. Since a consensus has to be reached for the standard to be accepted, many compromises have to be made. Thus consensus standards and, for that matter, all standards developed with input from several involved parties represent a minimum level of acceptance and are regarded generally as minimum standards. ANSI and ASTM standards generally fall into the consensus category.

TECHNICAL SOCIETIES AND TRADE ASSOCIATIONS. Technical societies and trade associations develop standards which are applicable to their constituents. These standards are also known as industrial standards and are not true consensus standards unless the public or users of the products are involved in the standards formulation.

One example occurs in the agricultural equipment industry. The Farm and Industrial Equipment Institute (FIEI) is the trade association to which most of the manufacturers belong. The FIEI proposes and assists in developing standards which are published by the American Society of Agricultural Engineers, or the Society of Automotive Engineers, or both. These standards include characteristics of farm crops (useful in harvesting, storing, and transporting), specifications for farm-implement mounting and operation so that farm equipment made by one manufacturer can be used with that made by another manufacturer, and safety and design specifications for items such as grain dryers, augers, and farm-implement controls.

COMPANY STANDARDS. Company standards are those developed by or within an individual company and include such things as specific fasteners, sizes of steel plates or shapes to be purchased, and drafting practices or design practices. Rarely are these standards used outside of a given company. These standards usually refer to or use outside standards wherever applicable.

STANDARDS OF GOOD ENGINEERING PRACTICE. The standards of good engineering practice are not as clearly defined as those previously discussed. Hammer [1-20] states that the mark of a good engineer, and inferentially, good engineering practice, is the design of a product or system to preclude failures, accidents, injuries, and damage. This increases safety and reliability when specific technical requirements do not exist or when conditions are other than ideal. Good engineering practice includes designing at least to minimum standards and generally beyond what the standards require in an effort to minimize failures and their effects, such as machine downtime, lost time, injuries, and damage. Some of the considerations in designing to good engineering practice standards are ease of operation, ease of manufacturability, accessibility for adjustments and service, ease of maintenance, ease of repair, safety, reliability, and overall economic feasibility.

STANDARDS OF CONSUMER AND USER EXPECTATIONS. Consumer and user expectations are another source of standards that are not clearly defined. In many cases, these expectation standards have been established in the marketplace and in the courts through product liability litigation.

When a consumer or user purchases or uses a product, certain expectations of performance, safety, reliability, and predictability of operation are present. For example, a person purchasing an automobile expects it to deliver the performance advertised by the manufacturer and the dealer: start reliably, stop predictably and reliably, and when in motion, the car should speed up, slow down, and steer in a predictably reliable manner. If a brake locks when applied or the steering does not respond, the automobile has not met what would be standard consumer expectations. The failure to meet these expectations provides impetus for product liability actions, depending on the effects of not meeting the expectations. This is particularly true if personal injury, death, or property damage results. A court decision, *Barker* v. *Lull Engineering Co., Inc.,* discussed in Sec 1-5 and accepted in many jurisdictions, established a legal criterion or standard to use in evaluating designs for meeting consumer and user expectations.

1-6-3 Categorization by Function

Functionally, all the standards discussed previously can be classified as follows:

1. Interchangeability standards
2. Performance standards
3. Construction standards
4. Safety standards
5. Test-procedure or test-method standards

There is much overlap in the functional categories. Although the standard may be listed as a safety standard, the safety may be specified in terms of machine construction or performance. For example, ANSI standard B15.1-1972 is entitled "Safety Standard for Mechanical Power Transmission Apparatus." It specifies performance requirements for the types of guarding which apply to mechanical power transmission apparatuses and shows some construction information.

Examples of interchangeability standards are SAE standard J403h, "Chemical Composition of SAE Carbon Steels," SAE standard J246, June 1980, "Spherical and Flanged Sleeve (Compression) Tube Fittings," and the ANSI standards in the C78 series which standardize incandescent light bulbs and screw bases. Because of these interchangeability standards, an SAE 1020 steel is the same in any part of the country, a hydraulic machine using compression fittings that were manufactured in one part of the country can be serviced or replaced with hydraulic compression tube fittings locally available in other parts of the country, and in the last case, when a bulb is blown in a lighting fixture, the fixture does not have to be taken to the store to be certain that the correct bulb is purchased.

Examples of test-procedure or test-method standards are SAE standard J406C, "Methods of Determining Hardenability of Steels," ASTM standard E84-67, "Standard Method of Test for Surface Burning Characteristics of Building Materials," and ASTM standard E108-58 (reapproved 1970), "Standard Methods of Fire Tests of Roof Coverings." Actually, the testing standards are written to assist in achieving interchangeable or repeatable test results; thus these two categories also overlap.

1-6-4 Sources of General Information

A further discussion of the history of standards and standards-making organizations can be found in Peters [1-27]. Further information about standards in general can be found in Talbot and Stephens [1-28] and in Refs. [1-29] to [1-32], taken from Klaas [1-33].

1-6-5 Use of Standards, Codes, and Governmental Regulations in Design

In design, the development of a product or a system requires the solution of a great many repetitive problems, such as the specification of a sheet metal thickness, the

Notes ▪ Drawings ▪ Ideas

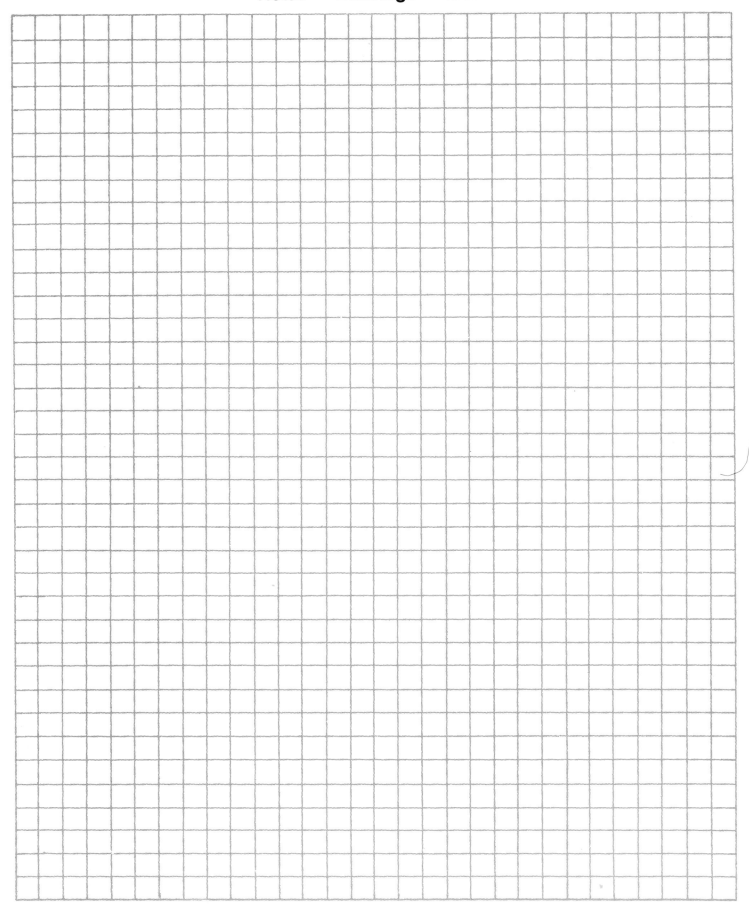

selection of fasteners, the construction of welded joints, the specification of materials in noncritical areas, and other recurring problems.

Standards provide the organized solution to recurring problems. For example, an engineer does not have to design a new cap screw each time a fastener is required. All that is needed is either a company standard or an SAE standard which details the screws already designed and the engineer can quickly select one and pursue other design problems. In fact, the presence of standards allows the designer more time to create or innovate, since solutions to recurring problems of the type discussed above are provided.

Standards can also provide economy by minimizing the number of items to be carried in inventory and the number of different manufacturing operations for a given product. Henderson [1-34] cites the example of a five-sided box formed from sheet metal which had 320 different holes of nine different diameters, of which 243 were tapped. The remaining nontapped holes were for machine screws with nuts and lock washers. Sixteen different screws and rivets were required and the labor costs required to make certain the correct fasteners were present were high.

In a design review, it was found that 304 of the 320 holes could be made the same size and 4 different fasteners could be used rather than the original 16. Specifying a single-diameter hole for 95 percent of the cases increased production while lowering costs significantly.

Standards allow the use of technicians or drafters to do the detail work and free the designer, since company standards will generally provide analyses and sizes and finishes of raw materials either available in stock or commercially available. Other standard manuals provide tap drill sizes, bushings, standard bores and shaft sizes for bearings, and other information in this regard.

In many cases, engineers and management will perceive standards as stifling originality or creativity and being an onerous burden. In many cases, what may be meant is that the standards do not allow or recommend design practices that are detrimental in terms of pollution, safety, or some other effect on the user, consumer, or society and will cost the manufacturer time and money in having the proposed product meet the standards. This argument usually arises when the engineer and/or management had very little input into creation of the standard and the provisions of the standard require redesign or elimination of the product in question.

Some of these products should not have been marketed in the first place. Some standards have required conditions of performance that were beyond the state of the art of measure when insufficient or arbitrary input was used to establish the standard. However, when standards are published, there is always inertia and resistance to change or a required modification because of a standard. The other extreme to resistance is use of the standard as a design specification with very little effort made to exceed the requirements of the standard.

In general, standards are minimum requirements, particularly when proposed as consensus standards, since much compromise is required to make a standard under these conditions. The competent designer, while not always unquestioningly accepting all the standards affecting the product, uses them as a guide and as a source of information to assist in the design and to identify areas of concern.

In the case of governmental regulations and standards, the use of these and other referenced standards is required by law. The use of other consensus or industry standards as a minimum usually indicates use of the standards of good engineering practice. However, if the standard is inadequate, meeting the standard does not guarantee that the design is satisfactory. In some cases, standards-making organizations have been found liable for an inadequate standard.

The engineer should be aware that designs and applications of standards in the design process may be evaluated not by peers, but by the courts. The final evaluations will be made by nontechnical people, users, consumers, and ultimately, by society in general.

A standards search should be initiated in the design process either at the stage where all available information is researched or at the stage where problem-solving and solution constraints are determined. Sources for locating standards are listed at the end of this chapter. In many cases, engineering departments will be involved in developing standards that affect their product and will have a file of applicable standards.

Since standards for a specific product, such as bakery equipment, reference general standards (for example, conveyors, power transmission apparatus), the general standards should also be available in the file.

1-7 SOURCES OF STANDARDS, CODES, GOVERNMENTAL REGULATIONS, INDEXES, AND STANDARDIZATION ACTIVITIES

1-7-1 General

The information provided for sources, indexes, and activities is taken in large part from Klass [1-33] and Talbot and Stephens [1-28] and is categorized as domestic mandatory standards, domestic voluntary standards, codes and recommended practices, and foreign standards. A general source guide for regulations, codes, standards, and publications is Miller [1-35].

1-7-2 Domestic Mandatory Standards

The domestic mandatory standards are published by the U.S. government and include AN, AND, and MS series of standards. (For sources see Refs. [1-36] and [1-37].)

Reference [1-38] lists all unclassified specifications and standards adopted by the Department of Defense. This reference includes listings by title and by specification and standard numbers as well as availability, number, and date of the latest edition. A subject classification is also listed [1-39].

Reference [1-40] indexes General Services Administration (GSA) nonmilitary standards for common items used by government agencies. The listings are alphabetical by title, numerical by specification, commercial item, or standard numbers, and by federal supply classification (FSC) numbers.

The executive departments and agencies of the federal government publish general and permanent rules in the *Code of Federal Regulation* (CFR) [1-41], which is published annually, and the *Federal Register* [1-42], which is published daily, providing current general and permanent rules between revisions of the CFR.

The Occupational Safety and Health Administration (OSHA), established in 1970, is responsible for producing mandatory standards for the workplace, which are available from Refs. [1-43] and [1-44] and are also published under Title 19 of the CFR [1-41].

The Consumer Product Safety Commission (CPSC), established in 1972, is responsible for producing mandatory standards for consumer products. These standards are also published in Title 16 of the CFR [1-41].

The Institute of Basic Standards of the National Bureau of Standards (NBS), a part of the Department of Commerce, prepares basic standards, including those for measurement of electricity, temperature, mass, and length. These standards and other associated publications may be obtained from the Superintendent of Documents, Washington, D.C. Information on ordering these documents is in Title 15 of the CFR, parts 200–299 [1-41]. The NBS also has standards on information processing [1-45] and an *Index of State Specifications and Standards* [1-46].

1-7-3 Domestic Voluntary Standards, Codes, and Recommended Practices

VOLUNTARY STANDARDS. The official coordinating organization in the United States for voluntary standards is the American National Standards Institute (ANSI) [1-47]. Other general standards organizations are the American Society for Testing and Materials (ASTM) and Underwriters Laboratories, Inc. (UL). In addition, professional societies, trade associations, and other organizations formed of people and organizations having like interests develop and promulgate voluntary standards.

The *American Society for Testing and Materials* is an international and nonprofit organization formed in 1898 to develop standards on the characteristics and performance of materials, products, systems, and services while promoting related knowledge. In addition, ASTM has become a managing organization for developing consensus standards. ASTM publishes standards and allied publications and provides a catalog and index which are continually being updated. For the latest catalogs, ASTM should be contacted directly [1-48]. Many of the ASTM standards are designated as ANSI standards also.

Underwriters Laboratories, Inc. was established in 1894 to develop standards and testing capabilities for fire resistance and electric devices. The standards were to include performance specifications and testing. A certification and testing service has evolved along with the development of safety standards for other products as well as those initially included. Many of the UL standards are also designated as ANSI standards. A listing of UL standards and other relevant information can be found in Ref. [1-49], which is available from UL.

Professional societies, trade associations, and other groups promulgate standards in their own areas of interest. Chumas [1-50] and Ref. [1-51] list the groups that fall into these categories.

Aids to finding U.S. voluntary standards are Slattery [1-52], Chumas [1-53], Parker et al. [1-54], and Hilyard et al. [1-55]. Although Slattery [1-52] is relatively old, the data base from which the reference was printed has been kept up to date and a computer printout of the up-to-date list, which provides key word access to standards, can be obtained from the National Bureau of Standards.

Standards or standards' titles and description search systems available are listed in Refs. [1-56] to [1-58]. Philo [1-25], which ostensibly is a publication for lawyers, is of particular interest in that it covers U.S. voluntary standards in Chaps. 17 and 18 and international safety standards and information sources in Chap. 19.

CODES. *Codes* are defined as a collection of rules or standards applying to one topic. In many cases they become a part of federal, state, or local laws, thus becoming mandatory in application.

The National Fire Protection Association (NFPA) publishes an annual set of codes [1-59], which includes the National Electric Codes as well as NFPA standards and additional safety and design publications emphasizing fire prevention. Many of these codes and standards are also designated ANSI standards.

Other well-known codes are the *National Electrical Safety Code* [1-60], the *ASME Boiler and Pressure Vessel Code* [1-61], the *Safety Code for Elevators and Escalators*

[1-62], and the *ASME Performance Test Codes* [1-63]. The *Structural Welding Code* [1-64], the *Uniform Plumbing Code* [1-65], and the *Uniform Mechanical Code* [1-66] are available and should be referred to by engineers, even though they do not appear to directly affect mechanical designers. In these and similar cases, the requirements of the codes dictate how products to be used in these areas should be designed. Another useful collection of codes was compiled by the International Labour Office and is available as *A Model Code of Safety Regulations for the Guidance of Governments and Industry* [1-67]. This discussion and listing of codes is not to be considered complete, but it does provide a listing of which mechanical designers should be aware for reference in designing products.

REFERENCES FOR GOOD ENGINEERING PRACTICE. There are many references that provide other standards, standard data, recommended practices, and good reference information that should be accessible to engineering designers. These and similar publications are considered standards of good engineering practice. The listing of references is not to be construed as all-encompassing, and the order listed does not indicate relative importance. It does include well-known and widely accepted and used references and data. Reference [1-20], as well as Refs. [1-68] to [1-78], are handbooks and compilations of reference data.

PROFESSIONAL SOCIETIES, TRADE ASSOCIATIONS, AND MISCELLANEOUS. In addition to the other references presented, professional societies and trade associations publish standards in specific areas that are accepted and used by machine designers. A representative listing is found in Refs. [1-79] to [1-103].

1-7-4 Foreign Standards

Standardization activity has become worldwide in nature to facilitate international exchange of goods and services and to provide a common international framework for scientific, technologic, and economic activity. Designers of products to be sold outside the United States must include considerations of applicable international and foreign standards to effectively market their products.

The International Organization for Standardization (ISO) is in all fields except electrical and electronic engineering and is located in Geneva, Switzerland. The International Electrotechnical Commission (IEC) covers electrical and electronic engineering and is located at the same address as the ISO in Geneva. The American National Standards Institute (ANSI) is a member body of the ISO and the IEC and, as such, is the sole sales agent for foreign and international standards in the United States. Catalogs of ISO and IEC standards, as well as their standards, may be ordered from ANSI. In addition, 17 countries have standards organizations listed as correspondent members. In this case, the standards organizations are not yet the official national standards organizations for the countries in this category. The latest ISO catalog lists all the members and correspondent members.

The ISO catalog provides names, addresses, and telephone, telegraph, and telex addresses for each of the member body organizations and names and addresses for the correspondent member organizations.

There are regional standardization activities in addition to those in the countries listed in the ISO catalog. Examples are:

1. Central America Research Institute for Industry, Institute de Recherches et de Technologie, Industrielles pour d'Amerique centrale (ICAITI), Guatemala City, Guatemala. Its members are Costa Rica, El Salvador, Guatemala, Honduras, Nicaragua, and Panama.

2. European Economic Community, which publishes *Journal Officiel des Communautés Européennes,* Rue De la Loi 200, B-1049, Bruxelles, Belgium. This journal is published daily and is the equivalent to the *U.S. Federal Register,* publishing laws, regulations, and standards.

Indexes for standards of a given country may be obtained either through ANSI or by contacting the official standards organization of the country. The most up-to-date listing of addresses is found in the ISO catalog of standards referred to previously.

Chumas [1-104] is an index by key word in context and includes addresses of standards organizations of various countries in 1974, in addition to 2700 standards titles of the ISO, IEC, the International Commission on Rules for the approval of Electrical Equipment (CEE), the International Special Committee on Radio Interference (CISPR), and the International Organization of Legal Metrology (OIML).

The World Standards Mutual Speedy Finder [1-105] is a six-volume set having tables of equivalent standards for the United States, the United Kingdom, West Germany, France, Japan, and the ISO in the following areas: vol. 1, Chemicals; vol. 2, Electrical and Electronics; vol. 3, Machinery; vol. 4, Materials; vol. 5, Safety, Electrical and Electronics Products; and vol. 6, Steel. The NBS Standards Information Service, library, and bibliography search referred to previously also include standards from many of the foreign countries.

REFERENCES

1-1   Edward V. Krick, *An Introduction to Engineering and Engineering Design,* John Wiley & Sons, Inc., New York, 1965.

1-2   C. R. Mischke, *Mathematical Model Building,* 2d rev. ed., Iowa State University Press, Ames, Iowa, 1980.

1-3   Percy H. Hill, *The Science of Engineering Design,* Holt, Rinehart and Winston, Inc., New York, 1970.

1-4   Harold R. Buhl, *Creative Engineering Design,* Iowa State University Press, Ames, Iowa, 1960.

1-5   John R. Dixon, *Design Engineering: Inventiveness, Analysis, and Decision Making,* McGraw-Hill, Inc., New York, 1966.

1-6   Thomas T. Woodson, *Introduction to Engineering Design,* McGraw-Hill, Inc., New York, 1966.

1-7   Warren E. Wilson, *Concepts of Engineering System Design,* McGraw-Hill, Inc., New York, 1965.

1-8   D. Henry Edel, Jr., *Introduction to Creative Design,* Prentice-Hall, Inc., Englewood Cliffs, N.J., 1967.

1-9   John R. M. Alger, and Carl V. Hays, *Creative Synthesis in Design,* Prentice-Hall, Inc., Englewood Cliffs, N.J., 1964.

1-10   Martin Kenneth Starr, *Production Design and Decision Theory,* Prentice-Hall, Inc., Englewood Cliffs, N.J., 1963.

1-11   Morris Asimov, *Introduction to Design,* Prentice-Hall, Inc., Englewood Cliffs, N.J., 1962.

1-12   Lee Harrisberger, *Engineersmanship. A Philosophy of Design,* Brooks/Cole, Division of Wadsworth, Inc., Belmont, Cal., 1966.

1-13　Ernest O. Doebelin, *System Dynamics: Modeling and Response,* Charles E. Merrill, Inc., New York, 1972.

1-14　D. J. Leech, *Management of Engineering Design,* John Wiley & Sons, Inc., New York, 1972.

1-15　George E. Dieter, *Engineering Design. A Materials and Processing Approach,* McGraw-Hill, Inc., New York, 1983.

1-15a　T. L. Janis and L. Mann, *American Scientist,* Nov.–Dec. 1976, pp. 657–667.

1-15b　C. H. Kepner and B. B. Tregoe, *The Rational Manager,* McGraw-Hill, Inc., New York, 1965.

1-16　E. B. Haugen, *Probabilistic Approaches to Design,* John Wiley & Sons, Inc., New York, 1968.

1-17　Yardley Beers, *Introduction to the Theory of Error,* 2d ed., Addison-Wesley, Inc., Cambridge, Mass., 1957.

1-18　F. A. Scerbo, and J. J. Pritchard, *Fault Tree Analysis: A Technique for Product Safety Evaluations,* ASME paper 75-SAF-3, American Society of Mechanical Engineers, 1975.

1-19　W. F. Larson, *Fault Tree Analysis,* technical report 3822, Picatinny Arsenal, Dover, N.J., 1968.

1-20　Willie Hammer, *Handbook of System and Product Safety,* Prentice-Hall, Inc., Englewood Cliffs, N.J., 1972.

1-21　Joseph Edward Shigley and Larry D. Mitchell, *Mechanical Engineering Design,* 4th ed., McGraw-Hill, Inc., New York, 1983.

1-22　Alvin S. Weinstein, Aaron D. Twerski, Henry R. Piehler, and William A. Donaher, *Products Liability and the Reasonably Safe Product,* John Wiley & Sons, Inc., New York, 1978.

1-23　James F. Thorpe and William H. Middendorf, *What Every Engineer Should Know About Product Liability,* Dekker, Inc., New York, 1979.

1-24　Vito J. Colangelo and Peter A. Thornton, *Engineering Aspects of Product Liability,* American Society for Metals, 1981.

1-25　Harry M. Philo, *Lawyers Desk Reference,* 6th ed. (2 vols.), Lawyers Cooperative Publishing Co., 1979 (updated).

1-26　Richard M. Goodman, *Automobile Design Liability,* Lawyers Cooperative Publishing Co, 1970; cumulative supplement, 1977 (updated).

1-27　L. C. Peters, *The Use of Standards in Design,* ASME paper 82-DE-10, American Society of Mechanical Engineers, New York, 1982.

1-28　T. F. Talbot and B. J. Stephens, *Locating and Obtaining Copies of Existing Specifications and Standards,* ASME paper 82-DE-9, American Society of Mechanical Engineers, New York, 1982.

1-29　J. Brown, *Standards,* in *Use of Engineering Literature,* Butterworths, Inc., 1976, chap. 7, pp. 93–114.

1-30　Rowen Gile (ed.), *Speaking of Standards,* Cahners Books, Inc., 1972.

1-31　Ellis Mount, *Specifications and Standards,* in *Guide to Basic Information Sources in Engineering,* Gale Research Co., Inc., Detroit, Mich., 1965, chap. 17, pp. 133–135.

1-32　Erasmus J. Struglia, *Standards and Specifications Information Sources in Engineering,* Gale Research Co., Detroit, Mich., 1965.

1-33　Janet E. Klaas, *A Selective Guide to Standards in the Iowa State University*

Library, Government Publications/Reference Department, Iowa State University Library (updated annually).

1-34 Ken L. Henderson, "Unpublished Notes on Standards," 1962; revised 1965. (Mimeographed.)

GENERAL SOURCE GUIDE

1-35 David E. Miller, *Occupational Safety, Health and Fire Index* (a source guide to voluntary and obligatory regulations, codes, standards, and publications), Dekker, Inc., New York, 1976.

SOURCES AND REFERENCES FOR DOMESTIC MANDATORY STANDARDS

1-36 *AN, AND and MS Series Standards,* Naval Publications and Forms Center, 5801 Tabor Avenue, Philadelphia, Pa. 19210.

1-37 *National Standards Association, AN, AND and MS Standards, Inc.,* Washington, D.C., updated, looseleaf.

1-38 U.S. Department of Defense, *Index of Specifications and Standards,* Superintendent of Documents, Washington, D.C., annual, bimonthly supplements.

1-39 U.S. Department of Defense, *Federal Supply Classification Listing of DOD Standards Documents,* Superintendent of Documents, Washington D.C., annual, bimonthly supplements.

1-40 General Services Administration Specifications and Consumer Information Distribution Section, *Index of Federal Specifications, Standards and Commercial Item Descriptions,* Superintendent of Documents, Washington D.C., annual, bimonthly supplements.

1-41 *Code of Federal Regulations,* Office of the Federal Register, Washington, D.C., annual, revised annually; Title 15, parts 200–299, *National Bureau of Standards;* Title 16, parts 1000–1799, *Consumer Product Safety Commissions;* Title 29, *Department of Labor, Occupational Health and Safety Administration,* part 1910, *General Industry,* part 1915, *Ship Repairing,* part 1916, *Ship Building,* part 1917, *Ship Breaking,* part 1918, *Longshoring,* part 1926, *Construction,* part 1928, *Agriculture.*

1-42 *Federal Register,* Office of the Federal Register, Washington, D.C., daily.

1-43 Occupational Safety and Health Administration, *OSHA Safety and Health Standards,* Superintendent of Documents, U.S. Government Printing Office, Washington, D.C. 20402.

1-44 Peter Hopf, *Designers Guide to OSHA,* McGraw-Hill, Inc., New York, 1975.

1-45 U.S. National Bureau of Standards, *Federal Information Processing Standards,* Washington, D.C., updated.

1-46 Linda L. Grossnickle (ed.), *An Index of State Specifications and Standards* (NBS special publication 375), National Bureau of Standards, Washington, D.C., 1973 (up-to-date computer printouts of the data base for this publication may be ordered from the same source).

SOURCES AND REFERENCES FOR VOLUNTARY STANDARDS

1-47 *ANSI Catalog* and *ANSI Standards,* American National Standards Institute, 1430 Broadway, New York, N.Y. 10018.

1-48 *ASTM Publications Catalog,* American Society for Testing and Materials, 1916 Race Street, Philadelphia, Pa. 19103.

1-49 *Catalog of Standards for Safety,* Underwriters Laboratories, Inc., 207 East Ohio Street, Chicago, Ill. 60611.

1-50 Sophie J. Chumas, ed., *Directory of United States Standardization Activities* (NBS special publication 417), National Bureau of Standards, Washington, D.C., 1975.

1-51 *Encyclopedia of Associations,* Gale Research Co., Inc., Detroit, Mich., updated.

1-52 William J. Slattery, ed., *An Index of U.S. Voluntary Engineering Standards* (NBS special publication 329), with supplement 1, 1972, and supplement 2, 1975, Washington, D.C., National Bureau of Standards, 1977.

1-53 Sophie J. Chumas, ed., *Tabulation of Voluntary Standards and Certification Programs for Consumer Products* (NBS technical note 948), Washington, D.C., National Bureau of Standards, 1977.

1-54 Andrew W. Parker, Jr., Charles H. Gonnerman, and Thomas Sommer, *Voluntary Products Standards: An Index Based on Hazard Category,* Washington, D.C., National Science Foundation, 1978.

1-55 Joseph F. Hilyard, Vern L. Roberts, and James H. McElhaney, *Product Stan-Standards Index,* Durham, North Carolina, Product Safety News, Safety Electronics, Inc., 1976.

STANDARDS OR STANDARDS TITLES AND DESCRIPTION SEARCH SYSTEMS THAT ARE AVAILABLE

1-56 Information Handling Services, *Industry/International Standards Locator Index* (microfilm), Englewood, Colorado, continually revised. (This index must be used in conjunction with Information Handling Services, Inc. Product/Subject Master Index.)

1-57 National Standards Association, *Standards and Specific Dialog Information Retrieval Service* (this is a computer data base), Washington, D.C., updated. (Copies of standards on paper or fiche can also be ordered.)

1-58 National Bureau of Standards–Standards Information Service (NBS-SIS), Key Word Search of Computer Data Bank, Washington, D.C.

SOURCES AND REFERENCES FOR CODES

1-59 National Fire Protection Association, *National Fire Codes,* 16 volumes, annual, 470 Atlantic Avenue, Boston, Mass. 02210.

1-60 Institute of Electrical and Electronics Engineers, Inc., *National Electrical Safety Code,* annual, 345 East 47th St., New York, N.Y. 10017. (Also available from ANSI.)

1-61 American Society of Mechanical Engineers, *ASME Boiler and Pressure Vessel Code,* 11 volumes, plus Code Case Book Interpretations, updated, United Engineering Center, 345 East 47th Street, New York, N.Y. 10017. (Also available from ANSI.)

1-62 American Society of Mechanical Engineers, *Safety Code for Elevators and Escalators,* updated, same publisher and availability as Ref. [1-60].

1-63 American Society of Mechanical Engineers, *ASME Performance Test Codes,* updated, same publisher and availability information as Ref. [1-60].

1-64   American Welding Society, *Structural Welding Code,* updated, Miami, Fla.

1-65   *Uniform Plumbing Code,* updated, International Association of Plumbing and Mechanical Officials, 5032 Alhambra Ave., Los Angeles, Cal. 90032.

1-66   *Uniform Mechanical Code,* updated, same as Ref. [1-65].

1-67   *Model Code of Safety Regulations for Industrial Establishments for the Guidance of Governments and Industry* (originally published by International Labour Office, Geneva, Switzerland, 1949), reprinted by Institute for Product Safety, 1410 Duke University Road, Durham, N.C. 27701.

STANDARDS, STANDARD REFERENCES, STANDARD DATA, AND RECOMMENDED PRACTICES SOURCES AND REFERENCES

1-68   Theodore Baumeister (ed.), *Marks' Standard Handbook for Mechanical Engineers,* 8th ed., McGraw-Hill, Inc., New York, 1979

1-69   Colin Carmichael (ed.), *Kent's Mechanical Engineers Handbook,* 12th ed., John Wiley & Sons, Inc., New York, 1950. (An old but still good basic reference.)

1-70   Erik Oberg, Franklin D. Jones, and Holbrook Horton, *Machinery's Handbook,* 21st ed., Industrial Press, New York, 1979.

1-71   C. B. Richey (ed.), *Agricultural Engineers Handbook,* McGraw-Hill, Inc., New York, 1961.

1-72   Harold A. Rothbart (ed.), *Mechanical Design and Systems Handbook,* McGraw-Hill, Inc., New York, 1964.

1-73   Wesley E. Woodson, *Human Factors Design Handbook,* McGraw-Hill, Inc., New York, 1981.

1-74   Henry Dreyfuss, *The Measure of Man. Human Factors in Design,* Whitney Library of Design, New York, 1967.

1-75   Albert Damon, Howard W. Staudt, and Ross A. McFarland, *The Human Body in Equipment Design,* Harvard University Press, Cambridge, Mass., 1966.

1-76   National Safety Council, *Accident Prevention Manual for Industrial Operations,* 7th ed., Chicago, Ill., 1974.

1-77   National Safety Council, *Industrial Safety, Data Sheet Series,* updated.

1-78   FMC Corporations, *Machinery Product Safety Signs and Labels,* 2d ed., Santa Clara, Cal., 1978.

1-79   Associated General Contractors of America, *Manual of Accident Prevention in Construction,* 6th ed., Washington, D.C., 1971.

REFERENCES FROM PROFESSIONAL SOCIETIES, TRADE ASSOCIATIONS, AND MISCELLANEOUS

1-80   Society of Automotive Engineers, Warrendale, Pennsylvania.
  a. SAE Handbook, annual.
  b. SAE Aerospace Index and Price List of AS Standards, ARP Recommended Practices, AIR Information Reports, updated.
  c. Aerospace Material Sepcifications, updated.
  d. Unified Numbering System for Metals and Alloys and *Cross Index of Chemically Similar Specifications,* 2d ed., 1977.

1-81   Aerospace Industries Association, Washington, D.C.
        a. Metric NAS Standards, updated.
        b. NAS Standards, updated.

1-82   American Society of Agricultural Engineers, *Agricultural Engineers Yearbook,* St. Joseph, Mich., annual through 1983.

1-83   American Society of Agricultural Engineers, *Standards 1984,* St. Joseph, Mich., updated each year.

1-84   National Electrical Manufacturers Association, *NEMA Standards,* New York, updated.

1-85   Lois M. Ferson (ed.), *Standards and Practices for Instrumentation,* 6th ed., Instrument Society of America, Research Triangle Park, N.C., 1980.

1-86   General Motors Corporation, *Engineering Materials and Process Standards,* Warren, Mich., updated.

1-87   American Concrete Institute; *ACI Manual of Concrete Practice,* Detroit, Mich., 1982 (updated).

1-88   Robert B. Ross, *Metallic Materials Specification Handbook,* 2d ed., Chapman and Hall, London, England. 1972.

1-89   Mechanical Properties Data Center, *Structural Alloys Handbook,* Traverse City, Mich., updated.

1-90   National Association of Corrosion Engineers, *NACE Standards,* Houston, Tex., updated.

1-91   American Institute of Steel Construction, *AISC Manual of Steel Construction,* 8th ed., New York, 1980.

1-92   The Aluminum Society, Inc., *Aluminum Standards and Data,* Washington, D.C., updated.

1-93   American Petroleum Institute, *API Standards,* Dallas, Tex., updated.

1-94   American Society of Heating, Refrigerating and Air Conditioning Engineers, Inc., New York.
        a. ASHRAE Handbook and Product Directory, Systems Applications Equipment, Fundamentals, updated.
        b. ASHRAE Standards, updated.

1-95   Air Conditioning and Regrigeration Institute, *Standards,* Arlington, Va., updated.

1-96   National Fluid Power Association, Inc., *Fluid Power Standards,* Milwaukee, Wisc, updated.

1-97   American Welding Society, *Welding Handbook,* 7th ed., Miami, Fla., 1976.

1-98   American Nuclear Society, *Standards,* LaGrange Park, Ill., updated.

1-99   American Railway Engineering Association, *Manual,* Washington, D.C. updated.

1-100   John H. Callender (ed.), *Time-Saver Standards for Architectural Design Data,* 5th ed., McGraw-Hill, Inc., New York, 1974.

1-101   Hardam S. Azod (ed.), *Industrial Wastewater Management Handbook,* McGraw-Hill, Inc. New York, 1976.

1-102   American Society of Sanitary Engineers, *ASSE Standards,* Cleveland, Ohio, updated.

1-103   National Sanitation Foundation, *Standards,* Ann Arbor, Mich., updated.

FOREIGN STANDARDS INDEXES

1-104   Sophie J. Chumas, *Index of International Standards* (NBS special publication 390), National Bureau of Standards, Washington, D.C., 1974.

1-105   The International Technical Information Institute, *World Standards Mutual Speedy Finder,* 6 volumes, Tokyo, updated.

Notes · Drawings · Ideas

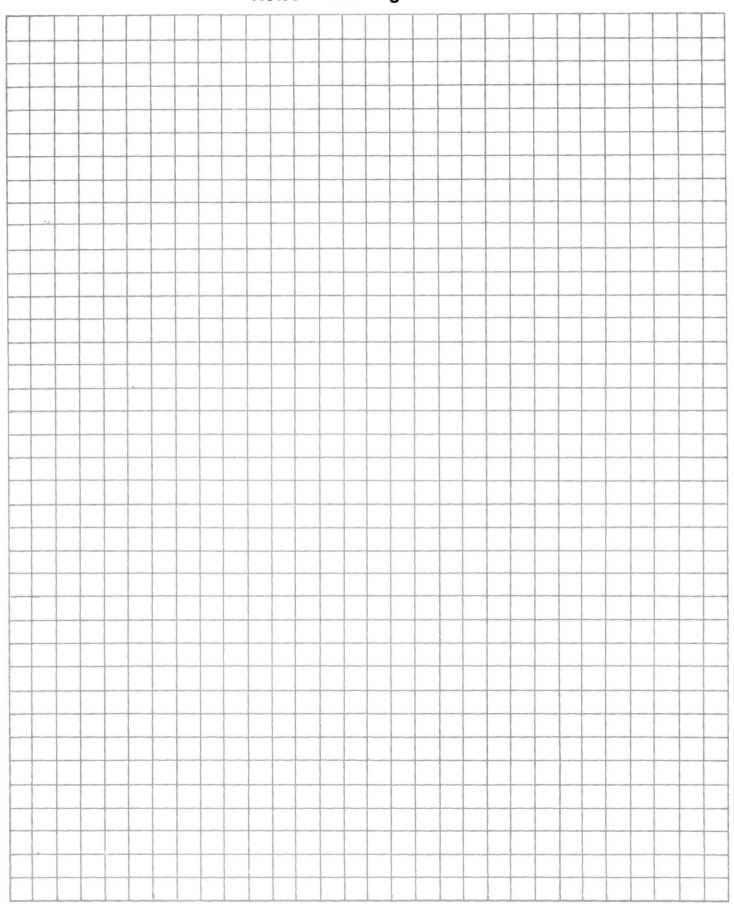

chapter **2**
STATISTICAL CONSIDERATIONS IN DESIGN AND INTERPRETATION OF DATA

EDWARD B. HAUGEN
Associate Professor Emeritus
The University of Arizona
Tucson, Arizona

GLOSSARY

d Wire diameter

D Mean coil diameter

f Probability density function

F Cumulative density function; force

G Shear modulus of elasticity

L Load; length or dimension

m Margin of safety

n Number of observations; design factor

N Number of active spring turns; normal distribution

p Probability

P Probability

R Reliability; probability of survival

s Sample standard deviation

S Strength

$S_{,,}$ Design strength

x Variate

X Variate; design variable

y End contraction of helical coil spring

η Factor of safety

μ Population mean

σ Stress

$\sigma_{,,}$ Working stress

σ Population standard deviation

τ Shear stress

2-1 STOCHASTIC (RANDOM) MODELS OF PHENOMENA

There is ample evidence of a growing interest in probabilistic and statistical methods in engineering. Probablistic design makes sense because engineering variables are modeled more completely by means of statistics and it has been found that stress-strength interactions are probabilistic. Only recently has a performance-related measure, reliability R, been used to state design adequacy or level of safety.

Some of the essentials that must be included in decisions and adequacy assessments based on probabilistic ideas include:

- Important concepts from probability theory—considering the ways they apply in engineering
- Distribution theory—which distributions describe engineering variables and which distributions constitute workable models
- Propagation of variability in functions of random variables—that is, how to determine the statistics of distributions of functions of random variables, each described by a distribution and by statistics (mean value and standard deviation)
- How to describe load-induced stress and significant strength—by means of defining distributions and their statistics
- A synthesis plan—given a required performance probability measure (R) and preceding item, a plan to carry out the design synthesis
- An optimization plan—having probabilistically synthesized a design, carry out an optimization at a specified reliability R

What must we consider in a study of probabilistic design? In addition to the interrelationships among design variables, the unique nature of these variables must be considered. A second tier of modeling is required, i.e., one which preserves the essential features of each variable in a function:

1. The multivalued aspects
2. Their random nature

Why design by reliability?

- Thoughtful engineers have been concerned with problems of design adequacy and its quantitative expression.
- Careful and rigorous analyses can be deprived of their merits if results are diluted through the use of empirical multipliers selected arbitrarily on bases not always rational or relevant.
- Conventional practice, evolved to circumvent variability problems, often produces overly conservative design.
- An analysis may or may not be realistic; there is no way of knowing which it is.

We need to consider the following questions:

1. How safe is a design, expressed by a measure related to performance?
2. How safe should a design be, related to the consequences of failure?
3. How can designs to specified levels of adequacy be accomplished?

Answers to these questions involve probabilistic methods.

The domain of engineering is fraught with uncertainty. Presently available mathematical tools have not been well suited to the task of dealing with uncertainty; i.e., the use of real numbers almost exclusively.

The algebra of real numbers produces unique single-valued answers in the evaluation of a function. As will be seen, we must take into account more than a single value (such as an average) in representing the behavior of a variable and accounting for uncertainty. Statistical uncertainty has been ignored, for instance, in the search for

1. Minimum guaranteed values
2. Limit loads
3. Ultimate loads, etc.

Consider the following classes of design variables:

1. Hardness
2. Geometry
3. Tensile ultimate strength
4. Loading, etc.

Thus if loading is expressed as $L = F(x_1, x_2, \ldots, x_n)$, it is a deterministic model, whereas if it is expressed as

$$(\overline{L}, {}_{\triangle L}) = f[(\overline{x}_1, {}_{\triangle x_1}), (\overline{x}_2, {}_{\triangle x_2}), \ldots, (\overline{x}_n, {}_{\triangle x_n})]$$

we have a statistical model.

The magnitudes of almost all engineering variables change in a random fashion. Variables are characterized by spectra of values, not by unique ones (see [2-1]). The results of a series of tests or measurements is a population of nonidentical observations:

$$x_1, x_2, \ldots, x_n$$

Plotted on a graph as magnitude versus frequency, such (histographic) displays tend to approach stable, predictable distributions, such as the normal, lognormal, gamma, Weibull, etc. (see Table 2-1).

Many engineering variables x are well represented by a mean value $\overline{x}$ and a measure of variation ${}_{\triangle x}$. These are estimators of μ_x and σ_x.

Example:

$$\overline{S}_y \text{ (psi)} = \text{sample mean tensile yield strength}$$

$${}_{\triangle S_y} \text{ (psi)} = \text{sample standard deviation of tensile yield}$$

Consequently, a variable may be described by a couple, $(\overline{S}_y, {}_{\triangle S_y})$ psi, and a statement of its distribution. These two numbers can uniquely describe any two-parameter distribution.

For classical strength-limited design, once the criterion of failure is identified, the rule for an adequate design is

Strength > stress

And to cover imponderables:

Strength > (design factor) stress

The concept of *design factor* conveys the idea that the mean strength and the mean stress have been intentionally separated sufficiently to provide the requisite level of safety.

There are frustrations in using the design factor. The inherent variability of stress

TABLE 2-1 Continuous Distributions

Distribution name	Parameters	Probability density function	Expected value	Variance
Normal	$-\infty < \mu < \infty, \sigma > 0$	$f(x) = \dfrac{1}{\sigma\sqrt{2\pi}} \exp\left[-\dfrac{1}{2}\left(\dfrac{x-\mu}{\sigma}\right)^2\right]$ $-\infty < x < \infty$	μ	σ^2
Gamma	$\lambda > 0, \eta > 0$	$f(x) = \begin{cases} \dfrac{\lambda^\eta}{\Gamma(\eta)} x^{\eta-1} \exp(-\lambda x) & x \geq 0 \\ 0 & \text{elsewhere} \end{cases}$	$\dfrac{\eta}{\lambda}$	$\dfrac{\eta}{\lambda^2}$
Exponential	$\lambda > 0$	$f(x) = \begin{cases} \lambda \exp(-\lambda x) & x \geq 0 \\ 0 & \text{elsewhere} \end{cases}$	$\dfrac{1}{\lambda}$	$\dfrac{1}{\lambda^2}$
Rayleigh	$\sigma > 0$	$f(x) = \begin{cases} \left(\dfrac{x}{\sigma^2}\right) \exp\left(\dfrac{-x^2}{2\sigma^2}\right) & x \geq 0 \\ 0 & \text{elsewhere} \end{cases}$	$\dfrac{(\sigma^2\pi)^{1/2}}{\sqrt{2}}$	$0.429\sigma^2$
Weibull	$\eta > 0, \theta > 0$	$f(x) = \begin{cases} \dfrac{\eta}{\theta}\left(\dfrac{x}{\theta}\right)^{\eta-1} \exp\left[-\left(\dfrac{x}{\theta}\right)^\eta\right] & x \geq 0 \\ 0 & \text{elsewhere} \end{cases}$	$\theta\Gamma\left(\dfrac{1}{\eta} + 1\right)$	$\theta^2\left[\Gamma\left(\dfrac{2}{\eta} + 1\right) - \left[\Gamma\left(\dfrac{1}{\eta} + 1\right)\right]^2\right]$
Lognormal	$-\infty < \mu < \infty;$ $\sigma > 0$	$f(x) = \dfrac{1}{\sigma x\sqrt{2\pi}} \exp\left[-\dfrac{1}{2\sigma^2}(\log x - \mu)^2\right]$ $x \geq 0$	$\exp\left(\mu + \dfrac{\sigma^2}{2}\right)$	$\exp(2\mu+\sigma^2)[\exp(\sigma^2) - 1]$

SOURCE: Haugen [2-2].

63

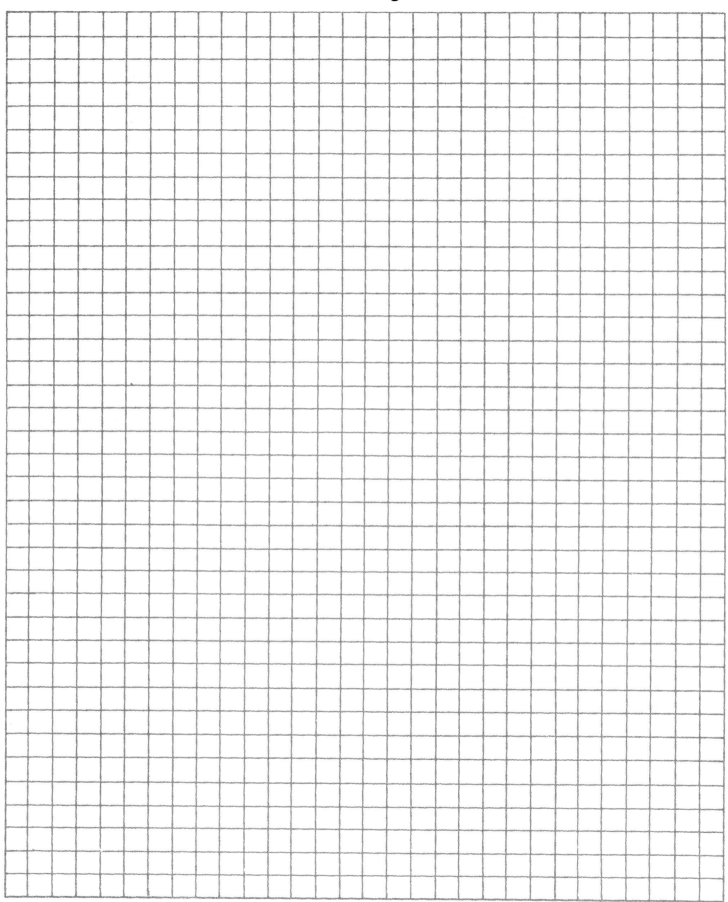

and stress factors and of strength and strength factors suggests the existence of stress and strength distributions. These distributions should be taken into account by engineers and designers.

When the distributions of strength and stress are known, the adequacy of a component or system may be estimated from the interference depicted in Fig. 2-1.

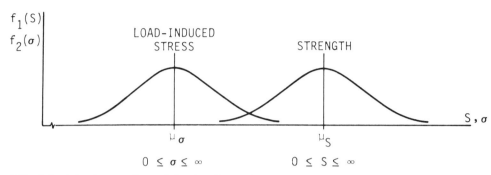

FIG. 2-1 The interaction of distributions of stress and strength when the mean strength exceeds the mean stress.

In the mathematical models of strength and stress distributions, an unavoidable overlap occurs in principle. The curves depicted in Fig. 2-1 predict a finite incidence of failure, which our experience verifies. It is to be noted that to support design, the algebra of statistics has recently been developed.

The following steps are necessary when including probabilistic methods:

- Invent a concept and give it a preliminary form.
- Describe external forces to be imposed on the devices or system a priori, as well as the range of loads and their relative frequencies.
- Analyze the preliminary system: quantitative estimates of force intensities expressed by statistical models.
- Select material based on physical and/or mechanical properties, considering economics, availability, and feasibility.
- Describe strength and failure characteristics of materials, including the probability density function, to account for variability.
- Make quantitative estimates of strength and failure characteristics at the component level.

In a strength-limited design, the results will be a joint probability function, where

$$P[S > \sigma] = P[S - \sigma > 0] \geq R$$

and

$$R = \int_{-\infty}^{\infty} f_1(S) \left[\int_{S}^{\infty} f_2(\sigma) \, d\sigma \right] dS. \tag{2-1}$$

where f_1 = strength probability density function
f_2 = load-induced stress probability density function
S = significant strength
σ = significant load-induced stress

The goal should be to design for

- Strength to resist static forces
- Strength to resist repeated applications of forces
- Finite life—to resist repeated forces for at least n cycles
- Finite deflection—to resist unvarying or repeated forces without exceeding a specified amount of distortion.

The task for a given design is to ensure that $S > \sigma$, where S = significant strength and σ = significant load-induced stress, in accordance with some failure criterion and meeting a reliability goal.

The definition of *failure* (the criterion) may be

- Fracture
- Yield
- Fatigue failure
- Deformation

Since a force F is applied on the one hand and resisted on the other hand by internal restoring forces, these must be expressed in compatible units. Since varia-

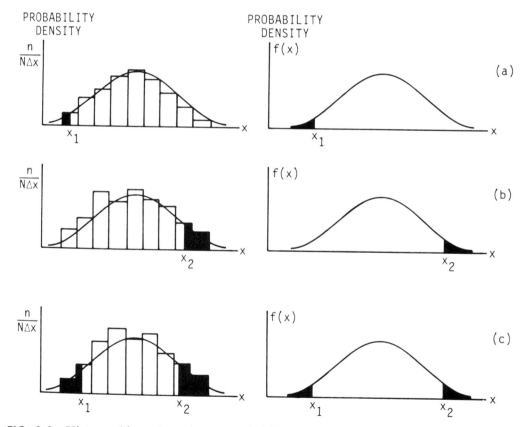

FIG. 2-2 Histographic and continuous probability density curves. (*a*) Shaded area is probability that $x < x_1$ and unshaded area is probability that $x > x_1$; (*b*) shaded area $p(x > x_2)$, unshaded area $p(x < x_2)$; (*c*) unshaded area $p(x_1 < x < x_2)$.

bility is encountered at every turn, it is necessary to consider some of the concepts from probability and statistics, the disciplines for dealing with uncertainty and variability.

Consider the following defintions for probability:

- The classical definition—requires a complete knowledge of all possible outcomes, such as in coin flipping or die rolling, i.e., in simple, well-defined situations having known sets of outcomes.
- The relative-frequency definition—applicable in more complicated situations where the outcomes cannot be easily listed and where the likelihood of outcomes may be in doubt. In such cases, we make a large number of trials of a test and then identify the various outcomes or values and count numbers of outcomes. This is the procedure followed in engineering and in practical statistical determinations. It is the only procedure available to us in studying natural phenomena. This has been denoted the relative-frequency approach. The estimations determined thereby are called *relative frequencies*.

Probability statements such as $p(x > x_1)$, $p(x < x_2)$, and $p(x_1 < x_2)$ may be interpreted as areas on histographic or continuous probability-density diagrams, such as depicted in Fig. 2-2.

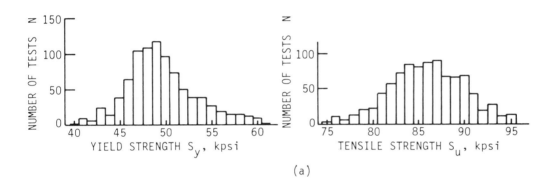

(a)

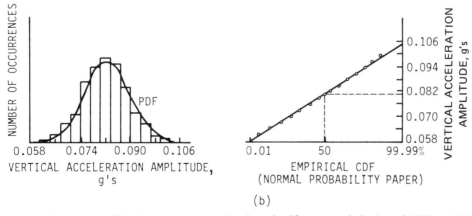

(b)

FIG. 2-3 Examples of design parameters having significant statistical variability. (*a*) Histograms of tensile properties of hot-rolled AISI 1035; (*b*) histogram and empirical cumulative density function for loading of floorpan of medium-weight passenger car—road surface, cobblestones; speed, 20 mi/h (32 km/h).

Notes ▪ Drawings ▪ Ideas

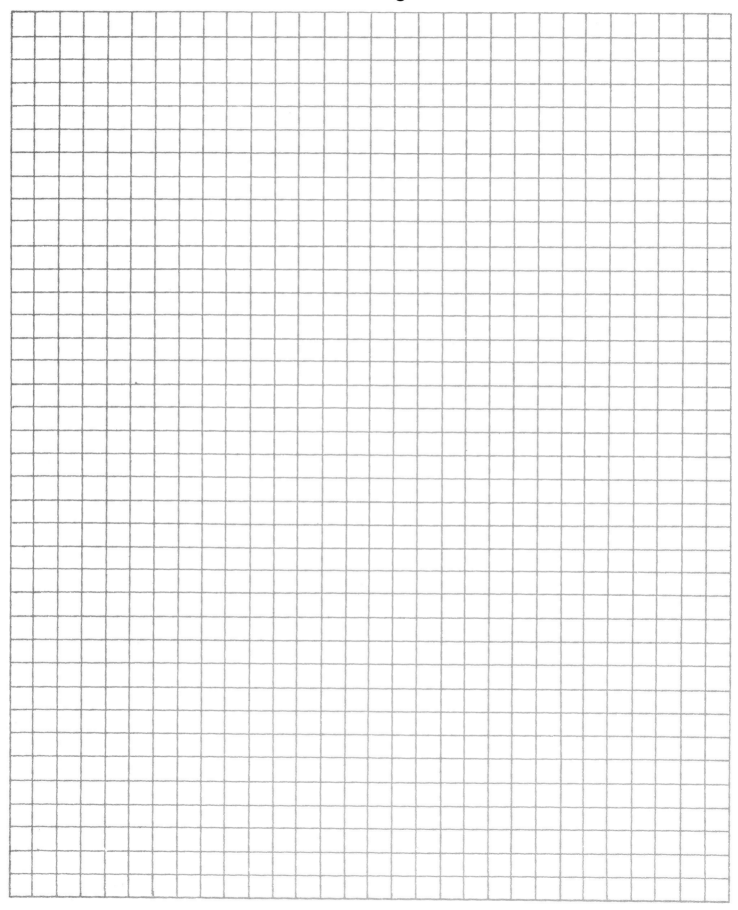

TABLE 2-2 Basic Definitions Utilized in Probability Theory

A **random variable** is a real number corresponding to the outcome of a nondeterministic experiment, e.g., the ultimate strength S_u of a material in a tensile test. S_u will take on different values when the experiment is repeated.

Probability (observational concept): Probability of occurrence of event D:

$$P(D) = \lim_{n \to \infty} \frac{n_o}{n}$$

where n = number of times that the experiment is repeated, and n_o = number of times that event D occurred during n trials.

Mathematical descriptions of a continuous random variable: X = random variable, x = specific value of X.

Cumulative distribution function (CDF):

$$F(x) = P(X \le x)$$

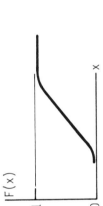

Probability density function (PDF):

$$\text{Area} = P(a \le X \le b)$$

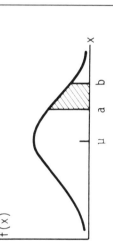

Mean (or average value): A measure of the central tendency of X:

$$\mu_x = \int_{-\infty}^{\infty} xf(x)\, dx$$

Geometric interpretation: Centroid of area of PDF.

Variance: A **measure** of the dispersion or variability of X:

$$\sigma_x^2 = \int_{-\infty}^{\infty} (x - \mu_x)^2 f(x)\, dx$$

Geometric interpretation: Second moment of area about centroid of PDF.

Standard deviation:

$$\sigma_X = \sqrt{\sigma_X^2}$$

This is often used by engineers in lieu of variance to describe dispersion because it has the same units as X and μ_X

Coefficient of variation: A dimensionless alternative measure of dispersion:

$$C_X = \frac{\sigma_X}{\mu_X}$$

This is commonly used in design because it has been observed that many design parameters, e.g., strength, have nearly constant coefficients of variation.

2-2 DESCRIPTIVE STATISTICS

The basic goal of engineering designers is to develop physical systems which represent the optimum economic balance between cost and risk in response to human needs. The probabilistic design methods for the analysis and synthesis of mechanical components appear to be an appropriate step, gradually replacing classical deterministic design procedures. In the *classical approach,* all design variables are idealized

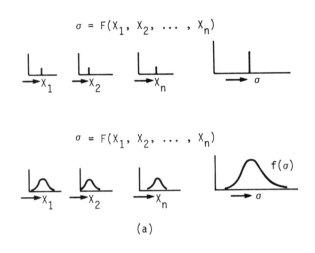

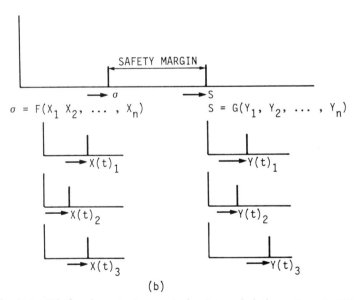

FIG. 2-4 Distinctions to be made in deterministic and probabilistic approaches. (*a*) Deterministic versus probabilistic representation of a load function; (*b*) design-deterministic approach; (*c*) design-probabilistic approach. (*Note:* The units are the same for stress σ and strength S, and t refers to service life.)

and treated as deterministic, and an empirical design factor provides the margin against uninvestigated or unforeseen variability. In the *probabilistic approach,* statistical information is employed in the design algorithms and maximum allowable probability of failure provides the proper margin against variability. Such a simple shift in the design viewpoint has far-reaching ramifications.

In the design of mechanical components for strength and/or deflection, attention centers on the characteristics of the variables that influence component behavior.

1. Evidence now supports the contention that engineering variables tend to be multivalued, i.e., are random variables (see Table 2-2 and Fig. 2-3). Most design random variables are continuous, and can be modeled by known continuous distributions. Also, design random variables interact functionally. Consider the classical (deterministic) and probabilistic treatment of load functions. If the real conditions were such that each variable $X_1, X_2, \ldots, X_n$ was single-valued and the relation of these variables to the variable x was described by the function $F(X_1, X_2, \ldots, X_n)$, then the transformation from $X_1, X_2, \ldots, X_n$ to σ would be a single value (Fig. 2-4a). If, however, the variables $X_1, X_2, \ldots, X_n$ were each multivalued, then the transformation for $X_1, X_2, \ldots, X_n$ to σ would be a distribution of probable values of σ (see Fig. 2-4b). This is similarly true for strength functions. In Table 2-3, a statistical algebra for simple functions of random variables is summarized.

2. It is more meaningful to state "This unit has a probability of 10^{-4} (a performance-related measure) of failing after 250 000 cycles of operation" than to state "This unit has a factor of safety of 2.3." Reliability is performance-related, a probability statement providing a valid and complete description of mechanical performance. Designers must increasingly utilize probabilistic design procedures (Fig. 2-4c).

3. Probabilistic-based information can be used to develop rational policies in pricing and in specifying warranties, spare-parts requirements, etc.

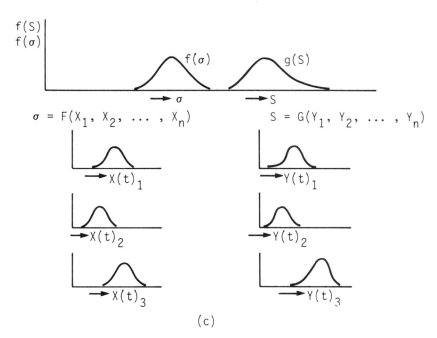

(c)

FIG. 2-4 (*Continued*)

TABLE 2-3 How to Compute Mean and Standard Deviations of Functions of Independent Random Variables X and Y (a is a constant)†

Function	Mean μ_Z	Standard deviation σ_Z
$Z = a$	a	0
$Z = aX$	$a\mu_X$	$a\sigma_X$
$Z = X \pm a$	$\mu_X \pm a$	σ_X
$Z = X \pm Y$	$\mu_X \pm \mu_Y$	$[\sigma_X^2 + \sigma_Y^2]^{1/2}$
$Z = XY$	$\mu_X\mu_Y$	$[\mu_X^2\sigma_Y^2 + \mu_Y^2\sigma_X^2]^{1/2}$ (1)
$Z = X/Y$	μ_X/μ_Y	$[\mu_X^2\sigma_Y^2 + \mu_Y^2\sigma_X^2]^{1/2}/\mu_Y^2$
$Z = X^2$	$\mu_X^2 + \sigma_X^2$	$[4\mu_X^2\sigma_X^2 + 2\sigma_X^4]^{1/2}$
$Z = 1/X$	$1/\mu_X$	σ_X/μ_X^2

†The algebra of random variables shares many elements in common with the algebra of real numbers:
- Uniqueness of sum/product.
- Associative law in addition/multiplication.
- Existence of identity element for addition/multiplication.
- Unitary minus operation leads to subtraction; multiplicative inverse leads to division.
- Commutative law in addition/multiplication.

In combinations of addition and multiplication, the distributive law holds. In general, if Z is a function of k independent random variables,

$$Z = Z(X_1, X_2, \ldots, X_k) \tag{2}$$

These approximate formulas give reasonable results if the coefficients of variation of each X_i are less than 0.20:

$$\mu_Z = Z(\mu_1, \mu_2, \ldots, \mu_k) \tag{3}$$

$$\sigma_Z^2 = \sum_{i=1}^{k}\left(\frac{\partial Z}{\partial X_i}\right)_\mu^2 \sigma_{X_i}^2 \tag{4}$$

where the partial derivatives are evaluated at the mean values. Note that when Z is a complicated function of the X_i's, a computer program may be used to evaluate Z, for example, as in finite-element analysis. This same program may be used to numerically estimate $\partial Z/\partial X_i$. See Refs. [2-2] and [2-10] for a more detailed discussion of mathematics and limitations and Ref. [2-16], App. C, for 45 useful equations.

MATHEMATICAL CONCEPTS. In the probabilistic approach, design variables are recognized as random variables. Definitions of random variables and other necessary basic concepts from probability theory are given in Table 2-2. A complete probabilistic description of a random variable S is contained in its cumulative distribution function (CDF) or probability density function (PDF) (Table 2-2). The mean value μ_X and standard deviation σ_X are real numbers which together with the PDF of the distribution of X uniquely describe the random variable (for any two-parameter distribution). Often an engineer's first contact with uncertainty in engineering phenomena occurs in studies of experimental data. If the data yield an estimate of the PDF or CDF, probability statements can be made of the sort depicted in Fig. 2-2. One aspect of statistics is that of constructing probability models from observed data (for example, see [2-2], Chap. 3).

It is necessary in probabilistic design to develop μ_X and σ_X for each design variable X and further to identify the likely form of the PDF in order to compute probabilities. Table 2-4 illustrates the statistical analysis of data. The sample mean value $\overline{X}$ and sample standard deviation s_X^* approximate μ_X and σ_X, respectively, and the shape of the histogram approximates that of the PDF. In general, the larger the sample size n, the closer the approximation [2-4]. The distribution of data can be approximated

TABLE 2-4 Elementary Statistical Analysis

The following data were obtained from an experiment to measure the loads in a strut of an aircraft landing gear upon landing impact. Loads are given in kips. A sample of size $n = 40$ replications, under a variety of flight conditions, was taken. Data are denoted as X_i, $i = 1, 2, 3, \ldots, 40$.

Let X be a random variable denoting a landing load. X has a PDF given as $f_x(x)$ and a mean of μ_X and standard deviation of σ_X all of which are unknown before the data are collected. The purpose of taking the data was to estimate these values.

2.88	2.41	2.42	2.72
1.79	1.97	3.20	2.61
3.02	2.86	2.59	2.68
3.12	3.05	2.27	2.46
2.40	2.80	2.19	3.10
2.79	2.52	2.82	2.07
2.37	2.48	2.63	2.71
1.90	2.10	2.57	2.32
2.74	2.90	3.14	2.81
2.80	3.32	2.70	2.63

The *sample mean* $\overline{X}$ is a measure of the "central tendency" of the data and is an estimate of μ_X.

$$\overline{X} = \frac{1}{n} \sum_{i=1}^{n} X_i$$

$$= \frac{1}{40} [104.86] = 2.62 \text{ kips}$$

The *sample standard deviation* s_X is a measure of the amount of variability of the data and is an estimate of σ_X.

$$\sigma_X = \left(\frac{1}{n-1} \sum X_i^2 - \frac{n}{n-1} \overline{X}^2 \right)^{1/2}$$

$$= \left[\frac{1}{39} (280.06) - \frac{40}{39} (6.864) \right]^{1/2} = 0.346 \text{ kips}$$

The sample coefficient of variation is another measure of the variability:

$$C_X = \frac{\sigma_X}{\overline{X}} = \frac{0.36}{2.60} = 0.14$$

graphically. The number of occurrences in each interval is plotted in a bar chart (or histogram) which indicates the form of the underlying PDF as the number of data n becomes large.

Many design variables suggest normal distributions, characterized by symmetrical bell-shaped PDFs (see Table 2-2). Other statistical models have been used to describe design parameters (see Refs. [2-2], [2-3], [2-4]), including the lognormal, gamma, Weibull, and exponential models (see also Refs. [2-5], [2-6], [2-7]).

ESTIMATION OF VARIABILITY FROM TOLERANCES. In engineering literature it is common to find variability in a design variable described in terms of a tolerance $\pm K$ or by a range r of values.

If tolerance is defined as $\pm \Delta L$ on a dimension L and $(L - \Delta L, L + \Delta L)$ describes the range of values generated by a particular process, then the standard deviation σ_L can be estimated as

$$\sigma_L \approx \frac{2\Delta L}{6} = \frac{\Delta L}{3} \tag{2-2}$$

provided n will be reasonably large (see Ref. [2-10]).

EXAMPLE. The yield strength S_y of the titanium alloy is reported to be in the range of 120 to 160 Kpsi. Estimate the mean and standard deviation of S_y.

Solution. The mean is estimated to be $\overline{S}_y \approx (120 + 160)/2 = 140$ kpsi, and the standard deviation is estimated as

$$\sigma_{S_y} \approx \frac{160 - 120}{6} = 6.67 \text{ kpsi} \tag{2-3}$$

The distributional PDF is unknown; however, the normal distribution is often an acceptable model for static material strengths.

FUNCTIONS OF RANDOM VARIABLES. For design purposes, from functional expressions of unit stress σ and unit strength S, components are synthesized. Each σ and/or S is often a function of several random design variables, and thus each is a random variable. For example, peak shearing stress τ in a helical spring can be written as (see Refs. [2-8] and [2-9])

$$\tau = \left(1 + \frac{d}{2D}\right) \frac{8FD}{\pi d^3} \tag{2-4}$$

where d = wire diameter, D = coil diameter, and F = axial force. If F, D, and d are random variables and have known PDFs, mean values μ, and standard deviations σ, the PDF of τ, as well as μ_τ and σ_τ, must usually be estimated.

Often, however, good approximations of μ_τ and σ_τ can be made. Table 2-3 summarizes methods for estimating μ and σ for a function of random variables.†

The designer can usually make reasonable estimates of μ and σ for each design variable, but doubt remains as to the exact form of the PDF. For the asymptotic limits of functions of arbitrary random variables, see Ref. [2-2], Chaps. 2 and 3.

EXAMPLE. This example illustrates estimation of the mean value and standard deviation of a function of several random variables utilizing Eqs. (1) and (2) in Table 2-3.

---

†For a comprehensive discussion of statistical algebra, see Haugen [2-2].

TABLE 2-5 Variability in Helical Coil Spring Parameters

Parameter	Mean μ	Standard deviation σ
Wire diameter d	0.092 in	0.399 (10^{-3}) in
Mean coil diameter D	0.658 in	0.3816 (10^{-2}) in
Shear modulus of elasticity G	11.5 (10^6) psi	23.0 (10^4) psi
Number of active coils N	14	0.0833
End contraction y	0.80 in	0.016 in

The shearing-stress amplitude of a helical spring is given as

$$\tau = \frac{(1 + d/2D)\, dGy}{\pi D^2 N} \qquad (2\text{-}5)$$

where the variables are defined in Table 2-5. (Also given in Table 2-5 are numerical values for the mean and variance of each of the variables.) Estimate the mean value and standard deviation of τ.

Solution. The mean value of τ, denoted as μ_τ, is estimated by applying Eq. (1) of Table 2-3 to Eq. (2-5) (see Ref. [2-8]):

$$\mu_\tau = \frac{(1 + \mu_d/2\mu_D)\mu_d\mu_G\mu_y}{\pi\mu_D^2\mu_N} \qquad (2\text{-}6)$$

Using mean-value data from Table 2-5,

$$\mu_\tau \approx 47\,550 \text{ psi}$$

The variance of τ, denoted as σ_τ^2, is estimated by applying Eq. (4) of Table 2-3 to Eq. (2-5):

$$\sigma_\tau^2 = \left(\frac{\partial\tau}{\partial d}\right)^2 \sigma_d^2 + \left(\frac{\partial\tau}{\partial D}\right)^2 \sigma_D^2 + \left(\frac{\partial\tau}{\partial G}\right)^2 \sigma_G^2 + \left(\frac{\partial\tau}{\partial N}\right)^2 \sigma_N^2 \qquad (2\text{-}7)$$

where $\partial\tau/\partial d$, etc. are evaluated at the mean values of the variables.

Evaluating σ_τ using data provided in Table 2-5 gives a value of 1430 psi. Since the coefficients of variation of all terms were relatively small, it is known that τ will have an approximately normal distribution and can be expressed as

$$\tau \approx N(47\,500,\ 1430) \text{ psi}$$

PROBABILISTIC DESIGN THEORY. In classical design practice, a factor of safety $\eta > 1$ is specified and the basic design criterion uses a design factor n so that the final adequacy assessment will reveal a factor of safety equal to or exceeding that specified. That is,

$$\eta = \frac{S_o}{\sigma_o}$$

where σ_o = working stress, and S_o = design strength. It has been established that both load-induced stress and strength are subject to statistical variability. Furthermore, since it is most meaningful to specify mechanical requirements by performance-related reliability statements, it is important that probability of adequacy, denoted R, be specified as a basic design requirement. The following explains the

TABLE 2-6 Interference Theory

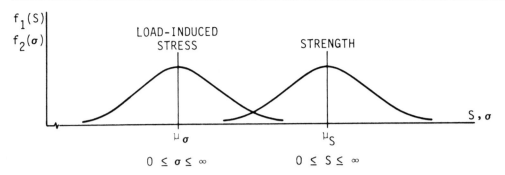

Overlap in density functions suggests that it is possible for $\sigma > S$.

Probability of failure: $P_f = P(\sigma \geq S)$ (1)
Reliability: $R = 1 - P(\sigma \geq S) = 1 - P_f$

Basic probabilistic design equations (Note that required geometric variables are contained in μ's and σ's.):

If σ and S are *normally* distributed:

$$z = -\frac{\mu_S - \mu_\sigma}{(\sigma_S^2 + \sigma_\sigma^2)^{1/2}} \qquad (2)$$

If σ and S are *lognormally* distributed:

$$\left(\frac{\mu_\sigma}{\mu_S}\right)^2 = \left(\frac{\mu_S^2 + \sigma_S^2}{\mu_\sigma^2 + \sigma_\sigma^2}\right)^{1/2} \exp\left[z \sqrt{\left(\frac{\sigma_S}{\mu_S}\right)^2 + \left(\frac{\sigma_\sigma}{\mu_\sigma}\right)^2}\right] \qquad (3)$$

P_f	$z = \phi^{-1}(1 - P_f)$	P_f	$z = \phi^{-1}(1 - P_f)$
10^{-2}	-3.326	10^{-7}	-5.199
10^{-3}	-3.090	10^{-8}	-5.610
10^{-4}	-3.719	10^{-9}	-5.997
10^{-5}	-4.265	10^{-10}	-6.361
10^{-6}	-4.753	10^{-11}	-6.700

where ϕ is the standard normal CDF.
Use this as an upper bound when you do not want to assume a specific distribution for σ and S:

For $\sigma_\sigma \neq \sigma_S$:

$$P_f(\sigma_\sigma - \sigma_S) = \sigma_\sigma \exp\left[\frac{-(\mu_S + \sigma_S - \mu_\sigma + \sigma_\sigma)}{\sigma_\sigma}\right] - \sigma_\sigma \exp\left[\frac{-(\mu_S + \sigma_S - \mu_\sigma + \sigma_\sigma)}{\sigma_S}\right] \qquad (4)$$

For $\sigma_\sigma = \sigma_S$:

$$P_f\sigma_\sigma = (\mu_S + 2\sigma_S - \mu_\sigma - \sigma_\sigma) \exp\left[\frac{-(\mu_S + \sigma_S - \mu_\sigma + \sigma_\sigma)}{\sigma_\sigma}\right]$$

NOTE: If σ or S is shown to be deterministic, then $\sigma = \mu_\sigma$ and $\sigma_\sigma = 0$, or $S = \mu_S$ and $\sigma_S = 0$ in Eqs. (2), (3), and (4).

TABLE 2-7 Normal Distribution Cumulative Density Function

$$F(x) = \int_{-\infty}^{x} \frac{1}{\sqrt{2\pi}} \exp\left(-\frac{t^2}{2}\right) dt$$

x	.00	.01	.02	.03	.04	.05	.06	.07	.08	.09
.0	.5000	.5040	.5080	.5120	.5160	.5199	.5239	.5279	.5319	.5359
.1	.5398	.5438	.5478	.5517	.5557	.5596	.5636	.5675	.5714	.5753
.2	.5793	.5832	.5871	.5910	.5948	.5987	.6026	.6064	.6103	.6141
.3	.6179	.6217	.6255	.6293	.6331	.6368	.6406	.6443	.6480	.6517
.4	.6554	.6591	.6628	.6664	.6700	.6736	.6772	.6808	.6844	.6879
.5	.6915	.6950	.6985	.7019	.7054	.7088	.7123	.7157	.7190	.7221
.6	.7257	.7291	.7324	.7357	.7389	.7422	.7454	.7486	.7517	.7549
.7	.7580	.7611	.7642	.7673	.7704	.7734	.7764	.7794	.7823	.7852
.8	.7881	.7910	.7939	.7967	.7995	.8023	.8051	.8078	.8106	.8133
.9	.8159	.8186	.8212	.8238	.8264	.8289	.8315	.8340	.8365	.8389
1.0	.8413	.8438	.8461	.8485	.8508	.8531	.8554	.8577	.8599	.8621
1.1	.8643	.8665	.8686	.8708	.8729	.8749	.8770	.8790	.8810	.8830
1.2	.8849	.8869	.8888	.8907	.8925	.8944	.8962	.8980	.8997	.9015
1.3	.9032	.9049	.9066	.9082	.9099	.9115	.9131	.9147	.9162	.9177
1.4	.9192	.9207	.9222	.9236	.9251	.9265	.9279	.9202	.9306	.9319
1.5	.9332	.9345	.9357	.9370	.9382	.9394	.9406	.9418	.9429	.9441
1.6	.9452	.9463	.9474	.9484	.9495	.9505	.9515	.9525	.9535	.9545
1.7	.9554	.9564	.9573	.9582	.9591	.9599	.9608	.9616	.9625	.9633
1.8	.9641	.9649	.9656	.9664	.9671	.9678	.9686	.9693	.9699	.9706
1.9	.9713	.9719	.9726	.9732	.9738	.9744	.9750	.9756	.9761	.9767
2.0	.9772	.9778	.9783	.9788	.9793	.9798	.9803	.9808	.9812	.9817
2.1	.9821	.9826	.9830	.9834	.9838	.9842	.9846	.9850	.9854	.9857
2.2	.9861	.9864	.9868	.9871	.9875	.9878	.9881	.9884	.9887	.9890
2.3	.9893	.9896	.9898	.9901	.9904	.9906	.9909	.9911	.9913	.9916
2.4	.9918	.9920	.9922	.9925	.9927	.9929	.9931	.9932	.9934	.9936
2.5	.9938	.9940	.9941	.9943	.9945	.9946	.9948	.9949	.9951	.9952
2.6	.9953	.9955	.9956	.9957	.9959	.9960	.9961	.9962	.9963	.9964
2.7	.9965	.9966	.9967	.9968	.9969	.9970	.9971	.9972	.9973	.9974
2.8	.9974	.9975	.9976	.9977	.9977	.9978	.9979	.9979	.9980	.9981
2.9	.9981	.9982	.9982	.9983	.9984	.9984	.9985	.9985	.9986	.9986
3.0	.9987	.9987	.9987	.9988	.9988	.9989	.9989	.9989	.9990	.9990
3.1	.9990	.9991	.9991	.9991	.9992	.9992	.9992	.9992	.9993	.9993
3.2	.9993	.9993	.9994	.9994	.9994	.9994	.9994	.9995	.9995	.9995
3.3	.9995	.9995	.9995	.9996	.9996	.9996	.9996	.9996	.9996	.9997
3.4	.9997	.9997	.9997	.9997	.9997	.9997	.9997	.9997	.9997	.9998

x	1.282	1.645	1.960	2.326	2.576	3.090	3.291	3.891	4.417
F(x)	.90	.95	.975	.99	.995	.999	.9995	.99995	.999995
2[1 − F(x)]	.20	.10	.05	.02	.01	.002	.001	.0001	.00001

SOURCE: **By permission from A. M. Mood,** *Introduction to the Theory of Statistics,* McGraw-Hill, 1950.

77

methodology of incorporating statistical information relating to stress and strength into the design process which will conform to a reliability requirement (see [2-1], [2-2], [2-5], and [2-6]).

DISTRIBUTION OF DESIGN VARIABLES. The size of a part designed by probabilistic procedures depends on the statistical distributions that model the design variables. Table 2-6 summarizes some of the distributional models commonly used by engineers. The normal distribution plays a central role in probabilistic mechanical design (see Table 2-7). The lognormal distribution also is of fundamental importance because of the central limit theorem for product series (see Hahn and Shapiro [2-5]).

PROBABILISTIC DESIGN ALGORITHMS. Define a random variable σ denoting stress and a random variable S denoting strength. Now $(\mu_\sigma, \sigma_\sigma)$ and (μ_S, σ_S) are the mean and standard deviation of stress and strength, respectively. It is customary to use unit stress and strength expressed in pounds per square inch or megapascals.† For a given component, it must be recognized (consistent with experience) that there is a finite probability that $\sigma > S$, defined as the occurrence of failure. Figure 2-5 illustrates the PDFs of σ and S (densities denoted as f_σ and f_S, respectively). Also, Fig. 2-5 provides definitions of probability of failure p_f and reliability R. Either p_f or R can be used as an index of structural performance, since they are equivalent expressions.

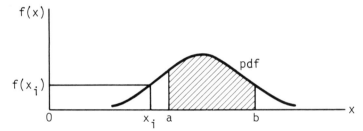

FIG. 2-5 Probability as an area. The probability $p(a < x < b)$ is the area under the PDF curve between abscissas a and b and is equal to $\displaystyle\int_a^b f(x)\, dx.$

Basic probabilistic design formulas are presented in Table 2-6 for two possible distributions of σ and S. Haugen [2-2] points out that often σ and/or S are products of several random design variables, and therefore, one or both may approximate lognormal distributions. It has also been shown (Ref. [2-5]) that the normal model for both σ and S usually produces conservative designs (relative to the lognormal and Weibull σ and S). Thus it is generally recommended (unless there is compelling contrary evidence) that the designer use Eq. (2) of Table 2-3. If the designer can make no assumptions regarding the distributional form of σ or S, Eq. (2) tends to yield conservative designs in such circumstances.‡

The task of design synthesis is to size a part. The geometric dimensions calculated will be functions of μ's and σ's in Eqs. (2), (3), or (4) of Table 2-3. Such solutions can

---

†Note that the units of mean value and standard deviation of a design random variable are the same.
‡For extensive discussion of probabilistic design theory, see Haugen [2-10], Chaps. 9 and 10.

now be obtained very efficiently using, for example, a small desktop programmable calculator.

An acceptable p_f may depend in part on the consequences of failure, a producer's warranty policy, or other performance requirements. However, with regard to public safety, it has been suggested that the average U.S. citizen is willing to accept fatality risks of roughly 10^{-6} per hour in commercial flying and operations of automobiles (Ref. [2-10], Chap. 10), i.e., risk roughly comparable to that of death due to common diseases in the United States. In theory, a design p_f can be established, as illustrated in Fig. 2-4. A practical problem is that of establishing anticipated profits and an economic equivalent of the consequences of failure as a function of p_f of a given system.

How is a system of several components, for example, a gear, a shaft, and two bearings, designed? If p_{f_i} is the probability of failure of the ith component, then it can be shown that the p_f is

$$p_f = \sum_{i=1}^{k} p_{f_i} \qquad (2\text{-}8)$$

where $$R = 1 - p_f$$

and k = number of components. An acceptable design requires that the right-hand side of Eq. (2-8) sum to less than p_f. In general, it may not be desirable to apportion all p_{f_i} the same. The consequences of failure among the different components may be very different. It may cost more to replace a shaft than a bearing, hence justifying a comparatively higher R value.

How is p_f computed when loading is repeated? After j independent applications of σ, the probability of failure of a component is

$$p_f^{(j)} = 1 - (1 - p_f)^j \qquad (2\text{-}9)$$

where p_f refers to a single application of σ. Equation (2-9) would be valid if fatigue failure is not assumed. Probabilistic design to avoid fatigue failure is considered later. More detailed discussion can be found in Refs. [2-2] and [2-10] to [2-14].

EXAMPLE 1 (RELIABILITY CALCULATION). Given the normal independent random variables describing strength and stress applied to a component, namely:

$$\text{Strength} = (\mu_S, \sigma_S) = (27\,000, 3200) \text{ psi}$$

$$\text{Stress} = (\mu_\sigma, \sigma_\sigma) = (18\,400, 1500) \text{ psi}$$

compute R and p_f.

Solution. (See Haugen [2-10], Chap. 9 for more complex examples.) If the stress margin m is expressed as $m = S - \sigma$, then from Table 2-3:

$$\mu_m = 27\,000 - 18\,400 = 8600 \text{ psi}$$

$$\sigma_m = \sqrt{(3200)^2 + (1500)^2} = 3534 \text{ psi}$$

The PDFs of S, σ, and $m = S - \sigma$ are shown in Fig. 2-6. The standardized normal random variable z_0 corresponding to $m = 0$ is

$$z_0 = \left.\frac{m - \mu_m}{\sigma_m}\right|_{m=0} = \frac{0 - \mu_m}{\sigma_m} = -\frac{\mu_m}{\sigma_m}$$

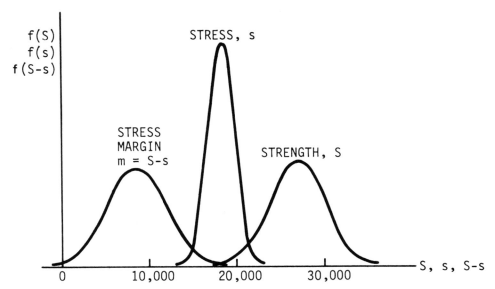

FIG. 2-6 The probability density functions for strength $S \approx N(27\ 000,\ 3200)$ psi, stress $\sigma \approx N(18\ 400,\ 1500)$ psi, and stress margin $m \approx N(8600,\ 3534)$ psi. Probability of failure P_f is the area under the stress margin PDF in the interval $-\infty < m < 0$.

Integration from z_0 to $z = \infty$ yields reliability R.
The lower limit is

$$z_0 = -\frac{8600}{3534} = -2.43$$

Utilizing standard normal area tables (Fig. 2-7),

$$R = \int_{-2.43}^{\infty} \frac{\exp\left(-z^2/2\right)}{\sqrt{2\pi}}\, dz = 0.9925$$

$$p_f = 1 - R = 0.0075$$

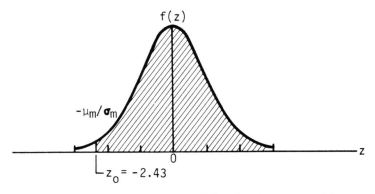

FIG. 2-7 Standard normal probability density curve with area corresponding to the reliability shaded for the circumstances of Example 1.

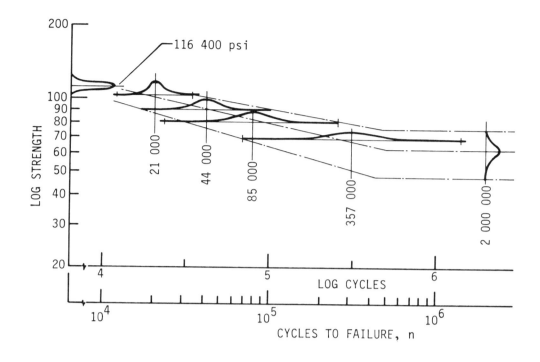

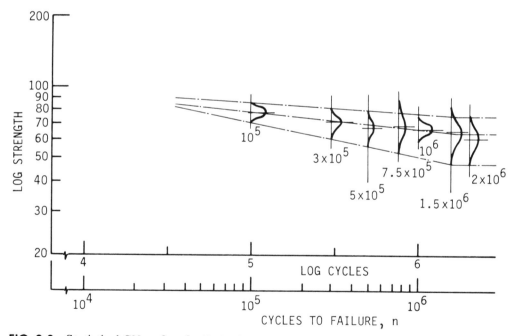

FIG. 2-8 Statistical *SN* surface for SAE 4340 steel wire, cold drawn and annealed. (*a*) Constant stress-to-failure distributions; (*b*) constant cycles-to-failure distributions. *(From D. Kececioglu and E. Haugen, "Interactions among the Various Phenomena Involved in the Design of Dynamic and Rotary Machinery and Their Effects on Reliability," 2d technical report to ONR, Washington, D.C., July 1969.)*

Notes · Drawings · Ideas

2-3 THE STATISTICAL NATURE OF ENGINEERING VARIABLES

2-3-1 Introduction

It has been accepted among knowledgeable engineers that application of probabilistic design theory promises to provide improvement in agreement between prediction and performance of mechanical and structural systems. Engineers have been slow to adopt probabilistic methods because of the scarcity of statistical data describing design parameters. However, recently efforts have been made to unify available statistical design information (for example, Refs. [2-1], [2-2], [2-10], and [2-15]) and make it available. For propagation of error equations, see Mischke [2-16], App. C.

The following are examples of available information pertaining to variability in design variables. They provide the designer with an idea of the magnitude of the variability to be expected in certain variables. However, one must also be aware of any use of simplifying assumptions.

2-3-2 Materials Strength Behavior

EXAMPLES OF AVAILABLE STATISTICAL DATA. Published statistically based data on strength (yield, ultimate, fatigue) and modulus of elasticity, etc. of metallic alloys have been collected and compiled in Ref. [2-1]. Typical values of μ (mean) and σ (standard deviation) of static strengths for widely used metallic alloys are given in Haugen [2-10], App. 1, and Mischke [2-15].

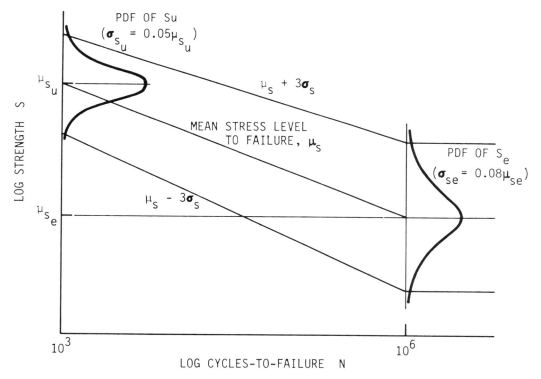

FIG. 2-9 One method of constructing an *SN* surface for steel using tensile-test and endurance-limit information.

Figure 2-8 indicates the large variability which exists in observed cycles to failure N in a constant-amplitude, fully reversed fatigue test, in this case 4340 steel wire. The degree of scatter in the cycles to failure data is typical of common metallic alloys.

In design practice, the required cycle life N is often specified. It is necessary to estimate the distribution of fatigue strength. Corresponding to N is the implication of experiencing and surviving $N - 1$ cycles of prior loading. Figure 2-9 portrays the usual statistical dynamic $S - N$ envelope of S at various values of N for a typical steel. Note that the coefficients of variation (σ/μ) of ultimate strength S_u and of endurance limits S_e are approximately 0.05 and 0.08, respectively. This description of variability is an estimate and should be used only in the absence of specific data. More extensive information on probabilistic design for fatigue loading (both harmonic and random stresses) is to be found in Refs. [2-1] to [2-5]. A distributional Goodman diagram is shown in Fig. 2-10. A summary of typical variability in material properties to be used in the absence of data is given in Tables 2-8, 2-9, and 2-10.

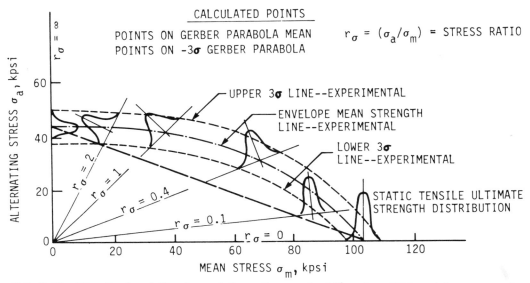

FIG. 2-10 Distributional Goodman fatigue diagram for 10^6 cycles of life and for stress ratios $r = \sigma_a/\sigma_m$ of 0, 0.1, 0.4, 1, 2, and ∞ for SAE 4130 steel. *(From D. Kececioglu and E. Haugen, "Interactions among the various Phenomena Involved in the Design of Dynamic and Rotary Machinery and Their Effects on Reliability," 2nd technical report to ONR, Washington, D.C., July 1969.)*

TABLE 2-8 Variability in Materials Properties†

Parameter	Coefficient of variation
Tensile ultimate strength of metallic materials	0.05
Tensile yield strength of metallic materials	0.07
Endurance limit for steel	0.08
Brinell hardness of steel	0.05
Fracture toughness of metallic materials	0.07

†Recommended for design purposes in absence of data. See Ref. [2-10], Chap. 8, for additional information.

TABLE 2-9 Examples of Variability in Materials Strength

Material	Condition	Tensile ultimate strength S_u, ksi		Tensile yield strength S_y, ksi	
		μ	σ	μ	σ
2024-T3 aluminum	(Bare sheet and plate) $<$ 0.250 in	73	3.7	54	2.7
6061-T6 aluminum	$\frac{1}{2}$-in sheet	46	1.9	42	2.9
7075-T6 aluminum	$\frac{1}{4}$-in plate, bare	85	3.4	76	3.8
A231B-0 magnesium	$\frac{1}{4}$-in plate, longitudinal	41	3.8	24	3.8
Ti-6A1-4V titanium alloy	Sheet and bar, annealed	135.	6.8	131	7.5
304 stainless steel	Round bars, annealed (0.050–4.6 in)	85.	4.1	38	3.8
ASTM-A7 steel	$\frac{1}{2}$-in plate	66	3.3	40	4.0
A1S1 1018	Cold drawn round bar (0.75–1.25 in)	88.	5.7	78	5.9

SOURCE: From Haugen [2–10], Chap. 4.

MATERIAL STIFFNESS. Little published data exist describing the variability of the modulus of elasticity E for metallic materials. Table 2-10 suggests that the variability may not be insignificant (see Ref. [2-1]).

GEOMETRY. Design engineers usually describe allowable variability in production operations in terms of tolerances. Table 2-11 summarizes typical tolerance capabilities for a variety of machining operations. From tolerances, standard deviations are estimated by setting 3σ equal to tolerance T, based on a rationale discussed in Ref. [2-1], Sec. 3.3.0.1. Table 2-12 exemplifies typical metal sheet thickness tolerances.

TABLE 2-10 Average Value of the Mean and Coefficient of Variation of Modulus of Elasticity for Metallic Materials

	Mean Mpsi	Coefficient of variation C
Steel	30.0	~0.03
Aluminum	10.0	~0.03
Titanium	14.7	~0.09
Nodular iron cast	23.1	~0.04

SOURCE: From Haugen [2–10].

Notes ▪ Drawings ▪ Ideas

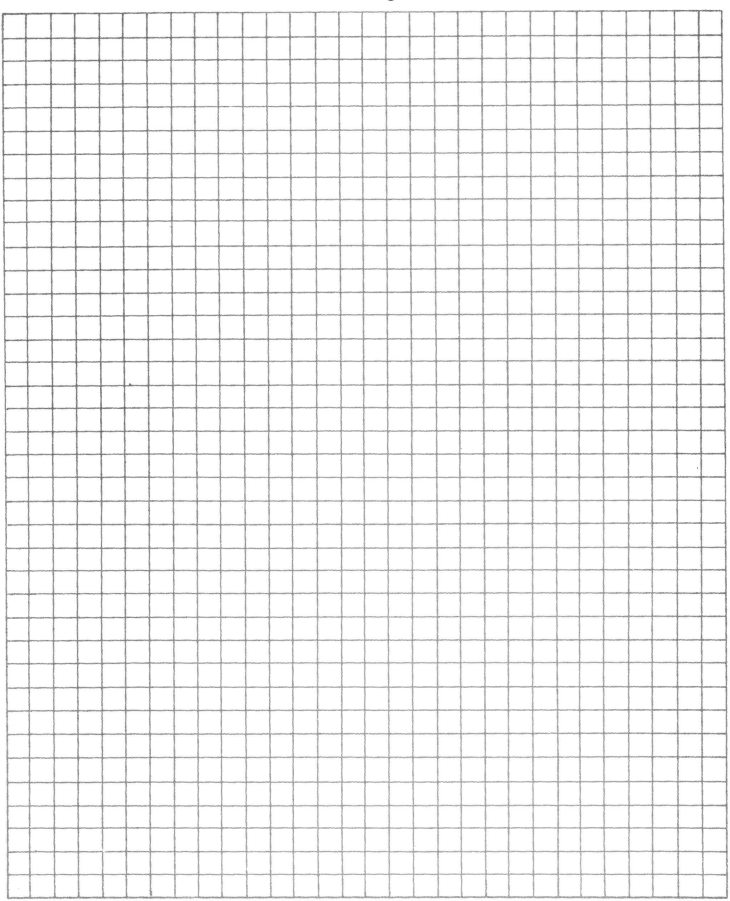

TABLE 2-11 Variability of Tolerances

Process	Tolerance† ±, in	Standard deviation σ, mils
Flame cutting	0.060	20.00
Sawing	0.020	6.67
Shaping	0.010	3.33
Broaching	0.005	1.67
Milling	0.005	1.67
Turning	0.005	1.67
Drilling	0.010	3.33
Reaming	0.002	.67
Hobbing	0.005	1.67
Grinding	0.001	0.33
Lapping	0.0002	.07
Stamping	0.010	3.33
Drawing	0.010	3.33

†It is assumed that tolerance equals 3σ.
SOURCE: From Haugen [2-10].

LOADING. Determination of the statistical actions of forces and moments on a component or system is usually treated on an individual basis. A wealth of statistical information on various environmental phenomena, such as wind gusts, ocean wave heights, road surface roughness, etc., is available (see Haugen [2-10], Chap. 3). Often the engineer must translate statistical environmental data into forces on systems.

MECHANICAL COMPONENTS. A considerable amount of statistical data is becoming available describing the statistical properties of mechanical components. Table 2-13 summarizes variability in design variables relating to helical spring performance. Table 2-14 provides data on the behavior of bolted and welded connections. It is recommended, for design purposes, that the coefficient of variation of strength of welded joints be taken as 0.15 for steel and aluminum (see Haugen [2-2]). Wear is subject to considerable statistical variability and rolling bearing life can be Weibull distributed, often with a coefficient of variation approximating 0.80. Note that the tolerances given in Table 2-11 include variability arising from operator (human) performance.

2-3-3 Elements in Nonstatistical Uncertainty

One purpose of the factor of safety in classical design practice has been to account for factors which were either nonstatistical, i.e., difficult if not impractical to observe, or for which data were lacking. The following list provides examples of uncertainty factors:

1. Uncertainty in the definition of system loads. Data in the past were often lacking.
2. If relatively complete statistical information on environmental phenomena was available, there was perhaps uncertainty in translating these data into forces. For example, although accurate wind gust velocity data were available, the designer

TABLE 2-12 Steel Sheet, Carbon, Cold-Rolled—Tolerances, Thickness† Tolerances (Plus or Minus)

Width	Thickness, in														
	0.2299 0.1875	0.1874 0.1800	0.1799 0.1420	0.1419 0.0972	0.0971 0.0822	0.0821 0.0710	0.0709 0.0568	0.0567 0.0509	0.0508 0.0389	0.0388 0.0344	0.0343 0.0314	0.0313 0.0255	0.0254 0.0195	0.0194 0.0142	0.0141 & less
<3½ incl.												0.003	0.002	0.002	
>3½–6 incl.												0.003	0.003	0.002	
>6–12	0.008	0.007	0.007	0.007	0.006	0.006	0.005	0.005	0.004	0.004	0.004	0.003	0.002	0.002	0.002
>12–15	0.008	0.008	0.008	0.008	0.007	0.007	0.006	0.005	0.005	0.004	0.003	0.003	0.003	0.002	
>15–20	0.009	0.009	0.009	0.008	0.007	0.007	0.006	0.006	0.005	0.004	0.004	0.003	0.003	0.002	
>20–32	0.009	0.009	0.009	0.009	0.008	0.007	0.006	0.006	0.005	0.004	0.004	0.003	0.003	0.002	
>32–40	0.010	0.010	0.010	0.010	0.008	0.007	0.006	0.006	0.005	0.004	0.004	0.003	0.003	0.002	
>40–48			0.010	0.010	0.008	0.007	0.006	0.006	0.005	0.004	0.004			0.002	0.002
>48–60			0.011	0.011	0.009	0.008	0.007	0.006	0.005	0.004	0.004				0.002
>60–70			0.012	0.012	0.009	0.008	0.007	0.007	0.006	0.005	0.004				
>70–80			0.012	0.012	0.010						0.005				
>80–90			0.012	0.012											
>90															

†Thickness is measured at any point on the sheet not less than ⅜ in from an edge [2-10].

88

TABLE 2-13 Variability of Design Variables in Helical Springs

Variable	Standard deviation
Wire diameter d, in	$\sigma_d = 1.58 \times 10^{-3}\sqrt{d}$ (hard-drawn carbon steel)
	$\sigma_d = 1.31 \times 10^{-3}\sqrt{d}$ (music wire)
Spring diameter D, in	$\sigma_D = (48 \times 10^{-4})D$ for $d < 0.1$ in
	$\sigma_D = \dfrac{1.90 \times 10^{-3}D}{\sqrt{d}}$ for $d \geq 0.1$ in
Number of coils N	$\sigma_N = \frac{1}{12}$
Shearing modulus of elasticity G	$C_G = 0.02$

SOURCE: From Wirsching and Haugen [2-8].

was unable to make precise estimates regarding wind forces on a particular system.

3. Given a description of forces on a complicated mechanical or structural system, uncertainty in component member loading was introduced as a result of the static and/or dynamic analysis procedures. Contemporary static and dynamic digital computer routines generally require assumptions ranging from homogeneous

TABLE 2-14 Statistical Data on Welded and Bolted Connections

	Mean μ	Standard deviation σ
$\dfrac{\text{Fillet weld shear strength}}{\text{Electrode tensile strength}} = (\mu, \sigma)$	0.769	0.097
Shear strength of longitudinal fillet welds		
E 60	56.4 kpsi	6.2 kpsi
E 70	63.5 kpsi	5.7 kpsi
Slip coefficient (bolted joint)		
$k_S = \dfrac{\text{slip load}}{(\text{clamping force})(\text{number of surfaces})} = (\mu, \sigma)$ No special treatment	0.336	0.070
$\dfrac{\text{Shear strength}}{\text{Tensile strength}} = (\mu, \sigma)$ (A325 and A490 bolts)	0.625	0.033

Notes ▪ Drawings ▪ Ideas

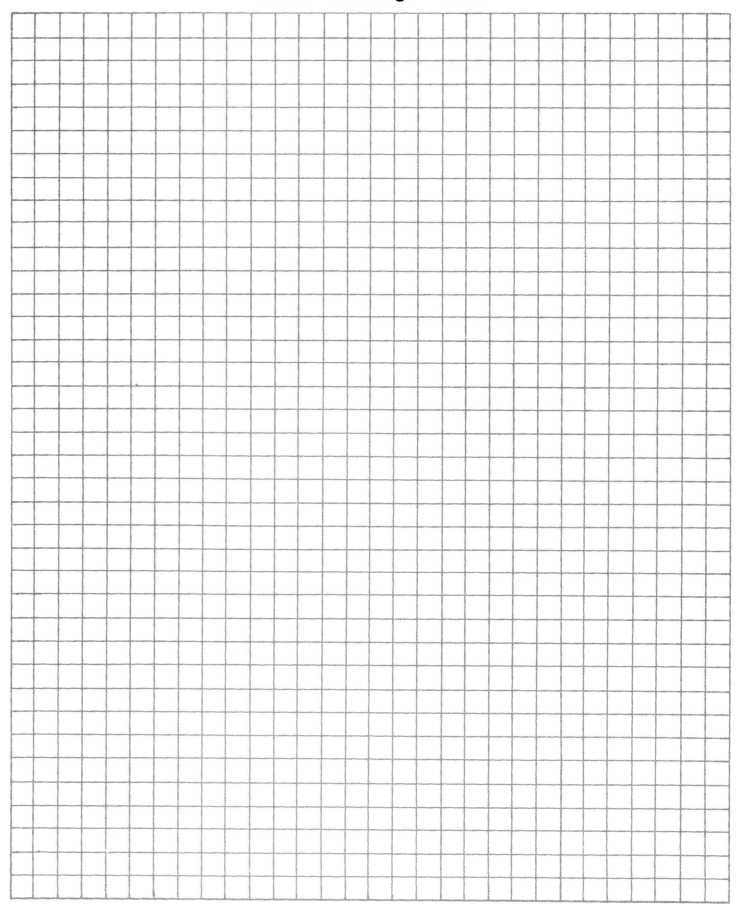

material properties and linear elastic behavior to small-amplitude responses. In the case of a bar member, loading may be most seriously affected by the degree of end fixity assumed; this may involve considerable uncertainty.

4. Given the forces on a component, subsequent stress analysis may require simplifying assumptions such that the designer lacks confidence in the accuracy of the estimated peak stresses.

5. Processing operations, such as cold working, grinding, and heat treating, and assembly operations, such as fastening, welding, and shrink fits, lead to uncertainties.

6. Material strength may be influenced by time, corrosion, and uncertain extreme thermal environments, sometimes to an unknown degree.

7. Questions of quality of workmanship may exist. How well will the system be manufactured? Will specified tolerances be maintained?

Finally, assumptions are often required in design procedures. In probabilistic design, the best a priori statistical information is utilized and the design is developed thereby. Reliability is ensured by methods such as those described in Haugen [2-2] (applied a posteriori).

2-3-4 Comments on Probabilistic Design

The adoption of probabilistic design theory and procedures has developed slowly because

1. Some knowledge of probability theory and statistics is required.
2. Necessary statistical data were not, in the past, readily available.
3. Probabilistic design algorithms initially appear to be somewhat more complicated than the classical form.

REFERENCES

2-1 *Metals Handbook,* vol. 1, 8th ed., American Society for Testing and Materials, Philadelphia, 1961.

2-2 E. B. Haugen, *Probabilistic Approaches to Design,* Wiley, New York, 1968.

2-3 E. B. Haugen and P. H. Wirsching, "Probabilistic Design Alternative to Miner's Cumulative Damage Rule," *Proceedings of the Annual Reliability and Maintainability Symposium,* Philadelphia, 1973.

2-4 H. R. Jaeckel and S. R. Swanson, *Random Loads Spectrum Test to Determine Durability of Structural Components of Automotive Vehicles,* Ford Motor Company, 1970.

2-5 G. J. Hahn and S. S. Shapiro, *Statistical Models in Engineering,* Wiley, New York, 1967.

2-6 J. A. Begley, "Fracture Mechanics in Materials Selection and Design," *Symposium on Fracture and Flaw,* University of New Mexico, Albuquerque, March 1–2, 1973.

2-7 J. Datsko, *Materials Properties and Manufacturing Processes,* Wiley, New York, 1966.

2-8   P. H. Wirsching and E. B. Haugen, "Probabilistic Design of Helical Springs," *Design Engineering,* Division of American Society of Mechanical Engineers, *in press.*

2-9   J. E. Shigley and L. D. Mitchell, *Mechanical Engineering Design,* 4th ed., McGraw-Hill, New York, 1983.

2-10 E. B. Haugen, *Probabilistic Mechanical Design,* Wiley, New York, 1980.

2-11 C. R. Mischke, "A Rationale for Mechanical Design to a Reliability Specification," *Proceedings of the Design Technology Transfer Conference of American Society of Mechanical Engineers,* New York, October 1974, pp. 221–233.

2-12 C. R. Mischke, "Implementing Mechanical Design to a Reliability Specification," *Proceedings of the Design Technology Transfer Conference of the American Society of Mechanical Engineers,* New York, October 1974, pp. 235–248.

2-13 C. R. Mischke, "Organizing the Computer for Mechanical Design," *Proceedings of the Design Technology Transfer Conference of the American Society of Mechanical Engineers,* New York, October 1974, pp. 51–64.

2-14 C. R. Mischke, "A Probabilistic Model of Size Effect in the Fatigue of Rounds in Bending and Torsion," *Transactions of the American Society of Mechanical Engineers, Journal of Mechanical Design,* vol. 102, Jan. 1980, pp. 32–37.

2-15 C. R. Mischke, "Some Tentative Weibullian Descriptions of the Properties of Steels, Aluminums and Titaniums," American Society of Mechanical Engineers Paper No. 71-Vibr-64, International Design Automation Conference, Toronto, Canada, September 1971.

2-16 C. R. Mischke, *Mathematical Model Building,* 2d rev. ed., Iowa State University Press, Ames, Iowa, 1980.

chapter 3
MEASUREMENT AND INFERENCE

JERRY LEE HALL, Ph.D., P.E.
Professor of Mechanical Engineering
Iowa State University
Ames, Iowa

3-1 THE MEASUREMENT PROBLEM

The essential purpose and basic function of all branches of engineering is design. Design begins with the recognition of a need and the conception of an idea to meet that need. One may then proceed to design equipment and processes of all varieties to meet required needs. Testing and experimental design are now considered a necessary design step integrated into other rational procedures. Experimentation is often the only practical way of accomplishing some design tasks, and this requires measurement as a source of important and necessary information.

To measure any quantity of interest, information or energy must be transferred from the source of that quantity to a sensing device. The transfer of information can only be accomplished by the corresponding transfer of energy. Before a sensing device or transducer can detect the signal of interest, energy must be transferred to it from the signal source. Because energy is drawn from the source, the very act of measurement alters the quantity to be determined. In order to accomplish a measurement successfully, one must minimize the energy drawn from the source or the measurement will have little meaning. The converse of this notion is that without energy transfer no measurement can be obtained.

The objective of any measurement is to obtain the most representative value $\bar{x}$ for the item measured as well as a determination of its uncertainty or precision w_x. In this regard one must understand what a measurement is and how to properly select and/or design the component transducers of the measurement system. One must also understand the dynamic response characteristics of the components of the resulting measurement system in order to properly interpret the readout of the measuring system. The measurement system must be calibrated properly if one is to obtain accurate results. A measure of the repeatability or precision of the measured variable is important as well as the accuracy of the resulting measurement. Unwanted information or "noise" in the output must also be considered when using the measurement system. Until these items are considered, valid data cannot be obtained.

Valid data are defined as those data which support measurement of the most representative value of the desired quantity and its associated precision or uncertainty. When calculated quantities employ measured parameters, one must naturally ask how the precision or uncertainty is propagated to any calculated quantity. Use of appropriate propagation-of-uncertainty equations can yield a final result and its associated precision or uncertainty. Thus the generalized measurement problem requires consideration of the measuring system and its characteristics as well as the statistical analysis necessary to place confidence in the resulting measured quantity. The considerations necessary to accomplish this task are illustrated in Fig. 3-1.

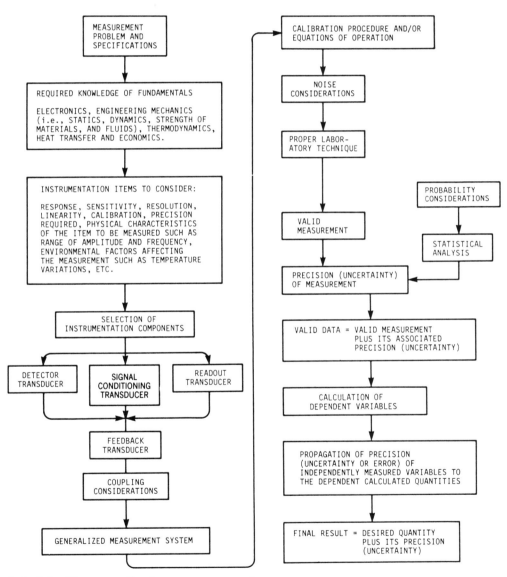

FIG. 3-1 The generalized measurement task.

Notes · Drawings · Ideas

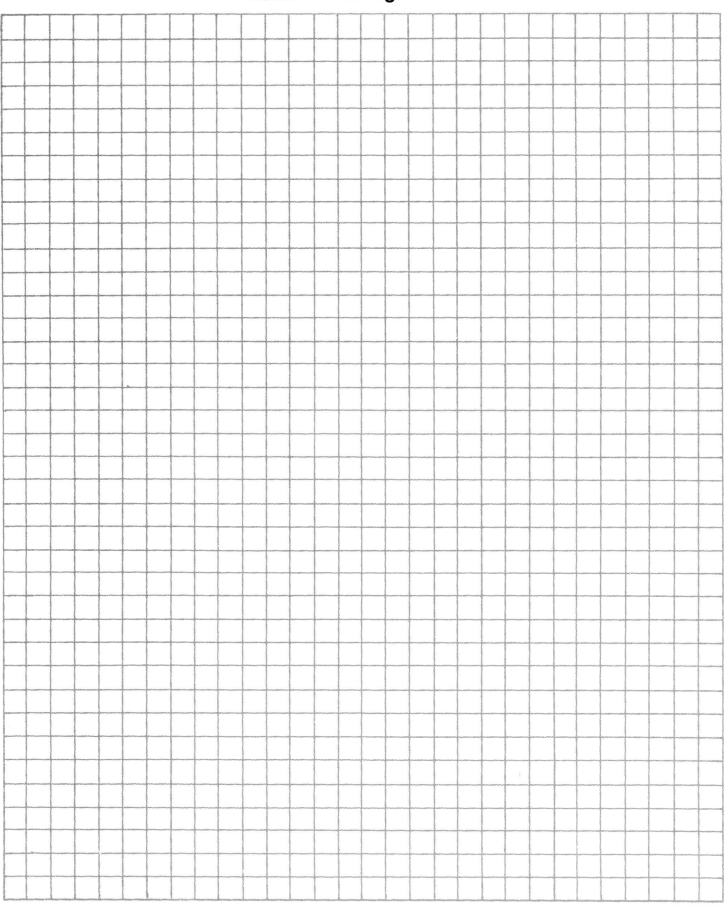

First, a statement of the variables to be measured along with their probable magnitude, frequency, and other pertinent information must be formulated. Next, one brings all the knowledge of fundamentals to the measurement problem at hand. This includes the applicable electronics, engineering mechanics, thermodynamics, heat transfer, economics, etc. One must have an understanding of the variable to be measured if an effective measurement is to be accomplished. For example, if a heat flux is to be determined, one should understand the aspects of heat-energy transfer before attempting to measure entities involved with this process.

Once a complete understanding of the variable to be measured is obtained and the environment in which it is to be measured is understood, one can then consider the necessary characteristics of the components of the measurement system. This would include response, sensitivity, resolution, linearity, and precision. Consideration of these items then leads to selection of the individual instrumentation components, including at least the detector-transducer element, the signal-conditioning element, and a readout element. If the problem is a control situation, a feedback transducer would also be considered. Once the components are selected or specified, they must be coupled to form the generalized measuring system. Coupling considerations to determine the isolation characteristics of the individual transducer must also be made.

Once the components of the generalized measurement system are designed (specified), one can consider the calibration technique necessary to ensure accuracy of the measuring system.

Energy can be transferred into the measuring system by coupling means not at the input ports of the transducer. Thus all measuring systems interact with their environment so that some unwanted signals are always present in the measuring system. Such "noise" problems must be considered and either eliminated, minimized, or reduced to an acceptable level.

If proper technique has been used to measure the variable of interest, then one has accomplished what is called a *valid measurement.* Considerations of probability and statistics then can result in determination of the precision or uncertainty of the measurement. If, in addition, calculations of dependent variables are to be made from the measured variables, one must consider how the uncertainty in the measured variables propagates to the calculated quantity. Appropriate propagation-of-uncertainty equations must be used to accomplish this task.

3-2 DEFINITION OF MEASUREMENT

A *measurement* is the process of comparing an unknown quantity with a predefined standard. For a measurement to be *quantitative,* the predefined standard must be accurate and reproducible. The standard must also be accepted by international agreement for it to be useful worldwide.

The units of the measured variable determine the standard to be used in the comparison process. The particular standard used determines the accuracy of the measured variable. The measurement may be accomplished by direct comparison with the defined standard or by use of an intermediate reference or calibrated system. The intermediate reference or calibrated system results in a less accurate measurement but is usually the only practical way of accomplishing the measurement or comparison process. Thus the factors limiting any measurement are the accuracy of the unit involved and its availability to the comparison process either through reference to the standard or to the calibrated system.

3-3   STANDARDS OF MEASUREMENT

The defined standards which currently exist are a result of historical development, current practice, and international agreement. The Système International d'Units (or SI system) is an example of such a system that has been developed through international agreement and subscribed to by the standard laboratories throughout the world, including the National Bureau of Standards of the United States.

The SI system of units consists of seven base units, two supplemental units, a series of derived units consistent with the base and supplementary units, and a series of prefixes for the formation of multiples and submultiples of the various units ([3-1], [3-2]).

The important aspect of establishing a standard is that it must be defined in terms of a physical object or device which can be established with the greatest accuracy by the measuring instruments available. The standard or base unit for measuring any physical entity should also be defined in terms of a physical object or phenomenon which can be reproduced in any laboratory in the world.

Of the seven standards, three are arbitrarily selected and thereafter regarded as fundamental units, and the others are independently defined units. The fundamental units are taken as mass, length, and time with the idea that all other mechanical parameters can be derived from these three. These fundamental units were natural selections because in the physical world one usually weighs, determines dimensions, or times various intervals. Electrical parameters require the additional specification of current. The independently defined units are temperature, electric current, the amount of a substance, and luminous intensity. The definition of each of the seven basic units follows.

At the time of the French Revolution, the unit of *length,* called a *meter* (m), was defined as one ten-millionth of the distance from the earth's equator to the earth's pole along the longitudinal meridian passing through Paris, France. This standard was changed to the length of a standard platinum-iridium bar when it was discovered that the bar's length could be assessed more accurately (to eight significant digits) than the meridian. Today the standard meter is defined to be the length equal to 1 650 763.73 wavelengths in a vacuum of the orange-red line of krypton isotope 86.

The unit of *mass,* called a *kilogram* (kg), was originally defined as the mass of a cubic decimeter of water. The standard today is a cylinder of platinum-iridium alloy kept by the International Bureau of Weights and Measures in Paris. A duplicate with the U.S. National Bureau of Standards serves as the mass standard for the United States. This is the sole base unit still defined by an artifact.

Force is taken as a derived unit from the Newton's second law. In the SI system, the unit of *force* is the *newton* (N), which is defined as that force which would give a kilogram mass acceleration of one meter per second per second.

The unit interval of *time,* called a *second,* is defined as the duration of 9 192 631 770 cycles of the radiation associated with a specified transition of the cesium 133 atom.

The unit of *current,* called the *ampere* (A), is defined as that current flowing in two parallel conductors of infinite length spaced one meter apart and producing a force of 2×10^{-7} N per meter of length between the conductors.

The unit of *luminous intensity,* called the *candela,* is defined as the luminous intensity of one six-hundred-thousandth of a square meter of a radiating cavity at the temperature of freezing platinum (2042 K) under a pressure of 101 325 N/m².

The *mole* is the *amount of substance* of a system which contains as many elementary entities as there are carbon atoms in 0.012 kg of carbon 12.

Unlike the other standards, temperature is more difficult to define because it is a measure of the internal energy of a substance, which cannot be measured directly but only by relative comparison using a third body or substance which has an observable property that changes directly with temperature. The comparison is made by means of a device called a *thermometer,* whose scale is based on the *practical international temperature scale* which is made as close as possible to agree with the theoretical thermodynamic scale of temperature. The *thermodynamic scale of temperature* is based on the reversible Carnot heat engine and is an ideal temperature scale which does not depend on the thermometric properties of the substance or object used to measure the temperature.

The practical temperature scale currently used is based on various fixed temperature points along the scale as well as interpolation equations between the fixed temperature points. The devices to be used between the fixed temperature points are also specified between certain fixed points on the scale. See Ref. [3-3] for more complete discussion of the fixed points used for the standards defining the practical scale of temperature.

3-4 THE MEASURING SYSTEM

A measuring system is comprised of devices called *transducers.* A transducer is defined as an energy-conversion device [3-4]. A configuration of a generalized measuring system is illustrated in Fig. 3-2.

The purpose of the detector transducer in the generalized system is to sense the quantity of interest and to transform this information (energy) into a form that will be acceptable by the signal-conditioning transducer. Similarly, the purpose of the signal-conditioning transducer is to accept the signal from the detector transducer and to modify this signal in any way required so that it will be acceptable to the readout transducer. For example, the signal-conditioning transducer may be an amplifier, an integrator, a differentiator, or a filter.

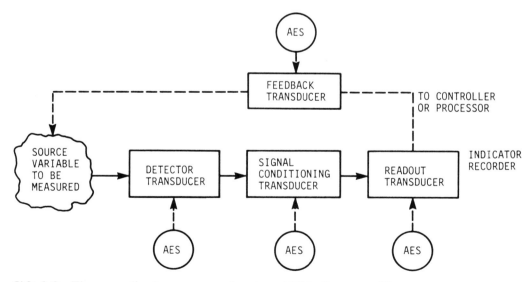

FIG. 3-2 The generalized measurement system. AES indicates auxiliary energy source, dashed line indicates that the item may not be needed.

Notes ▪ Drawings ▪ Ideas

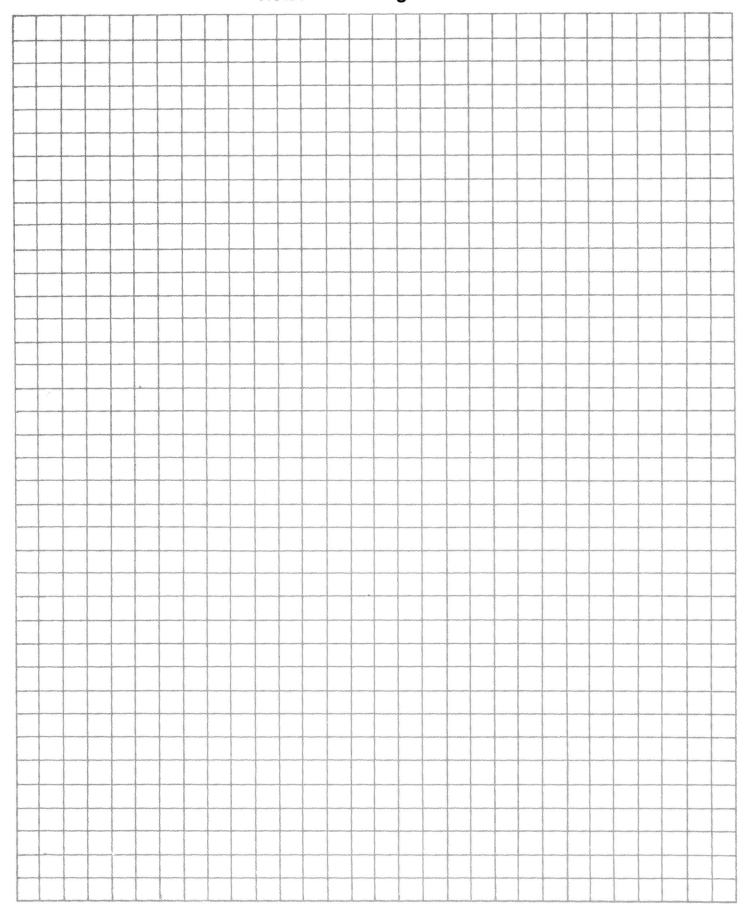

The purpose of the readout transducer is to accept the signal from the signal-conditioning transducer and to present an interpretable output. This output may be in the form of an indicated reading (e.g., from the dial of a pressure gauge), or it may be in the form of a strip-chart recording, or the output signal may be passed to either a digital processor or a controller. With a control situation, the signal transmitted to the controller is compared with a desired operating point or set point. This comparison dictates whether or not the feedback signal is propagated through the feedback transducer to control the source from which the original signal was measured.

An *active transducer* transforms energy between its input and output without the aid of an auxiliary energy source. Common examples are thermocouples and piezoelectric crystals. A *passive transducer* requires an auxiliary energy source (AES) to carry the input signal through to the output. Measuring systems using passive transducers for the detector element are sometimes called *carrier systems.* Examples of transducers requiring such an auxiliary energy source are impedance-based transducers such as strain gauges, resistance thermometers, and differential transformers. All impedance-based transducers require auxiliary energy to carry the information from the input to the output and are therefore passive transducers.

The components which comprise a measuring system can be illustrated with the ordinary thermometer, as shown in Fig. 3-3. The thermometric bulb is the detector or sensing transducer. As heat energy is transferred into the thermometric bulb, the thermometric fluid (for example, mercury or alcohol) expands into the capillary tube of the thermometer. However, the small bore of the capillary tube provides a signal-conditioning transducer (in this case an amplifier) which allows the expansion of the thermometric fluid to be amplified or magnified. The readout in this case is the comparison of the length of the filament of thermometric fluid in the capillary tube with the temperature scale etched on the stem of the thermometer.

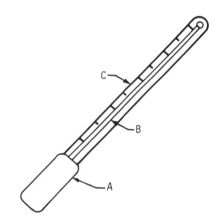

FIG. 3-3 Components of a simple measuring system. A, detector transducer (thermometer bulb with thermometric fluid); B, signal conditioning stage (amplifier); C, readout stage (indicator).

Another example of an element of a measuring system is the Bourdon-tube pressure gauge. As pressure is applied to the Bourdon tube (a curved tube of elliptical cross section), the curved tube tends to straighten out. A mechanical linkage attached to the end of the Bourdon tube engages a gear or pinion which in turn is attached to an indicator needle. As the Bourdon tube straightens, the mechanical linkage to the gear on the indicator needle moves, causing the gear and indicating needle to rotate, giving an indication of a change in pressure on the dial of the gauge. The magnitude of the change in pressure is indicated by a pressure scale marked on the face of the pressure gauge.

The accuracy of either the temperature measurement or the pressure measurement previously indicated depends on how accurately each measuring instrument is calibrated. The values on the readout scales of the devices can be determined by means of comparison (calibration) of the measuring device with a predefined standard or by a reference system which in turn has been calibrated in relation to the defined standard.

Notes · Drawings · Ideas

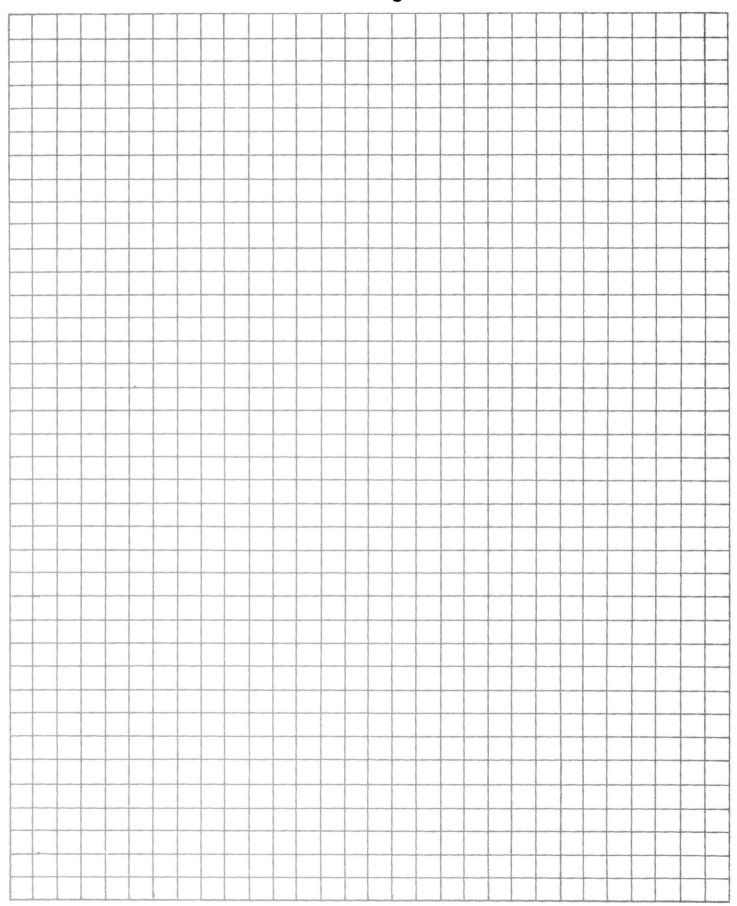

3-5 CALIBRATION

The *process of calibration* is comparison of the reading or output of a measuring system to the value of known inputs to the measuring system. A complete calibration of a measuring system would consist of comparing the output of the system to known input values over the complete range of operation of the measuring device. For example, the calibration of pressure gauges is often accomplished by means of a device called a *dead-weight tester* where known pressures are applied to the input of the pressure gauge and the output reading of the pressure gauge is compared to the known input over the complete operating range of the gauge.

The type of calibration signal should simulate as nearly as possible the type of input signal to be measured. A measuring system to be used for measurement of dynamic signals should be calibrated using known dynamic input signals. Static, or level, calibration signals are not proper for calibration of a dynamic measurement system because the natural dynamic characteristics of the measurement system would not be accounted for with such a calibration. A typical calibration curve for a general transducer is depicted in Fig. 3-4. It might be noted that the sensitivity of the measuring system can be obtained from the calibration curve at any level of the input signal by noting the relative change in the output signal due to the relative change in the input signal at the operating point.

3-6 DESIGN OF THE MEASURING SYSTEM

The design of a measuring system consists of selection or specification of the transducers necessary to accomplish the detection, transmission, and indication of the desired variable to be measured. The transducers must be connected to yield an interpretable output so that either an individual has an indication or recording of the information or a controller or processor can effectively use the information at the output of the measuring system. To ensure that the measuring system will perform the measurement of the specified variable with the fidelity and accuracy required of the test, the *sensitivity, resolution, range,* and *response* of the system must be known. In order to determine these items for the measurement system, the individual transducer characteristics must be known as well as the loading effect between the individual transducers in the measuring system. Thus by knowing individual

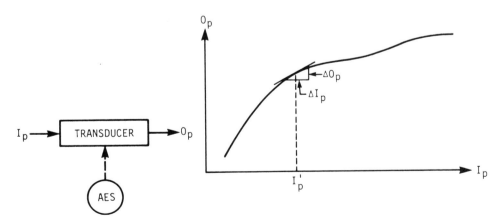

FIG. 3-4 Typical calibration curve. Sensitivity at $I_p' = (\Delta O_p/\Delta I_p)$.

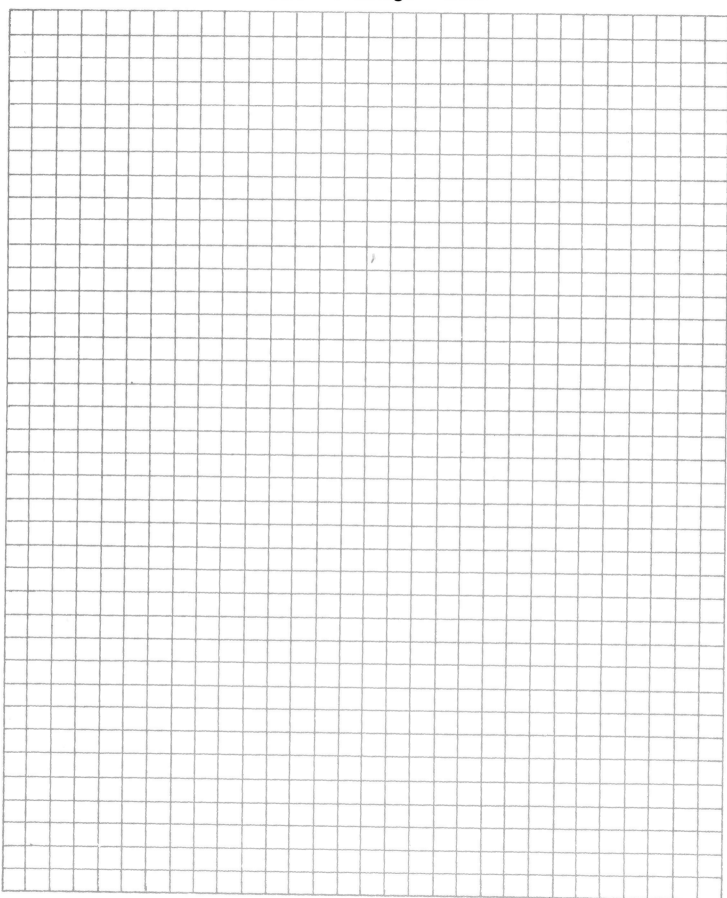

transducer characteristics the system characteristics can be predicted. If the individual transducer characteristics are not known, one must resort to testing the complete measuring system in order to determine the desired characteristics.

The system characteristics depend on the mathematical order (for example, first-order, second-order, etc.) of the system as well as the nature of the input signal. If the measuring system is a first-order system, its response will be significantly different from a measuring system that can be characterized as a second-order system. Furthermore, the response of an individual measuring system of any order will be dependent on the type of input signal. For example, the response characteristics of either a first- or second-order system would be different for a step input signal as compared to a sinusoidal input signal.

3-6-1 Energy Considerations

In order for a measurement of any item to be accomplished, energy must move from a source to the detector-transducer element. Correspondingly, energy must flow from the detector-transducer element to the signal-conditioning device, and energy must flow from the signal-conditioning device to the readout device in order for the measuring system to function to provide a measurement of any variable. Energy can be viewed as having intensive and extensive or primary and secondary components. One can take the primary component of energy as the quantity that one desires to detect or measure. However, the primary quantity is impossible to detect unless the secondary component of energy accompanies the primary component. Thus a force cannot be measured without an accompanying displacement, or a pressure cannot be measured without a corresponding volume change. Note that the units of the primary component of energy multiplied by the units of the secondary component of energy yield units of energy or power (an energy rate). Figure 3-5 illustrates both the active and passive type of transducers with associated components of energy at the input and output terminals of transducers. In Fig. 3-5 the primary component of energy I_p is the quantity that one desires to sense at the input to the transducer. A secondary component I_s accompanies the primary component, and energy must be transferred before a measurement can be accomplished. This means that pressure changes I_p cannot be measured unless a corresponding volume change I_s occurs. Likewise, voltage change I_p cannot be measured unless charges I_s are developed, and force change I_p cannot be measured unless a length change I_s occurs. Thus the units of the product $I_p I_s$ must always be units of energy or power (energy rate). Some important transducer characteristics can now be defined in terms of the energy components shown in Fig. 3-5. These characteristics may have both magnitude and direction, so that generally the characteristics are complicated in mathematical nature. A more complete discussion of the following characteristics is contained in Stein [3-4].

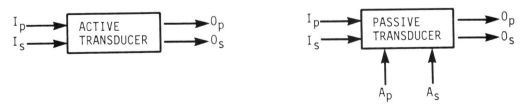

FIG. 3-5 Energy components for active and passive transducers.

3-6-2 Transducer Characteristics

Acceptance ratio of a transducer is defined in Eq. (3-1) as the ratio of the change in primary component of energy at the transducer input to the change in secondary component at the transducer input. It is similar to an input impedance for a transducer with electric energy at its input:

$$A = \frac{\Delta I_p}{\Delta I_s} \tag{3-1}$$

Emission ratio of a transducer is defined in Eq. (3-2) as the ratio of the change in primary component of energy at the transducer output to the change in the secondary component of energy at the transducer output. This is similar to output impedance for a transducer with electric energy at its output:

$$E = \frac{\Delta O_p}{\Delta O_s} \tag{3-2}$$

Transfer ratio is defined in Eq. (3-3) as the ratio of the change in primary component of energy at the transducer output to the change in primary component of energy at the transducer input:

$$T = \frac{\Delta O_p}{\Delta I_p} \tag{3-3}$$

Several different types of transfer ratios may be defined which involve any output component of energy with any input component of energy. However, the main transfer ratio involves the primary component of energy at the output with the primary component of energy at the input. The main transfer ratio is similar to the *transfer function,* which is defined as that function describing the mathematical operation that the transducer performs on the input signal to yield the output signal at some operating point. The transfer ratio at a given operating point or level of input signal is also the *sensitivity* of the transducer at that operating point.

When two transducers are connected, they will interact, and energy will be transferred from the source, or first, transducer to the second transducer. When the transfer of energy from the source transducer is zero, it is said to be *isolated* or *unloaded.* A measure of isolation (or loading) is determined by the *isolation ratio,* which is defined by

$$I = \frac{O_{p,a}}{O_{p,i}} = \frac{O_{p,L}}{O_{p,NL}} = \frac{A}{A + |E_s|} \tag{3-4}$$

where *a* means actual; *i,* ideal; *L,* loaded; and *NL,* no load.

When the *emission ratio* E_s from the source transducer is zero, the isolation ratio becomes unity and the transducers are isolated. The definition of an *infinite source* or a *pure source* is one that has an emission ratio of zero. The concept of the emission ratio approaching zero is that for a fixed value of the output primary component of energy O_p, the secondary component of energy O_s must be allowed to be as large as is required to maintain the level of O_p at a fixed value. For example, a pure voltage source of 10 V (O_p) must be capable of supplying any number (this may approach infinity) of charges (O_s) in order to maintain a voltage level of 10 V. Likewise, the pure source of force (O_p) must be capable of undergoing any displacement (O_s) required in order to maintain the force level at a fixed value.

FIG. 3-6 Measuring-system sensitivity.

EXAMPLE 1. The transfer ratio (measuring-system sensitivity) of the measuring system shown in Fig. 3-6 is to be determined in terms of the individual transducer transfer ratios and the isolation ratios between the transducers.

Solution

$$T = \frac{O_3}{I_1} = \frac{O_3}{O_{2,L}} \frac{O_{2,L}}{O_{2,NL}} \frac{O_{2,NL}}{O_{1,L}} \frac{O_{1,L}}{O_{1,NL}} \frac{O_{1,L}}{I_1} = T_3 {}_2I_3 T_2 {}_1I_2 T_1$$

= (product of transfer ratios) (product of isolation ratios)

3-6-3 Sensitivity

The *sensitivity* is defined as the change in the output signal relative to the change in the input signal at an operating point k. Sensitivity S is given by

$$S = \lim_{\Delta I_p \to 0} \left(\frac{\Delta O_p}{\Delta I_p} \right)_{I_p = k} = \left(\frac{dO_p}{dI_p} \right)_k \qquad (3\text{-}5)$$

3-6-4 Resolution

The *resolution* of a measuring system is defined as the smallest change in the input signal that will yield an interpretable change in the output of the measuring system at some operating point. Resolution R is given by

$$R = \Delta I_{p,\min} = \frac{\Delta O_{p,\min}}{S} \qquad (3\text{-}6)$$

It can be determined by taking the smallest change in the output signal which would be interpretable (as decided by the observer) and dividing by the sensitivity at that operating point.

EXAMPLE 2. A pressure transducer is to be made from a spring-loaded piston in a cylinder and a dial indicator, as shown in Fig. 3-7. Known information concerning each element is also listed below:

Pneumatic cylinder

    Spring deflection
    factor = 14.28 lbf/in = K

    Cylinder bore = 1 in

    Piston stroke = $\frac{1}{2}$ in

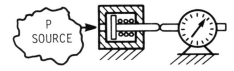

FIG. 3-7 Pressure transducer in the form of a spring-loaded piston and a dial indicator.

Dial indicator

Spring deflector factor $= 1.22$ lbf/in $= k$

Maximum stroke of plunger $= 0.440$ in

Indicator dial has 100 equal divisions per 360°

Each dial division represents a plunger deflection of 0.001 in

The following items are determined:

1. Block diagram of measuring system showing all components of energy (see Fig. 3-8)
2. Acceptance ratio of pneumatic cylinder:

$$A_{PC} = \frac{\Delta I_p}{\Delta I_s} = \frac{P}{V} = \frac{F/A}{AL} = \frac{K}{A^2} = \frac{14.28(16)}{\pi^2} = 23.1 \text{ psi/in}^2$$

3. Emission ratio of pneumatic cylinder:

$$E_{PC} = \frac{\Delta O_p}{\Delta O_s} = \frac{L}{F} = \frac{1}{K} = \frac{1}{14.28} = 0.070 \text{ in/lbf}$$

4. Transfer ratio of pneumatic cylinder:

$$T_{PC} = \frac{\Delta O_p}{\Delta I_p} = \frac{L}{P} = \frac{LA}{F} = \frac{A}{K} = \frac{\pi}{4(14.28)} = 0.055 \text{ in/psi}$$

5. Acceptance ratio of dial indicator:

$$A_{Di} = \frac{\Delta I_p}{\Delta I_s} = \frac{L}{F} = \frac{1}{k} = \frac{1}{1.22} = 0.82 \text{ in/lbf}$$

6. Transfer ratio of dial indicator:

$$T_{DI} = \frac{\Delta O_p}{\Delta I_p} = \frac{\theta}{L} = (3.6° \text{ per division})/(0.001 \text{ in per division})$$

$$= 3600°/\text{in (or 1000 divisions/in)}$$

7. Isolation ratio between pneumatic cylinder and dial indicator:

$$I = \frac{A_{DI}}{A_{DI} + E_{PC}} = \frac{1/k}{1/k + 1/K} = \frac{0.82}{0.82 + 0.07} = 0.921$$

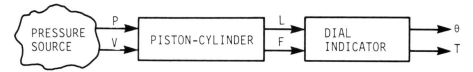

FIG. 3-8 Pressure-transducer block diagram.

8. System sensitivity in dial divisions per psi:

$$S = \frac{\text{output}}{\text{input}} = \frac{DI \text{ output}}{DI \text{ input}} \times \frac{DI \text{ input}}{PC \text{ output}} \times \frac{PC \text{ output}}{PC \text{ input}}$$

$$= T_{DI}T_{PC} = 0.055(0.921)(1000) = 50.7 \text{ divisions/psi}$$

9. Maximum pressure that the measuring system can sense:

$$\text{Maximum input} = \frac{\text{input}}{\text{output}} \times \text{maximum output}$$

$$= \frac{1}{S}(440 \text{ dial divisions}) = 8.7 \text{ psi}$$

10. Resolution of the measuring system in psi:

$$\text{Minimum input} = \frac{\text{input}}{\text{output}} \times \text{minimum readable output}$$

$$= \frac{1}{S}(1 \text{ dial division}) = 0.02 \text{ psi}$$

3-6-5 Response

When time-varying signals are to be measured, the dynamic response of the measuring system is of crucial importance. The components of the measuring system must be selected and/or designed such that they can respond to the time-varying input signals in such a manner that the input information is not lost in the measurement process. Several measures of response are important to know if one is to evaluate a measuring system's ability to detect and reproduce all the information in the input signal. Some measures of response involve time alone, whereas other measures of response are more involved. Various measures of response are defined in the following paragraphs.

Amplitude response of a transducer is defined as the ability to treat all input amplitudes uniformly [3-5]. The typical amplitude-response curve determined for either an individual transducer or for a complete measuring system is depicted in Fig. 3-9.

A typical amplitude-response specification is as follows:

$$\left| \frac{O_p}{I_p} \right| = M \pm T \qquad I_{p,\text{min}} < I_p < I_{p,\text{max}} \tag{3-7}$$

The amplitude-response specification includes a nominal magnitude ratio M between output and input of the transducer measuring system along with an allowable tolerance T and a specification of the range of the magnitude of the primary input variable I_p over which the amplitude ratio and tolerance are valid.

Frequency response can be defined as the ability of a transducer to treat all input frequencies uniformly [3-5] and can be specified by a frequency-response curve such as that shown in Fig. 3-10. A typical frequency-response specification would be the nominal magnitude ratio M of output to input signals plus or minus some allowable

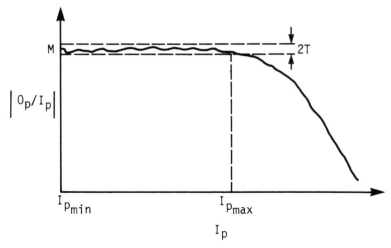

FIG. 3-9 Typical amplitude-response characteristic.

tolerance T specified over a frequency range from the low-frequency limit f_L to the high-frequency limit f_H as follows:

$$\left|\frac{O_p}{I_p}\right| = M \pm T \qquad f_L < f < f_H \tag{3-8}$$

It is the usual practice to use the decibel (dB) for the ordinate of the frequency-response curve rather than the actual magnitude ratio. The decibel, as defined in Eq. (3-9), is used in transducers and measuring systems in specifying frequency response:

$$\text{Decibel} = 20 \log_{10} \frac{O_p}{I_p} \tag{3-9}$$

The decibel scale allows large gains or attenuations to be expressed as relatively small numbers.

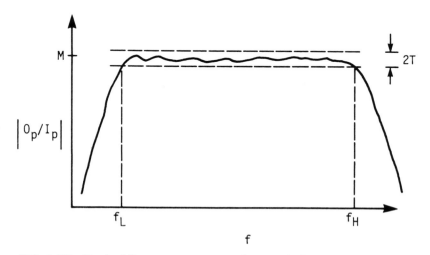

FIG. 3-10 Typical frequency-response characteristic.

Phase response can be defined as the ability of a transducer to treat all input-phase relations uniformly [3-5]. For a pure sine wave the phase shift would be a constant angle or a constant time delay between input and output signals. Such a constant phase shift or time delay would not affect the waveform shape or amplitude determination when viewing at least one complete cycle of the waveform. For complex input waveforms, each harmonic in the waveform may be treated slightly differently in the measuring system, resulting in what is known as *phase distortion,* as illustrated in Ref. [3-5].

Response times are valid measures of response of transducers and measuring systems. An understanding of the response-time specifications requires that the mathematical order of the system be known and that the type of input signal or forcing function be specified.

Rise time of a transducer or measuring system is defined for any order system subjected to a step input. The *rise time* is defined as that time for the transducer or measuring system to respond from 10 to 90 percent of the step-input amplitude and is depicted in Fig. 3-11.

Delay time is another response time which is defined for any order system to a step input. The *delay time* is defined to be that time for the transducer or measuring system to respond from 0 to 50 percent of the step-input amplitude and is depicted in Fig. 3-11.

Time constant is specifically defined for a first-order system subjected to a step input. The *time constant* τ is defined as the time for the transducer or measuring system to respond to 63.2 percent (or $1 - e^{-1}$) of the step-input amplitude. The time constant is specifically illustrated in Fig. 3-12, where the response x of the first-order system to step input x_s is known to be exponential as follows:

$$x = x_s(1 - e^{-t/\tau}) \tag{3-10}$$

When the time t is equal to the time constant τ, the first-order system has responded to 63.2 percent of the step-input amplitude. In a time span equivalent to 3 time constants the system has responded to 95.0 percent of the step-input amplitude, and in a time span of 5 time constants the system has responded to 99.3 percent of the step-input amplitude. Thus for a first-order system subjected to a step input,

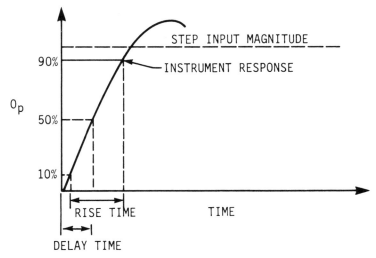

FIG. 3-11 Rise time and delay time used as response times.

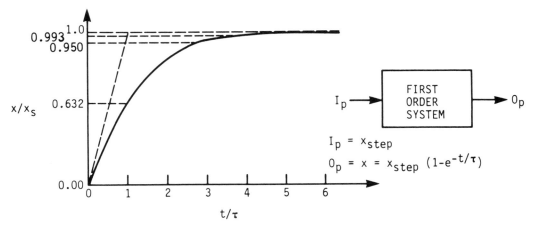

FIG. 3-12 Response of a first-order system to a step input.

to yield a correct reading of the input variable one must wait a time period of at least 5 time constants before the first-order system can respond sufficiently to give a correct indication of the measured variable.

TRANSDUCER DYNAMICS. Because of the time delay or phase shift a transducer or measuring system may have, one must be very careful to ensure that the measuring system can respond adequately if the input signal to the measuring system is varying with time. If the time response of the measuring system is inadequate, it may never read the correct value. Thus if one believes the output indication of the measuring system to be a reproduction of the actual value of the input (measured) variable without understanding the dynamics of how the measuring system is responding to the input signal, a crucial error can be made.

In order to understand dynamic response one must recognize that the components of the measuring system have natural physical characteristics and the measuring system will tend to respond according to these natural characteristics when perturbed by any external disturbance. In addition, the input signal supplied to a transducer or measuring system provides a forcing function for that transducer or measuring system. The equation of operation of a transducer is a differential equation whose order is defined as the order of the system. The response of the system is determined by solving this differential equation of operation according to the type of input signal (forcing function) supplied to the system. If the measuring system is modeled as a linear system, the differential equation of operation will be ordinary and linear with constant coefficients. This is the type of differential equation that can be solved by well-known techniques. The nature of the solution depends on the nature of the forcing function as well as the nature of the physical components of the system. For example, the thermometric element of the temperature-measuring device can be modeled as shown in Fig. 3-13. For this model,

$$q_{in} = q_{lost} + q_{stored} = \text{rate of heat energy entering control region}$$

and
$$q_{in} = hA(T_\infty - T)$$

$$q_{lost} = 0 \text{ (assumed)}$$

$$q_{stored} = \rho c v \frac{dT}{dt}$$

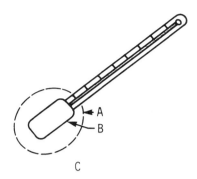

FIG. 3-13 Thermometric element modeled as a first-order system. A, control region; B, thermometric element at temperature T; C, environment at temperature T_∞.

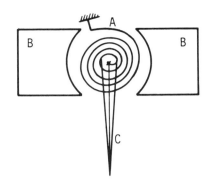

FIG. 3-14 D'Arsonval movement. A, spring-retained armature; B, field magnets; C, indicating needle.

where A = surface area
  h = surface-film coefficient of convective heat transfer
  ρ = density of thermometric element
  c = specific heat capacity of thermometric element
  T = temperature of thermometric element
  t = time

The resulting equation of the operation is given as follows for the step input $x_s = T_\infty - T_o$:

$$T - T_o = (T_\infty - T_o)(1 - e^{-t/\tau}) \tag{3-11}$$

where $\tau = \rho v c / h A$. The response $x = T - T_o$ is shown in Fig. 3-12.

Another example of a first-order system is the electric circuit composed of resistance and capacitive elements or the so-called *RC* circuit. Masses falling in viscous media also follow a similar exponential characteristic.

If the system is characterized by a second-order linear ordinary differential equation, the solution becomes more complex than that for the first-order system. The system behavior depends on the amount of friction or damping in the system. For example, the meter movement of a galvanometer or D'Arsonval movement of Fig. 3-14 such as exists in many electrical meters can be modeled as shown in Fig. 3-15. Applying first principles to this model yields the equation of motion

$$\Sigma T = J\ddot{\theta} = T(t) - T_s - T_f$$

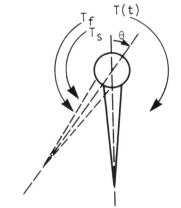

FIG. 3-15 Torques applied to the D'Arsonval movement.

where $T_s = k\theta$ for torsional damping
  $T_f = \sigma\dot{\theta}$ for viscous friction
  $T(t)$ = driving or forcing function

then
$$J\ddot{\theta} + \sigma\dot{\theta} + k\theta = T(t)$$

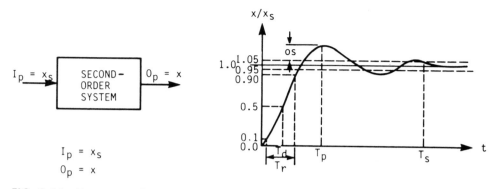

FIG. 3-16 Response of a second-order system to a step input.

or

$$\ddot{\theta} + 2\gamma\omega_n\dot{\theta} + \omega_n^2\theta = \frac{T(t)}{J} \tag{3-12}$$

where $\omega_n = \sqrt{k/J}$ = natural undamped frequency

$\omega_d = \omega_n\sqrt{1 - \gamma^2}$ = natural damped frequency

$\omega_p = \omega_n\sqrt{1 - 2\gamma^2}$ = frequency at peak of frequency response curve

$\gamma = \sigma/\sigma_c$ = damping ratio

$\sigma_c = \sqrt{4kJ}$ = critical value of damping

$\quad$ = lowest value of damping where no natural oscillation of system occurs

If the damping is modeled as viscous friction, the possible solutions to the equation of motion are given by Eqs. (3-13), (3-14), and (3-15) for the step input. The underdamped solution of Eq. (3-12) is shown in Fig. 3-16.

For $\sigma < 1$ (underdamped),

$$\frac{x}{x_s} = 1 - \{1 - \gamma^2\}^{-1/2} \exp(-\gamma\omega_n t) \sin(\omega_d t + \phi) \tag{3-13}$$

$$\phi = \tan^{-1}\sqrt{\frac{1 - \gamma^2}{\gamma}}$$

For $\sigma = 1$ (critical damping),

$$\frac{x}{x_s} = 1 - (1 + \omega_n t) \exp(-\omega_n t) \tag{3-14}$$

For $\sigma > 1$ (overdamped),

$$\frac{x}{x_s} = 1 - \left(\frac{\beta}{\beta - 1}\right)\left[\exp\left(\frac{-\omega_n t}{\sqrt{\beta}}\right) - \frac{1}{\beta}\exp(-\sqrt{\beta}\,\omega_n t)\right] \tag{3-15}$$

$$\beta = \frac{\gamma + \sqrt{\gamma^2 - 1}}{\gamma - \sqrt{\gamma^2 - 1}}$$

If the system is underdamped, the response of the transducer or measuring system overshoots the step-input magnitude and the corresponding oscillation occurs with a first-order decay. This type of response leads to additional response specifications which may be used by transducer manufacturers. These specifications include *overshoot OS, peak time T_p, settling time T_s, rise time T_r*, and *delay time T_d* as depicted in Fig. 3-16. If the viscous damping is at the critical value, the measuring system responds only up to the step-input magnitude after a very long period of time. If the damping is more than critical, the response of the measuring system never reaches a magnitude equivalent to the step input. Measuring-system components following a second-order behavior are normally designed and/or selected such that the damping is less than critical. With underdamping the second-order system responds with some time delay and a characteristic phase shift.

If the natural response characteristics of each measuring system are not known or understood, the output reading of the measurement system can be erroneously interpreted. Figure 3-17 illustrates the response of a first-order system to a square wave input. Note the system with inadequate time response never yields a valid indication of the magnitude of the step input. Figure 3-18 illustrates a first-order system with time constant adequate ($\tau \ll 1/f$) to yield a valid indication of step-input magnitude. Figure 3-19 illustrates the response of an underdamped second-order system to a square wave input. A valid indication of the step-input magnitude is obtained after the settling time has occurred.

If the input forcing function is not a step input but a sinusoidal function instead, the corresponding differential equations of motion to the first- and second-order systems are given in Eq. (3-16) and (3-17), respectively:

$$\dot{x} + \frac{x}{\tau} = A \cos \omega_f t \tag{3-16}$$

where A = amplitude of input signal transformed to units of the response variable derivative(s)

ω_f = frequency of input signal (forcing function)

τ = time constant

$$\ddot{x} + 2\sigma\omega_n\dot{x} + \omega_n^2 x = A \cos \omega_f t \tag{3-17}$$

In addition, the parameters of the steady-state responses of the first- and second-order system are given by Eqs. (3-18) and (3-19), respectively, and are shown in Figs. 3-20 and 3-21. The steady state solutions are of the form

$$x_{ss} = B \cos (\omega_f t + \phi)$$

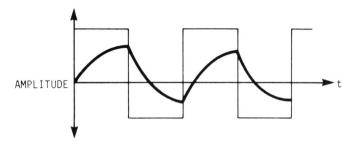

FIG. 3-17 Response of a first-order system with inadequate response to a square-wave input ($\tau > 1/f$).

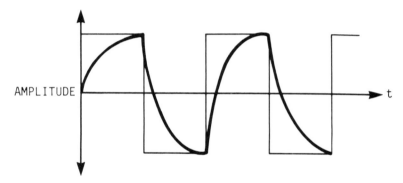

AMPLITUDE

t

FIG. 3-18   Response of a first-order system with barely adequate response to a square-wave input ($\tau \ll 1/f$).

where, for the first and second order systems respectively,

$$B_1 = \frac{A}{\sqrt{(\tau\omega_f)^2 + 1}} \qquad \phi_1 = -\tan^{-1}(\tau\omega_f) \tag{3-18}$$

$$B_2 = \frac{A}{\sqrt{[1 - (\omega_f/\omega_n)^2]^2 + (2\gamma\,\omega_f/\omega_n)^2}} \qquad \phi_2 = -\tan^{-1}\frac{2\gamma\,\omega_f/\omega_n}{1 - (\omega_f/\omega_n)^2} \tag{3-19}$$

From these results it can be noted that both the first- and second-order system, when responding to sinusoidal input functions, experience a magnitude change and a phase shift in response to the input function.

Many existing transducers behave according to either a first- or second-order system. One should understand thoroughly how both first- and second-order systems respond to both the step input and sinusoidal input in order to understand how a transducer is likely to respond to such input signals. Table 3-1 is a listing of the steady-state responses of both the first- and second-order systems to a step function, ramp function, impulse function, and sinusoidal function. (See also [3-6] and [3-7].)

Understanding how a transducer might respond to a complex transient waveform can be understood by considering a sinusoidal response of the system, since any complex transient forcing function can be represented by a Fourier series equivalent [3-5]. Consideration of each separate harmonic in the input forcing function would then yield information as to how the measuring system is likely to respond.

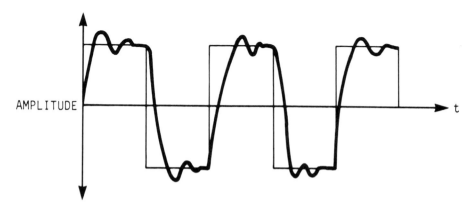

AMPLITUDE

t

FIG. 3-19   Response of an underdamped second-order system to a square wave.

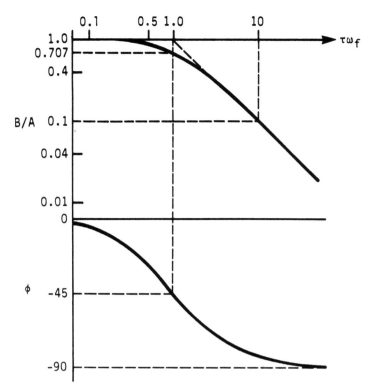

FIG. 3-20 Frequency and phase response of a first-order system to a sinusoidal input.

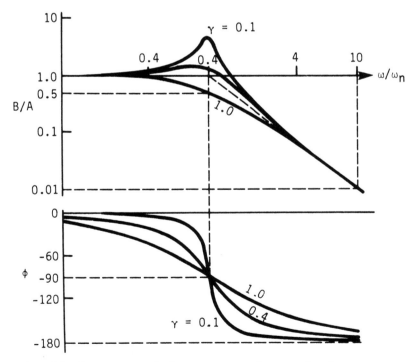

FIG. 3-21 Frequency and phase response of a second-order system to a sinusoidal input.

117

TABLE 3-1 Response of First- and Second-Order Systems to Various Input Signals

First-order system	Second-order system

Equation of Motion

First-order system:

$$c\dot{x} + kx = F(t)$$

$$\tau\dot{x} + x = \frac{F(t)}{k}$$

$$\tau = \frac{c}{k}$$

Second-order system:

$$M\ddot{x} + c\dot{x} + kx = F(t)$$

$$\ddot{x} + 2\gamma\omega_n\dot{x} + \omega_n^2 x = \frac{F(t)}{M}$$

$$\text{where } \gamma = \frac{c}{c_c} \qquad c_c = \sqrt{4kM} \qquad \omega_n = \sqrt{\frac{k}{M}}$$

Step input: $F(t) = F \qquad t > 0$

First-order system:

$$\frac{x}{F/k} = 1 - \exp(-t/\tau)$$

Second-order system:

(a) $\gamma < 1$: $\dfrac{x}{F/k} = 1 - \dfrac{\exp(-\gamma\omega_n t)}{\sqrt{1-\gamma^2}} \sin\left(\sqrt{1-\gamma^2}\,\omega_n t + \phi\right)$

$$\phi = \tan^{-1}\frac{\sqrt{1-\gamma^2}}{\gamma}$$

(b) $\gamma = 1$: $\dfrac{x}{F/k} = 1 - (1 + \omega_n t)\exp(-\omega_n t)$

(c) $\gamma > 1$: $\dfrac{x}{F/k} = 1 - \dfrac{\nu}{\nu-1}\left[\exp\dfrac{-\omega_n t}{\sqrt{\nu}} - \dfrac{1}{\nu}\exp\left(-\sqrt{\nu}\,\omega_n t\right)\right]$

$$\nu = \frac{\gamma + \sqrt{\gamma^2-1}}{\gamma - \sqrt{\gamma^2-1}}$$

Impulse input: $I = \int_0^t F\,dt \quad t \to 0$

(a) $\gamma < 1$: $\dfrac{x\sqrt{Mk}}{I} = \dfrac{\exp(-\gamma\omega_n t)}{\sqrt{1-\gamma^2}}\sin\left(\sqrt{1-\gamma^2}\,\omega_n t\right)$

(b) $\gamma = 1$: $\dfrac{x\sqrt{Mk}}{I} = \omega_n t\,\exp(-\omega_n t)$

(c) $\gamma > 1$: $\dfrac{x\sqrt{Mk}}{I} = \dfrac{\sqrt{v}}{v-1}\exp\left(\dfrac{-\omega_n t}{\sqrt{v}}\right) - \exp\left(\sqrt{v}\omega_n t\right)$

$\dfrac{xk\tau}{I} = \exp(-t/\tau)$

Ramp input: $F(t) = \beta t$

(a) $\gamma < 1$: $\dfrac{x\omega_n k}{\beta} = \dfrac{1}{\sqrt{1-\gamma^2}}\exp(-\gamma\omega_n t)\sin\left(\sqrt{1-\gamma^2}\,\omega_n t + \phi\right) - 2\gamma + \omega_n t$

$\phi = \tan^{-1}\dfrac{\gamma\sqrt{1-\gamma^2}}{\gamma^2 - \frac{1}{2}}$

(b) $\gamma = 1$: $\dfrac{x\omega_n k}{\beta} = (2 + \omega_n t)\exp(-\omega_n t) + \omega_n t - 2$

(c) $\gamma > 1$: $\dfrac{x\omega_n k}{\beta} = \dfrac{v\sqrt{v}}{v-1}\exp\left(\dfrac{-\omega_n t}{\sqrt{v}}\right) - \dfrac{1}{v^2}\exp\left(-\sqrt{v}\omega_n t\right) - \dfrac{v+1}{\sqrt{v}} + \omega_n t$

$\dfrac{xk}{\beta\tau} = \dfrac{t}{\tau} - [1 - \exp(-t/\tau)]$

TABLE 3-1 Response of First- and Second-Order Systems to Various Input Signals (*continued*)

First-order system	Second-order system

Sinusoidal input: $F(t) = F_0 \cos \Omega t$ or $F(t) = $ (real part of) $F_0 \exp{(i\Omega t)}$

First-order system:

$$\frac{x}{(F_0/k)} = \frac{\cos(\Omega t + \phi)}{\sqrt{1 + (\Omega \tau)^2}}$$

$$-\phi = \tan^{-1} \Omega \tau$$

Second-order system:

$$\frac{x}{F_0/k} = \frac{\cos{(\Omega t + \phi)}}{\sqrt{(1 - \beta^2)^2 + (2\gamma\beta)^2}}$$

$$\phi = \tan^{-1} \frac{-2\gamma\beta}{1 - \beta^2}$$

$$\beta = \frac{\Omega}{\omega_n}$$

EXAMPLE 3. A thermistor-type temperature sensor is found to behave as a first-order system and its experimentally determined time constant τ is 0.4 s. The resistance-temperature relation for the thermistor is given as

$$R = R_0 \exp\left[\beta\left(\frac{1}{T} - \frac{1}{T_0}\right)\right]$$

where β has been experimentally determined to be 4000 K. This temperature sensor is to be used to measure the temperature of a fluid by suddenly immersing the thermistor into the fluid medium.

How long one must wait to ensure that the thermometer reading will be in error by no more than *5 percent of the step change in temperature* is calculated as follows:

$$x = x_s(1 - e^{-t/\tau})$$

$$x = T - T_0 = 0.95(T_\infty - T_0)$$

$$x_s = T_\infty - T_0$$

$$\therefore \quad 0.95 = 1 - e^{-t/0.4}$$

$$\ln 0.05 = \frac{-t}{0.4} = -2.9957$$

$$\therefore \quad t = 1.198 \text{ s} = 1.2 \text{ s}$$

Determine the sensitivity of the thermometer at a temperature of 300 K if the resistance R is 1000 ohms (Ω) at this temperature:

$$S = \left.\frac{dR}{dT}\right|_{op} = R_0 \exp\left[\beta\left(\frac{1}{T} - \frac{1}{T_0}\right)\right]\beta(-1)T^{-2}$$

$$= -\frac{R\beta}{T^2} = \frac{1000(4000)}{(300)^2}$$

$$= -44.44 \ \Omega/K$$

Determine the resolution of the thermometer if one can observe changes in resistance of 0.50 Ω on a Wheatstone bridge used as a readout device at the temperature of 300 K:

$$R = \frac{\Delta Q_{op}|_{min}}{S} = \frac{-0.50}{-44.44} = 0.0113 \text{ K}$$

The expected response of the thermometer if it were subjected to step changes in temperature between 300 and 500 K in a square wave fashion and at a frequency of 1.0 hertz (Hz) is shown in Fig. 3-22, where $x = x_s(0.7135)$. Note that the thermistor never responds sufficiently to give an accurate indication of the step-amplitude temperature. However, if the time constant of the thermistor were selected to be less than 0.1 s, the step-amplitude temperature would be indicated in 0.5 s (5 time constants).

EXAMPLE 4. A strip-chart recorder (oscillograph) has been determined to behave as a second-order system with damping ratio of 0.5 and natural frequency of 60 Hz.

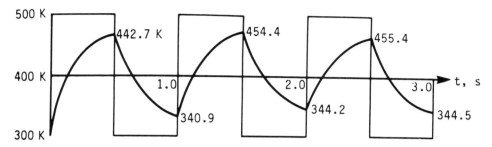

FIG. 3-22 Thermistor temperature response of Example 3.

At what frequency would the output amplitude of the recorder "peak" even with a constant-amplitude input signal? The frequency may be calculated as follows:

$$\omega_p = \omega_n \sqrt{1 - 2\gamma^2} = 60\sqrt{1 - 2(0.5)^2} = 42.4 \text{ Hz}$$

What is the maximum sine wave frequency of input signal that would allow no more than 5 percent error in amplitude? See Fig. 3-23. The amplitude factor (AF) is calculated as follows:

$$1.05 = \text{AF} = \frac{1}{\sqrt{[1 - (\omega_f/\omega_n)^2]^2 + (2\gamma\,\omega_f/\omega_n)^2}} = \frac{1}{\sqrt{1 - z + z^2}}$$

where $z \equiv (\omega_f/\omega_n)^2$. The result is $\omega_{f_{\max}} = 19.2$ Hz.

A complex waveform comprised of a fundamental frequency of 10 Hz and 8 harmonics in terms of its Fourier series representation is desired to be recorded. Will the oscillograph described above suffice?

The basic equation is

$$\text{maximum frequency} = (n + 1)(\text{fundamental}) = 90 \text{ Hz}$$

$$\text{AF} = \frac{1}{\sqrt{[(1 - (90/60)^2]^2 + (90/60)^2}} = 0.51$$

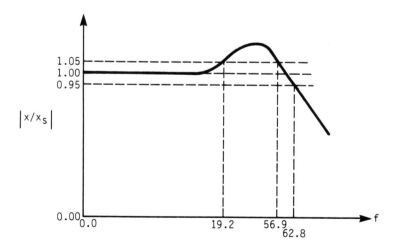

FIG. 3-23 Frequency response of strip-chart recorder of Example 4.

$$\psi = \tan^{-1} \frac{2(0.5)90/60}{1 - (90/60)^2} = -55.2° \qquad \text{(oscillograph will not suffice)}$$

If both the frequency and phase-response characteristics for the oscillograph are given below, show how the input signal to the oscillograph, also given below, will be changed, and give the resulting relation expected:

$$e = 10 + 5.8 \cos 5t + 3.2 \cos 10t + 1.8 \cos 20t$$

Input frequency ω, rad/s	Amplitude, V		Phase angle (lag), °
	Input	Output	
0	10.0	10.0	0
5	10.0	10.0	10
10	10.0	10.2	20
15	10.0	10.6	30
20	10.0	11.0	45
25	10.0	12.2	90

It follows that

$$e_o = 10 \left(\frac{10}{10}\right) + 5.8 \left(\frac{10.0}{10.0}\right) \cos \left(5t - \frac{10\pi}{180}\right) + 3.2 \left(\frac{10.2}{10.0}\right) \cos \left(10t - \frac{20\pi}{180}\right)$$

$$+ 1.8 \left(\frac{11.0}{10.0}\right) \cos \left(20t - \frac{45\pi}{180}\right)$$

$$= 10 + 5.8 \cos (5t - 0.174) + 3.26 \cos (10t - 0.349)$$

$$+ 1.98 \cos (20t - 0.785)$$

3-7 SELECTED MEASURING-SYSTEM COMPONENTS AND EXAMPLES

3-7-1 Operational Amplifiers

Operational amplifiers [3-8] used in measuring systems have the basic configuration shown in Fig. 3-24. The *operational amplifier* is comprised of a high-gain voltage amplifier coupled with both input and feedback impedances. The characteristics of the operational amplifier depend on the feedback impedance Z_f and input impedance Z_i selected according to the Eq. (3-20):

$$\frac{e_o}{e_i} = - \frac{Z_f}{Z_i} \tag{3-20}$$

The relations between input and output voltage for the specific configurations shown in Fig. 3-24 are as follows:
Voltage amplifier:

$$\frac{e_o}{e_i} = - \frac{R_f}{R_i} \tag{3-21}$$

Notes · Drawings · Ideas

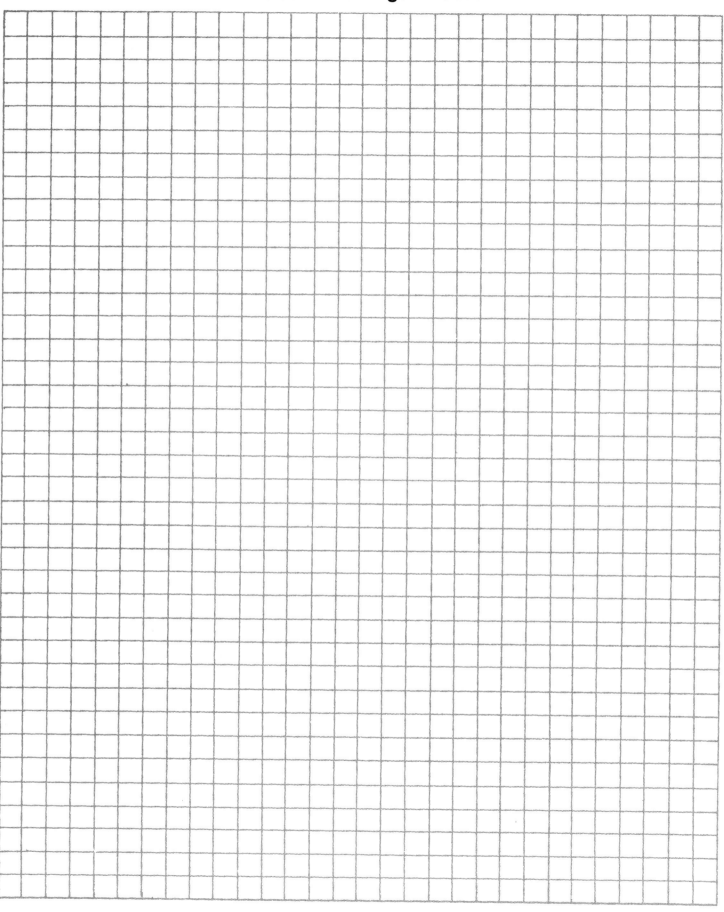

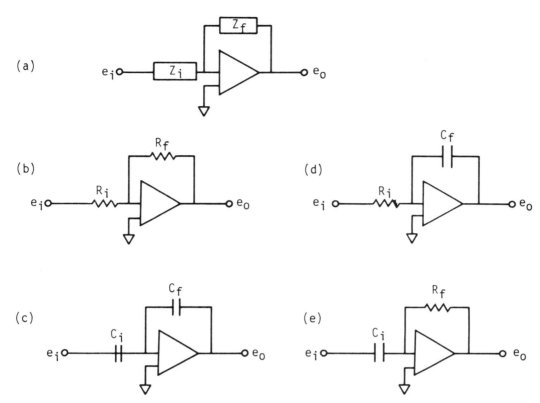

FIG. 3-24 Operational amplifier circuit. (*a*) General; (*b*) voltage amplifier; (*c*) charge amplifier; (*d*) integrator; (*e*) differentiator.

Charge amplifier:

$$\frac{e_o}{e_i} = -\frac{C_i}{C_f} \qquad (3\text{-}22)$$

Integrator:

$$e_o = -\frac{1}{R_i C_f} \int_0^t e_i \, dt + e_o(0) \qquad (3\text{-}23)$$

Differentiator:

$$e_o = -R_f C_i \frac{de_i}{dt} \qquad (3\text{-}24)$$

3-7-2 Piezoelectric Crystal

Piezoelectric crystals [3-9] are specific crystals of such materials as quartz, barium titinate, and lead zirconate which, when properly heated and quenched, demonstrate the piezoelectric phenomenon. The *piezoelectric phenomenon* is that the crystal, when stressed, produces an electric charge on its surfaces. If the crystal is a wafer of thickness t and its surfaces are coated with (or touching) conductive plates, the plates become a capacitor of plate area A, spacing t, and dielectric property ε of the piezo-electric material. The voltage developed from the piezoelectric crystal from any input (force, pressure, acceleration, stress, etc.) is

$$e_o = S_e x \qquad (3\text{-}25)$$

where S_e = voltage sensitivity, and x = input variable. The voltage sensitivity depends on the fundamental charge sensitivity of the piezoelectric crystal:

$$S_e = \frac{S_q}{C_c} \qquad (3\text{-}26)$$

where $S_q = q/x$, and C_c = crystal capacitance, given by

$$C_c = \frac{KA\varepsilon}{t} \qquad (3\text{-}27)$$

K is a constant which depends on the geometry and the units of the parameters in the preceding equation.

When the piezoelectric crystal is coupled via lead wires with capacitance, the voltage sensitivity and output voltage are reduced according to the relation

$$e_o = S_e x = \frac{S_q}{C_T} x \qquad (3\text{-}28)$$

where C_T = total capacitance of the combination of piezoelectric crystal, lead wires, and readout device and is equal to

$$C_T = C_c + C_{lw} + C_{rd} \qquad (3\text{-}29)$$

The equivalent circuits of the piezoelectric crystal are given in Fig. 3-25. The piezoelectric crystal has a dynamic response that is approximately that of an undamped second-order system. The circuit components of the piezoelectric crystal have a dynamic response that is approximately that of a first-order system. The typical frequency response of the piezoelectric transducer is that shown in Fig. 3-26 and is the combination of the crystal and circuit responses.

When the piezoelectric crystal is coupled with a voltage amplifier, the output voltage of the measuring system is dependent on lead-wire capacitance according to the relation

$$e_o = -\frac{R_f}{R_i} S_e x = -\frac{R_f}{R_i}\frac{S_q}{C_T} x \qquad (3\text{-}30)$$

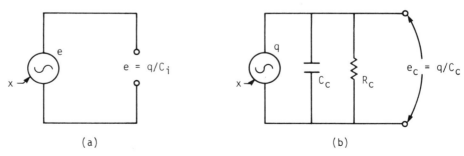

(a)   (b)

FIG. 3-25 Equivalent circuits of a piezoelectric crystal. (*a*) Voltage generator equivalent circuit; (*b*) charge generator equivalent circuit.

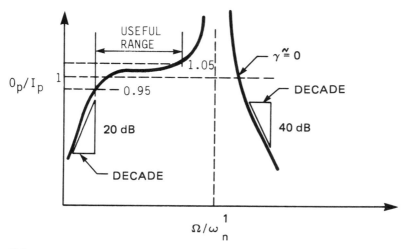

FIG. 3-26 Composite frequency response of a piezoelectric transducer.

where $C_T = C_c + C_{lw} + C_a$, and R_f/R_i = the ratio of feedback-to-input resistance on the operational amplifier used for voltage amplification. Thus long lead wires or high lead-wire capacitance will significantly decrease the output voltage of the measuring system when using a voltage amplifier. The use of a charge amplifier avoids the problem of capacitance of the input lead wires, as shown by the relation

$$e_o = -\frac{C_i}{C_f} S_e x = -\frac{C_i}{C_f} \frac{S_q}{C_T} x \qquad (3\text{-}31)$$

where C_i equals C_T and is the total capacitance at the input to the charge amplifier. Thus with a charge amplifier the voltage sensitivity S_e of the system depends only on the basic crystal charge sensitivity S_q and the charge amplifier feedback capacitance C_f and not on the input capacitance.

EXAMPLE 5. A piezoelectric accelerometer is to be used to measure the vibration of an automotive engine as installed in a particular test cell. The pertinent characteristics of the transducer, cable, charge amplifier, and cathode-ray oscilloscope used in the acceleration measuring system are given in the following table:

Characteristic	Piezoelectric accelerometer	Cable	Charge amplifier	Cathode-ray oscilloscope	Voltage amplifier
Charge sensitivity, pC/g	123				
Natural frequency, Hz	30 000				
Capacitance, pF	8 600	300			
Resistance, Ω	10^{12}	Negligible			
Feedback capacitance, pF	. . . . .	. . . .	10^3		
Input resistance, Ω	. . . . .	. . . .	10^8	10^6	
Input capacitance, pF	. . . . .	. . . .	50	50	
$\dfrac{R_f}{R_i}$	. . . . .	. . . .	. .	. .	0.123

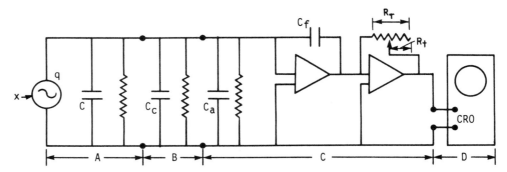

FIG. 3-27   Circuit diagram of the vibration-measuring system. A, piezoelectric crystal; B, cable; C, charge amplifier coupled to a voltage amplifier; D, cathode-ray oscilloscope.

The circuit diagram is shown in Fig. 3-27.

Determine the sensitivity of the *measuring system* if the "charge sensitivity" setting on the charge amplifier is adjusted to a value of 0.123.

The following equation gives the sensitivity:

$$\frac{R_t}{R_T} = 0.123 \qquad \frac{e_o}{x} = \frac{R_T}{R_t}\frac{S_q}{C_f} = \frac{123}{0.123}\frac{1}{10^3} = 1 \text{ V/g}$$

What sensitivity setting should be selected on the cathode-ray oscilloscope?

For 1 g/cm, use 1 V/cm.

For 0.1 g/cm, use 0.1 V/cm.

What range of acceleration can be measured if a maximum output of 10 V is available?

Range of acceleration is found as follows:

$$x_{\max} = \frac{e_o|_{\max}}{S} = \frac{10}{1 \text{ V/g}} = 10.0 \text{ g}$$

What is the voltage sensitivity of the accelerometer?

1. If the charge amplifier is used,

$$\frac{e_i}{x} = \frac{q/x}{C_i} = \frac{S_q}{C_i} \qquad \frac{e_o}{x} = -\frac{e_i}{x}\frac{C_i}{C_f} = -\frac{S_q}{C_f}$$

Thus   Voltage sensitivity $= \dfrac{123 \text{ pC/g}}{10^3 \text{ pF}} = 123 \text{ mV/g}$

2. If the accelerometer is connected directly to the cathode-ray oscilloscope (no charge amplifier),

$$\frac{e_o}{e_i} = -G \qquad \frac{e_o}{x} = -G\frac{e_i}{x} = -G\frac{S_q}{C_i} = -\frac{G(123) \text{ pC/g}}{(8600 + 300 + 50) \text{ pF}}$$

Thus   Voltage sensitivity $= -13.7G$ mV/g

If the accelerometer has zero damping, what would be the largest frequency of input vibration allowable to have no more than a 1 percent error? If the engine has eight cylinders and operates at 4000 rpm, will the measuring system work?

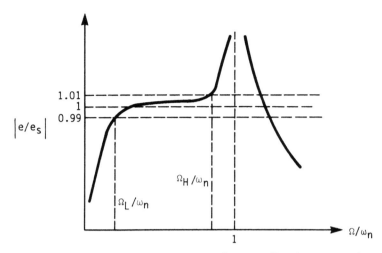

FIG. 3-28 Frequency response of the vibration-measuring system.

The computations are as follows:

$$\frac{8(4000)}{60} = 533.3 \text{ Hz} = \text{vibration frequency expected}$$

$$\text{AF}_{\text{HF}} = \frac{1}{1 - (\Omega/\omega n)^2} = 1.01 \qquad \Omega/\omega_n = 0.0995 \qquad \Omega_{\text{H}} = 2985 \text{ Hz}$$

$$\text{AF}_{\text{LF}} = \frac{1}{\sqrt{1 + (\tau\Omega)^2}} = 0.99$$

$$\tau = R_T C_T = 10^6(8650 \times 10^{-12}) = 0.00865 \text{ s.}$$

$$\tau\Omega = 0.1425 \qquad \Omega_{\text{L}} = 15.83 \text{ rad/s} = 2.5 \text{ hZ}$$

The frequency response of the vibration measurement system is satisfactory and is shown in Fig. 3-28.

3-7-3 Ballast-Type Circuit

A basic circuit used in measurement applications is the ballast-type circuit shown in Fig. 3-29. The relation between input and output voltage is given by

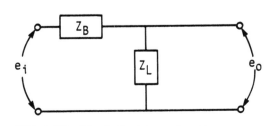

FIG. 3-29 The ballast-type circuit.

$$\frac{e_o}{e_i} = \frac{Z_L}{Z_B + Z_L} \qquad (3\text{-}32)$$

where Z_L = load impedance, and Z_B = ballast impedance.

When Z_L and Z_B are capacitance C and resistance R, respectively, the circuit is used as a low-pass filter with output voltage and phase shift given by Eqs. (3-

33) and (3-34), respectively, where ω is the frequency of the input signal:

$$\left|\frac{e_o}{e_i}\right| = \sqrt{\frac{1}{1 + (RC\omega)^2}} \tag{3-33}$$

$$\phi = \tan^{-1}(RC\omega) \tag{3-34}$$

When Z_L and Z_B are resistance and capacitance, respectively, the circuit is used as a high-pass filter.

The output voltage and phase shift are then given by Eqs. (3-35) and (3-36), respectively:

$$\left|\frac{e_o}{e_i}\right| = \sqrt{\frac{(RC\omega)^2}{1 + (RC\omega)^2}} \tag{3-35}$$

$$\phi = \tan^{-1}\left(\frac{1}{RC\omega}\right) \tag{3-36}$$

An example of this type of circuit is the ac coupling circuit at the input of a cathode-ray oscilloscope. When Z_L is that of an impedance-based detector transducer such as a resistance thermometer or strain gauge, the voltage e_i is that of the auxiliary energy source and Z_B is an impedance used to limit the current flow to the detector transducer. If Joule (I^2R) heating would affect the transducer measurement, such as in resistance-thermometer or strain-gauge applications, the ability to limit current is important.

EXAMPLE 6. The circuit of Fig. 3-30a is used as a coupling circuit between a detector transducer and a readout device. Determine and sketch the amplitude and phase characteristics of the coupling circuit (see Fig. 3-30b, c, and d). Determine the loading error if a readout device having an input impedance equal to R is connected to the circuit.

The equations are as follows:

$$e_o = IR$$

$$e_i = I(Z_L + R)$$

$$\left.\frac{e_o}{e_i}\right|_U = \left(\frac{R}{j\omega L + R}\right)\left(\frac{-j\omega L + R}{-j\omega L + R}\right) = \frac{R^2 - jRL\omega}{R^2 + (\omega L)^2} = \frac{R^2}{D} - \frac{jRL\omega}{D}$$

$$\left.\left|\frac{e_o}{e_i}\right|\right|_U = \sqrt{\left(\frac{R^2}{D}\right)^2 + \left(\frac{RL\omega}{D}\right)^2}$$

$$= \sqrt{\frac{R^4 + R^2L^2\omega^2}{R^4 + 2R^2\omega^2L^2 + (\omega L)^4}} = \sqrt{\frac{R^2(R^2 + L^2\omega^2)}{[R^2 + (\omega L)^2]^2}}$$

$$= \sqrt{\frac{R^2}{R^2 + (\omega L)^2}} = \sqrt{\frac{1}{1 + (\omega L/R)^2}}$$

$$\left.\frac{e_o}{e_i}\right|_L = \frac{R_{eq}^2}{D} - \frac{jR_{eq}L\omega}{D}$$

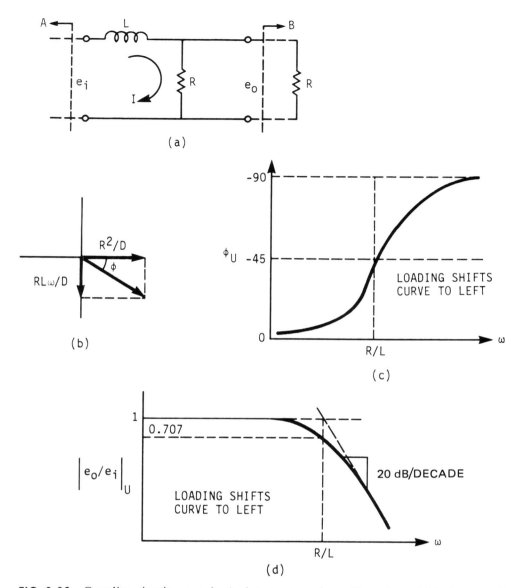

FIG. 3-30 Coupling circuit example. A, detector transducer; B, readout. (*a*) Inductor and resistance in a ballast-type circuit; (*b*) real and complex components; (*c*) phase-shift characteristic; (*d*) frequency-response characteristic.

and

$$\left|\frac{e_o}{e_i}\right|_L = \sqrt{\frac{1}{1 + (\omega L/R_{eq})^2}} = \sqrt{\frac{1}{1 + (2\omega L/R)^2}}$$

$$LE \equiv \frac{|e_o/e_i|_U - |e_o/e_i|_L}{|e_o/e_i|_U} = 1 - \frac{e_o|_L}{e_o|_U} = 1 - I$$

$$= 1 - \sqrt{\frac{1 + (\omega L/R)^2}{1 + 4(\omega L/R)^2}}$$

$$\phi_L = \tan^{-1}\frac{2\omega L}{R} \qquad \phi_U = \tan^{-1}\frac{L\omega}{R}$$

Tables 3-2 and 3-3 give several examples of both ballast and bridge circuits used in instrumentation systems.

3-7-4 Bridge Circuit

The bridge circuit used in measurement circuits is shown in Fig. 3-31. For voltage excitation, e_i, the output Δe_o corresponds to the change in output voltage due to the change in the arm impedances of the bridge. The relationship between output voltage and impedance change in one arm of the bridge is given as follows:

$$\frac{e_o + \Delta e_o}{e_i} = \frac{(Z_1 + \Delta Z_1)Z_4 - Z_2 Z_3}{(Z_1 + \Delta Z_1 + Z_2)(Z_3 + Z_4)} \qquad (3\text{-}37)$$

If initially the bridge is said to be "balanced," the output voltage e_o is zero and the relationship for the impedances in the bridge is given by the balance equation

$$\frac{Z_1}{Z_2} = \frac{Z_3}{Z_4} \qquad (3\text{-}38)$$

TABLE 3-2 Typical Ballast-Type Circuits Used in Instrumentation Circuits

Ballast-type circuits	Magnitude response and phase shift
(a) Low-pass RC	$\left\|\dfrac{e_o}{e_i}\right\| = \dfrac{1}{\sqrt{1 + \omega^2\tau^2}} \approx \dfrac{1}{\omega\tau}$ $\phi = -\tan^{-1} R\omega C$
(b) High-pass RC	$\left\|\dfrac{e_o}{e_i}\right\| = \dfrac{1}{\sqrt{1 + 1/\omega^2\tau^2}} \approx \omega\tau$ $\phi = \tan^{-1}\dfrac{1}{R\omega C}$
(c) Low-pass RL	$\left\|\dfrac{e_o}{e_i}\right\| = \dfrac{1}{\sqrt{1 + \omega^2\tau^2}} \approx \dfrac{1}{\omega\tau}$ $\phi = -\tan^{-1}\dfrac{\omega L}{R}$
(d) High-pass RL	$\left\|\dfrac{e_o}{e_i}\right\| = \dfrac{1}{\sqrt{1 + 1/\omega^2\tau^2}} \approx \omega\tau$ $\phi = \tan^{-1}\dfrac{R}{\omega L}$

TABLE 3-3 Typical Bridge Circuits Used in Instrumentation Circuits

Bridge circuits	Balance relations

ac Wheatstone bridge

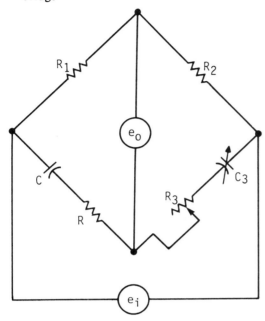

$$C = \frac{C_3 R_2}{R_1}$$

$$R = \frac{R_3 R_1}{R_2}$$

Wein bridge

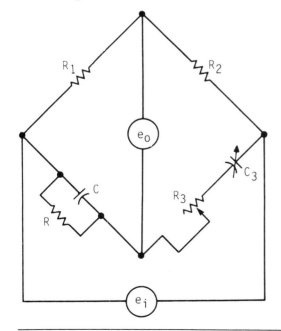

$$\frac{C}{C_3} = \frac{R_2}{R_1} - \frac{R_3}{R}$$

$$CC_3 = \frac{1}{\omega^2 R_3 R}$$

If $C_3 = C$ and $R_3 = R$,

$$f = \frac{1}{2\pi R_3 C_3}$$

Bridge circuits	Balance relations

Resonance bridge

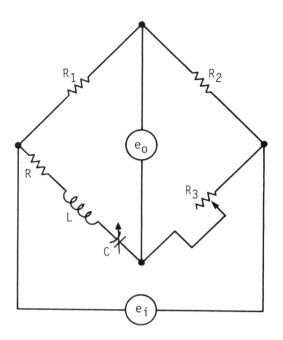

$$\omega^2 LC = 1$$

$$R = \frac{R_3 R_1}{R_2}$$

At balance

$$f = \frac{1}{2\pi \sqrt{LC}}$$

Maxwell bridge

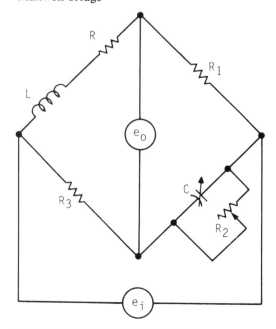

$$L = R_1 R_3 C$$

$$R = \frac{R_1 R_3}{R_2}$$

Bridge circuits	Balance relations

Owen bridge

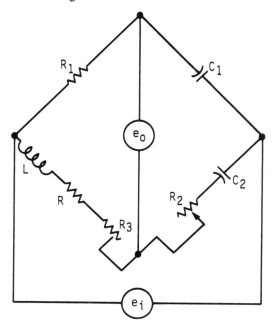

$$L = C_1 R_1 R_2$$

$$R = \frac{C_1 R_1}{C_2} - R_3$$

Hay bridge

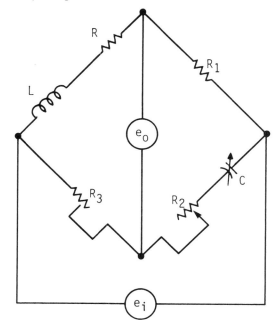

$$L = \frac{R_1 R_3 C}{1 + \omega^2 C^2 R_2^2}$$

$$R = \frac{\omega^2 C^2 R_1 R_2 R_3}{L + \omega^2 C^2 R_2^2}$$

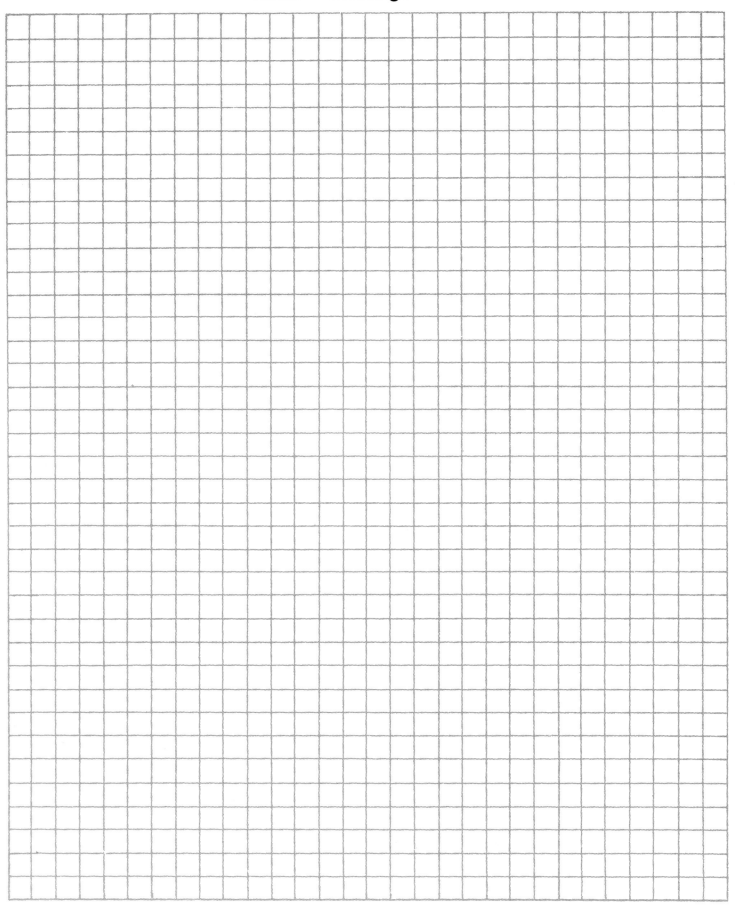

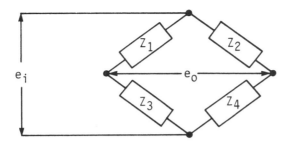

FIG. 3-31   The bridge circuit.

This relation is used to measure an unknown impedance connected in a bridge circuit with three other impedances which are known. The reader is referred to Prensky [3-10] and to Table 3-3 for further information in this regard.

The ability of the bridge circuit to "zero" the output at any level of input transducer impedance allows the circuit to be used for the "balance" type of measurement which is more accurate than the "unbalance" type of measurement commonly employed when using the ballast-type circuit.

When all impedances are initially equal, the bridge is balanced, and the impedance change from an input signal is small compared to the original impedance, the bridge output voltage is linearized to

$$\Delta e_o \approx \frac{\Delta Z}{4Z} e_i \qquad (3\text{-}39)$$

This equation can be used to predict the output of impedance-based transducers such as variable capacitors, variable inductances, or variable resistances (such as resistance thermometers or strain gauges) used in voltage-sensitive bridge circuits.

3-7-5 Strain Gauges

The strain gauge is a resistance R (usually in the form of a grid) wire or foil that changes when strained according to the relation

$$R = \rho \frac{L}{A} \qquad (3\text{-}40)$$

where L = wire or foil length, A = wire or foil cross section, and ρ = electrical resistivity of the strain-gauge material. The strain-gauge sensitivity is the *"gauge factor"* GF given by the relation

$$\text{GF} = \frac{\Delta R/R}{\Delta L/L} = 1 + 2\mu + \frac{\Delta \rho/\rho}{\Delta L/L} \qquad (3\text{-}41)$$

where μ = Poisson's ratio for the strain-gauge material.

The strain gauge is often the sensing element in force transducers (load cells), pressure transducers, and accelerometers. The use of a strain gauge is illustrated in the following example.

EXAMPLE 7. Figure 3-32 shows a rectangular cross section of a cantilever beam of width b and depth h with a bending load F applied at a distance L from where the strain is desired. A voltage-sensitive bridge circuit is used for excitation of 120-Ω, gauge factor 2.0 strain gauges.

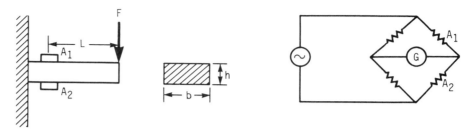

FIG. 3-32 Cantilever beam with strain gauges.

The strain-gauge characteristics coupled with the bridge circuit and beam characteristics yield the following output voltage with respect to input load producing the strain:

$$e_o = Ke_i \left(\frac{\Delta R}{4R} \right) = \frac{Ke_i}{4} (\text{GF}) \, \epsilon = \frac{K}{4} e_i (\text{GF}) \frac{6FL}{Ebh^2} \qquad (3\text{-}42)$$

K is the "bridge factor" in this equation and is a constant giving the magnification factor for using more than one active gauge in the bridge circuit. With two active gauges as shown the bridge factor is 2 and the gauge arrangement gives complete compensation for temperature change of the beam. The temperature-induced strains are detected by the strain gauges but are effectively canceled in the bridge circuit if the gauges are oriented to measure the same strain magnitude and if they have the same sensitivity; that is, matched transducers are used to cancel the "noise" signal caused by temperature change.

3-8 SOURCES OF ERROR IN MEASUREMENTS

The basic problem of every quantitative experiment is that of trying to identify the true value of the measured quantity. Philosophically, the measurement process is like viewing a deterministic event through a foggy window. Refinement of the measuring system to the ultimate should result in the measurement being the true value. However, because errors occur in all measurements, one can never establish the true value of any quantity. Continued refinement of the methods used in any measurement will yield closer approximations to the true value, but there is always a limit beyond which refinement cannot be made. Furthermore, the fact that the measuring system draws energy from the source of the variable to be measured results in the measurement process changing the characteristics of both the signal source and the measured variable. Thus some difference, however small, always occurs between the indicated value of the measured quantity and the original quantity to be measured.

3-8-1 Systematic Errors

Systematic errors are of consistent form. They result from conditions or procedures that cause a consistent error which is repeated every time the measurement is performed, such as faulty calibrations of the measuring system or changes in the measuring-system components due to factors such as aging.

Another form of systematic error can occur as a result of the observer. Parallax is an example of such an error. If the observer does not correctly align the indicating needle of the instrument, the reading may be consistently high or low depending on the individual observer. This type of error is difficult to detect because it is repeated with every measurement under identical conditions. However, one means of detecting systematic error is to measure something whose magnitude is accurately and independently known. For example, a check on a thermometer at one or more fixed points on the temperature scale will determine if the temperature scale on the thermometer is yielding a systematic error. Use of gauge blocks in checking micrometers and calipers is another example of checking a measuring system to eliminate systematic errors.

Calibration of the measuring system frequently, by use of accurately known input signals, can give an indication of the development of systematic errors in the measuring system. Measurement of the variable with two different measuring systems can often help detect the presence of a fixed error in the measurement system or measurement process.

3-8-2 Illegitimate Errors

Illegitimate errors are mistakes and should not exist. They may be eliminated by using care in the experimental procedure and by repetition in checking the measurement. Faulty data logging is an example of illegitimate error. This might occur by reading the wrong value from a scale, by writing down a wrong number, or by transposing the digits of a number. Another example of illegitimate error is that of using linear interpolation between scale divisions on a readout device when the scale is nonlinear. For example, some readout scales may be logarithmic, but it is quite common for observers to interpolate between these scale divisions in a linear fashion. Repeating the measurement and rechecking suspicious values can help eliminate such mistakes.

3-8-3 Random Errors

Random errors are accidental errors that occur in all measurements. They are characterized by their stochastic natures in both magnitude and time. One cannot determine their origin in the measurement process. These errors can only be estimated by statistical analysis. However, if both systematic and illegitimate errors can be eliminated, the uncertainty in the measurement due to the remaining random error can be estimated by statistical analysis of the data obtained in the experiment.

3-8-4 Loading Error

The loading error can be reduced in some measurement systems by means of a technique called *balancing*. A balance-type measurement is one where a reference signal is fed into the measurement system and a direct comparison between the reference and the measured signal is made. The reference signal is adjusted such that when its value is the same as the measured signal the two signals balance one another and the output reading from the measurement system is zero. With the reference signal balancing out the measured signal, the net energy flow from the source at the balance condition is zero. Thus the balance method usually provides a more accurate measurement than the unbalance method. Examples of the balance type of measurement are the use of bridge circuits in strain-gauge measurement and the use of a voltage-balancing potentiometer with thermocouples when measuring temperatures. It should be noted that the balance type of measurement is usually difficult to achieve when dynamic or time-varying signals are being measured. The loading error is a type of fixed error in the measuring system and can be determined by appropriate calibration.

3-8-5 Noise-Measurement Systems

"Noise" in a measurement system is any output which is not generated by the input quantity to be measured ([3-4], [3-11], [3-12]). It must be remembered that all measuring systems are placed in an environment and interact in some way with that environment. Any interaction of a measuring system with the environment that is not related to the input quantity to be measured can result in an unwanted output (noise) of the measuring system. For noise to exist at a measurement-system output there must be both a source and a receiver of the noise. There must also be a coupling method between the source and the receiver of the noise.

The noise signal at the output of the measuring system can come from two general sources. One source is internally from the transducers in the measuring system and the other source is from the environment of the transducers of the measuring system. Examples of internally generated signals are the thermal or Johnson noise [3-4] created in a resister of an electric circuit. Another example is the shot noise [3-4] generated by tubes in electric circuits. External sources can cover a variety of possibilities, such as vibrations, electrical interference from the electromagnetic spectrum, and switching or discharge of storage elements causing transient signals to be induced in the power and signal lines of a measuring system. Any physical change in the environment can induce externally generated noise signals. These include temperature change, humidity change, pressure change, sound-level change, etc.

The noise signal can be *active* or *self-generating* in the sense that the noise is directly coupled to the measuring system without the aid of an auxiliary energy source. These might be thermoelectric or electromagnetic in nature. For example, a constantan strain gauge connected with copper lead wires could have a noise voltage generated by the thermocouple effect at the two junctions where the constantan gauge and copper lead wires are connected if the junctions are at different temperatures.

Noise effects that require the use of an auxiliary energy source to be carried into the measuring system are called *passive noise signals*. Examples of such noise signals are the temperature effects that occur with strain gauges and the strain effects that occur with resistance thermometers.

The effects of the noise on the output of the measuring system may be additive, multiplicative, or a combination of additive and multiplicative. If the noise level is an additive effect with no frequency content, the output signal due to the noise is called *zero shift*. This is a very common type of noise and can be easily detected by calibration. It is usually eliminated by a "bias" control on the measuring instrument. Noise levels that have a multiplicative effect on the system output usually affect the gain or sensitivity of the components of the measuring system. These effects can sometimes be detected by calibration.

At least four methods of handling noise are known ([3-4], [3-11], [3-12]). These include removal of the noise source, elimination of the noise by cancellation, minimization of the noise by division (filtering), and minimization of the noise by frequency-selective filtering. Removal of the noise source is not usually possible, and one must generally resort to the other techniques. However, if the noise source can be eliminated, this would be the most effective method of preventing the noise problem.

When the effects which create the noise are consistent to the extent that one can expect two matched transducers to detect identical noise signals at the same instant of time in the same environment, it is possible to arrange for cancellation of these signals by subtraction. For example, the weight of a balance-scale pan may be subtracted (or balanced out) by placing an equal weight on the other side of the balance scale. Another example is the temperature-induced noise in strain gauges illustrated in Example 7. The temperature-induced resistance change in a strain gauge can be canceled out by placing two identical strain gauges (matched transducers) in the same thermal environment and by using proper placement of the gauges in a bridge circuit to provide subtraction of the noise signals. This is called *temperature compensation*. Another example is the noise-canceling microphone, in which two sensing elements are placed opposite one another. Voice input is supplied to only one element while external noise is sensed by both elements and is effectively balanced out or canceled. This technique is often used in aircraft applications. The use of this technique for noise elimination depends on being able to have two identical sensing elements which detect and respond to the noise signal to which they are exposed in exactly the same way and at the same time. Such detector elements are called *matched transducers*.

When the effects which create the noise level are not consistent, one cannot expect that two noise sources under identical environmental conditions will emit the same noise at every instance of time. In this case, noise is minimized by division so that only a small fraction of the original noise propagates through the system. For example, contact-resistance phenomena in switching gear and slip rings cause this type of noise. Electric circuitry in the measuring system is designed so that these resistance changes will have a minimal effect on the output reading. Electromagnetic radiation can also cause this type of noise input. Appropriate shielding of lead wires and circuits is necessary and is commonly used to minimize this type of noise.

Frequency-selecting filtering can be used if the noise and the desired signal can be made to exist at different frequencies [3-4]. When this is the case, a simple filter may then be used to minimize the noise signal. If the signal and the noise exist in the same frequency range, one must resort to a technique of modulation where the signal frequency is moved to a frequency range sufficiently separated from the noise frequency that the noise frequency can be effectively filtered from the signal frequency. This technique of frequency-selective filtering can only be used to minimize active noise in a passive transducer, since the carrier wave of the auxiliary energy source is used via modulation to shift the signal frequency upward and separate it from the noise frequency. If the noise is passive noise (depends on the auxiliary source of energy) in the transducer, the signal and noise would both be modulated upward to the same frequency band and separation could not be achieved. References [3-11] and [3-12] give specific details on how noise can be eliminated or minimized in a given measurement situation.

3-8-6 Precision and Accuracy

Accuracy is the difference between a measured variable and the true value of the measured variable. Normally, one is not able to determine accuracy. *Precision* is the difference between a measured variable and the best estimate (as obtained from the measured variable) of the true value of the measured variable. Thus precision is a measure of repeatability. It should also be noted that one may have excellent precision in a measurement but very poor accuracy. Calibration of a measuring system is essential toward determining its accuracy. Precision is specified by quantities called *precision indices* (denoted by W_x) that are calculated from the random errors of a set of measurements.

When a variable is measured, it is just as important to state the precision of the

Notes · Drawings · Ideas

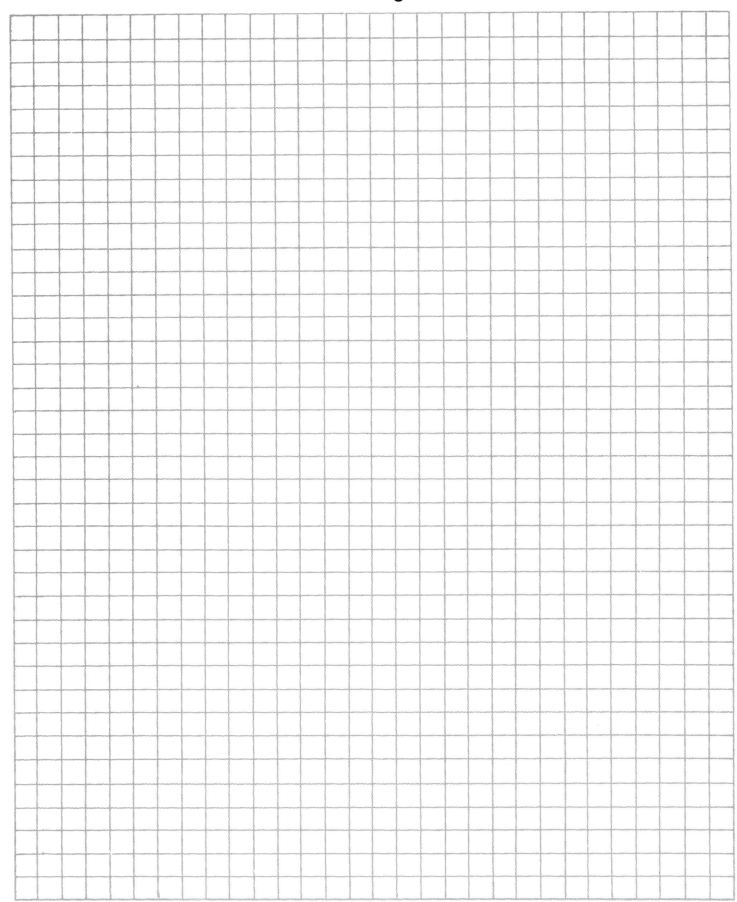

measurement as it is to state the most representative value of the quantity. Thus we desire W_x to be specified for every measured variable. The confidence or probability for obtaining the range $\pm W_x$ is generally specified directly or else is implied by the particular type of precision index being used.

3-9 ANALYSIS OF DATA

The basic problem in every quantitative experiment is that of obtaining the unbiased estimate $\hat{\mu}$ of the true value μ of a quantity as well as an unbiased estimate $\hat{W}$ of the dispersion or uncertainty in the measured variable. Data sets or samples typically display the two very important characteristics of central tendency (or most representative value) and dispersion (or scatter). Other characteristics, such as skewness and flatness (or peakness), may also be of importance but are not considered in the items that follow.

If we were given a list of measured values of the same variable, the question is raised as to what value shall be taken as being nearest to the true value. In order to determine what relation the measured value has with the true value, we must be able to specify in any experiment the unbiased estimate $\hat{\mu}$ of the true value of a measurement and its uncertainty (or precision) interval W based on a given confidence level (or probability of occurrence).

3-9-1 Unbiased Sampling

An *unbiased estimator* exists if the mean of its distribution is the same as the quantity being estimated [3-13]. Thus for sample mean $\bar{x}$ to be an unbiased estimator of population mean μ, the mean of the distribution of sample means $\bar{\bar{x}}$ must be equal to the population mean.

It can be shown that the unbiased estimator $\hat{\mu}$ for the population mean μ is the sample mean $\bar{x}$. In this section the measure of dispersion is selected to be the standard deviation σ or its square σ^2, called the *variance*. Determination of the unbiased estimator of the standard deviation or variance depends on the type of sampling method used.

Figure 3-33 illustrates that different samples from a population yield slightly different estimates of population mean and variance. However, if the data from the individual samples are combined, even better estimates of population mean and variance can be achieved. The mean of the sample means $\bar{\bar{x}}$ is a better estimate of μ than any of the individual sample means $\bar{x}$. Also, the dispersion of the distribution

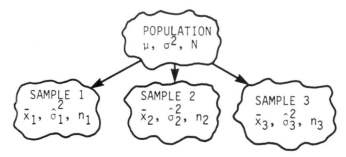

FIG. 3-33 Sampling from a population.

TABLE 3-4 Unbiased Estimates of Mean, Variance, and Variance of the Mean†

Statistic	Sampling with replacement	Sampling without replacement
Mean	$\hat{\mu} = \dfrac{\Sigma x_i}{n} = \bar{x}$	$\hat{\mu} = \dfrac{\Sigma x_i}{n} = \bar{x}$
Variance	$\hat{\sigma}^2 = \dfrac{\Sigma(x_i - \bar{x})^2}{n - 1} = S^2\left(\dfrac{n}{n-1}\right)$	$\hat{\sigma}^2 = S^2\left(\dfrac{n}{n-1}\right)\left(\dfrac{N-1}{N}\right)$
Variance of the mean	$\sigma_{\bar{x}}^2 = \dfrac{\hat{\sigma}^2}{n}$	$\hat{\sigma}_{\bar{x}}^2 = \dfrac{\hat{\sigma}^2}{n}\left(\dfrac{N-n}{N-1}\right)$

†S^2 = sample variance = $\Sigma(x_i - \bar{x})^2/n$ and $n/(n - 1)$ = Bessel's correction.

of $\bar{x}$ values is much less than the dispersion of items within an individual sample, as indicated by the central limit theorem.

The *central limit theorem* yields the result that if one obtains random samples of size n from a large population of mean μ and variance σ^2, the distribution of sample means approaches Gaussian as n becomes large with a mean μ and a variance σ^2/n. This is valid regardless of the nature of the distribution of the population from which the sample values were obtained.

A *random sample* is a sample collected such that every member of the population from which one is sampling has an equal probability of selection in every trial. This may be done with or without replacement. For a sample of size n, the probability of selection from the population of each member of the sample is $1/n$.

Unbiased estimates for determining population mean, population variance, and variance of the sample means depend on the type of sampling procedure used. Unbiased estimates of population mean μ, population variance σ^2, and variance of the mean are listed in Table 3-4 for sampling both with and without replacement. Note from the relations in Table 3-4 that sampling without replacement from an extremely large population is essentially equivalent to sampling with replacement (random sampling) since $(N - 1)/N$ and $(N - n)/(N - 1)$ approach unity.

EXAMPLE 8. The following data set is obtained by sampling from a population of 15 items:

x_i	$(x_i - \bar{x})$	$(x_i - \bar{x})^2$
65.0	−15.3	234.09
73.1	− 7.2	51.84
83.0	+ 2.7	7.29
100.1	+19.8	392.04
Σ = 321.2	00.0	685.26

1. Determine the mean and standard deviation of the *original data.*

$$n = 4 \qquad \bar{x} = \frac{321.2}{4} = 80.3$$

$$s = \sqrt{\frac{\Sigma(x_1 - \bar{x})^2}{n}} = \sqrt{\frac{685.26}{4}} = \sqrt{171.3} = \pm 13.09$$

2. What are the estimates of *population mean* and *variance* if the sampling occurred *with* replacement?

$$\hat{\mu} = \bar{x} = 80.3$$

$$\hat{\sigma}^2 = s^2 \frac{n}{n-1} = 171.3 \frac{4}{3} = 228.4$$

3. What are the estimates of population mean and variance if the sampling occurred *without* replacement?

$$\hat{\mu} = \bar{x} = 80.3$$

$$\hat{\sigma}^2 = s^2 \frac{n}{n-1} \frac{N-1}{N} = 171.3 \frac{4}{3} \frac{14}{15} = 213.2$$

4. What is the variance associated with the distribution of $\bar{x}$ values if sampling occurred *without* replacement?

$$\hat{\sigma}_x^2 = \frac{N-n}{N-1} \frac{\hat{\sigma}_x^2}{n} = \frac{(15-4)213.17}{(15-1)4} = 41.87$$

3-9-2 Uncertainty Interval

When several observations of a variable have been obtained to form a data set (multisample data), the best estimates of the most representative value (mean) and dispersion (standard deviation) are obtained from the formulas in Table 3-3. When only a single measurement exists (or when the data are taken so that they are similar to a single measurement), the standard deviation cannot be determined and the data are said to be "single sample" data. Under these conditions, the only estimate of the true value is the single measurement and the uncertainty interval must be estimated by the observer. Kline and McClintock [3-14] address this problem in detail. It is recommended that the precision index be estimated as the maximum error and that it correspond approximately to the 99 percent confidence level associated with multisample data.

Once the unbiased estimates of mean and variance are determined from the sample data, the *uncertainty interval* can be expressed as

$$\mu = \hat{\mu} \pm \hat{W} = \hat{\mu} \pm k(\nu, \gamma)\hat{\sigma} \qquad (3-43)$$

where $\hat{\mu}$ = the most representative value of the measured data, and $\hat{W}$ = the uncertainty interval or precision index associated with the estimate of μ. The magnitude of the precision index or uncertainty interval depends on confidence level γ (or probability chosen), sample size n, and type of probability distribution governing the distribution of measured items.

The uncertainty interval $\hat{W}$ can be replaced by $k\hat{\sigma}$, where $\hat{\sigma}$ is the standard deviation (measure of dispersion) of the population as estimated from the sample, and k

is a constant that depends on the probability distribution, the confidence level γ, and the sample size n. For example, with a Gaussian distribution, the 95 percent confidence limits $\hat{W} = 1.96\hat{\sigma}$, where $k = 1.96$ and in this case is independent of n. For a t distribution, $k = 2.78$, 2.06, and 1.96 for sample sizes of 5, 25, and ∞, respectively, at the 95 percent confidence level. The t distribution becomes the Gaussian distribution as $n \to \infty$. The uncertainty interval $\hat{W}$ in Eq. (3-43) assumes a set of measured values with only random error present. Furthermore, the set of measured values is assumed to have unbounded significant digits and to have been obtained with a measuring system having infinite resolution. When finite *resolution* exists and *truncation of significant digits* occurs, the uncertainty interval will be larger than that predicted by consideration of only the random error [3-15]. The uncertainty interval can never be less than the resolution limits or truncation limits of the measured values. If $\{s_n\}$ is the theoretically possible set of measurements of unbounded resolution and $\{x_n\}$ is the actual set of measurements expressed to m significant details from a measuring system of finite resolution R, the quantity $s_i - x_i = \pm e_i$ is the resolution or truncation deficiency caused by the measurement process. The unbiased estimates of mean and variance are

$$\hat{\mu} = \frac{\Sigma s_i}{n} = \bar{s} \qquad \hat{\sigma}^2 = \frac{\Sigma(s_i - \bar{s})^2}{n - 1} \tag{3-44}$$

Noting that the experimenter has the set $\{x_n\}$ rather than $\{s_n\}$, the mean and variance become

$$\hat{\mu} = \frac{\Sigma x_i}{n} \pm \frac{\Sigma e_i}{n} = \bar{x} \pm \frac{\Sigma e_i}{n} \qquad \hat{\sigma}^2 = \frac{\Sigma(x_i - \bar{x})^2}{n - 1} \tag{3-45}$$

Thus the truncation or resolution has no effect on the estimate of variance but does effect the estimate of the mean.

The truncation errors e_i are not necessarily distributed randomly and may all be of the same sign. Thus $\bar{x}$ can be biased as much as $\Sigma e_i/n = \bar{e}$ high or low from the unbiased estimate of the value of μ, so that $\hat{\mu} = \bar{x} \pm \bar{e}$.

If e_i is a random variable, such as when observing a variable with a measuring system of finite resolution, the values of e_i may be plus or minus, but their upper bound is R (the resolution of the measurement). Thus the resolution error is no larger than R, and $\mu = \bar{x} \pm R$.

If the truncation is never more than that dictated by the resolution limits R of the measuring system, the uncertainty in $\bar{x}$ as a measure of the most representative value of μ is never larger than R plus the uncertainty due to the random error. Thus $\hat{\mu} = \bar{x} \pm (\hat{W} + R)$. It should be emphasized that the uncertainty interval can never be less than the resolution bounds of the measurement no matter how small the random error might be. The resolution bounds cannot be reduced without changing the measurement system.

When x_i is observed to m significant digits, the uncertainty (except for random error) is never more than $\pm(5/10^m)$ and the bounds on s_i are equal to $x_i \pm (5/10^m)$, so that

$$x_i - \frac{5}{10^m} < s_i < x_i + \frac{5}{10^m} \tag{3-46}$$

The relation for $\hat{\mu}$ for m significant digits is then

$$\hat{\mu} = \bar{x} \pm \frac{\Sigma e_i}{n} = \bar{x} \pm \frac{\Sigma 5/10^m}{n} = \bar{x} \pm \frac{5}{10^m} \tag{3-47}$$

When the uncertainty due to significant digits is combined with the resolution limits and random error, the uncertainty interval on μ becomes

$$\mu = \hat{\mu} \pm \left(\hat{W} + R + \frac{5}{10^m} \right) \qquad (3\text{-}48)$$

This illustrates that the number of significant digits of a measurement should be carefully chosen in relation to the resolution limits of the measuring system so that $5/10^m$ has about the same magnitude as R. Additional significant digits would imply more accuracy to the measurement than would actually exist based on the resolving ability of the measuring system.

3-9-3 Amount of Data to Take

Exactly what data to take and how much data to take are two important questions to be answered in any experiment. Assuming that the correct variables have been measured, the amount of data to obtain can be determined by using the relation

$$\mu = \hat{\mu} \pm \left(\hat{W}_x + R + \frac{5}{10^m} \right) \qquad (3\text{-}49)$$

where it is presumed that several samples may exist for estimation of μ. This equation can be rewritten such that

$$\mu = \overline{\overline{x}} \pm \left[k(\nu, \alpha) \frac{\hat{\sigma}}{\sqrt{n}} + R + \frac{5}{10^m} \right] \qquad (3\text{-}50)$$

If one wishes to know the value of n to achieve the difference in $\mu - \overline{x}$ within a stated percent of μ, the relation can be solved for n to yield

$$n^2 = \frac{k(\nu, \gamma)\hat{\sigma}}{(\text{percent}/100)\hat{\mu} - R - (5/10^m)} \qquad (3\text{-}51)$$

This equation can only yield valid values of n once estimates of $\hat{\mu}$, $\hat{\sigma}$, k, R, and m are available. This means that the most correct value of n can only be obtained once the measurement system and data-taking procedure have been specified so that R and m are known. Furthermore, either a preliminary experiment or a portion of the actual experiment should be performed to obtain good estimates of $\hat{\mu}$ and $\hat{\sigma}$. Because k depends on the type of data distribution, the sample size n yields an iterative reduction. Thus the most valid estimates of the amount of data to take can only be obtained after the experiment has begun. This requires that estimates of the mean and the standard deviation must be obtained by performing part of the experiment. However, the equation can be quite useful for prediction purposes if one wishes to estimate values of $\hat{\mu}$, $\hat{\sigma}$, k, R, and m. This is especially important in experiments where the cost of a single run may be relatively high.

EXAMPLE 9. The life (mileage) for a certain type of automotive tire is known to follow a Gaussian (normal) distribution function. The mean and standard deviation of the mileage are estimated for these tires to be 84 000 and 2100 mi, respectively, from a sample of nine tires. Determine the 90 percent confidence limits for the means of all such tires manufactured by the company if the resolution of these measurements is 5 mi. On the basis of the sample, how much data (i.e., what is the sample size?) are required to establish the life of this type of tire to within ± 1 percent with 90 percent confidence and a resolution of 5 mi?

Notes · Drawings · Ideas

Solution

$$\mu = \mu \pm (t\sigma_x + R)$$

$$\sigma_x = 2230 \text{ mi}$$

$$\hat{\sigma}_x = \frac{\sigma_x}{n} = \frac{\Sigma(x_i - \overline{x})^2}{n-1} = \pm 743 \text{ mi}$$

$$t = t(\nu, \gamma) = t(8, 0.90) = 1.860\dagger$$

$$\mu = 84000 \pm [1.860(743) + 5]$$

$$= 84000 \pm 1387 \text{ mi}$$

$$\mu = \hat{\mu} \pm (t\hat{\sigma}_x + R)$$

$$\mu - \hat{\mu} = 0.01\overline{x} = t\frac{\hat{\sigma}_x}{\sqrt{n}} + R$$

$$\frac{t}{\sqrt{n}} = \frac{0.01\overline{x} - R}{\hat{\sigma}_x} = \frac{835}{2230} = 0.374$$

Use of Table A-8 in Ref. [3-7] yields the final result of $n = 122$.

3-10 CONFIDENCE LIMITS

A "confidence" limit or uncertainty interval is associated with a probability. The area under a probability-density curve between any two limits give the value of probability or confidence that any item sampled at random from the population will have a value between the two limits chosen. For example, the area under the Gaussian (or normal) probability-density function $p(x)$ between values of x_1 and x_2 is given by

$$\int_{x_1}^{x_2} p(x)\,dx = \int_{x_1}^{x_2} \frac{1}{\sigma\sqrt{2\pi}} \exp\left[-\frac{(x-\mu)^2}{2\sigma^2}\right] dx = \gamma \qquad (3\text{-}52)$$

and represents (as shown in Fig. 3-34) the probability that any one item selected at random from the population of values will have a magnitude between x_1 and x_2. In this figure, x_1 and x_2 are called *precision indices*. The symbol W_x is used to denote the values of x to be taken as a precision index or uncertainty interval. For the Gaussian distribution, a value of the precision indices of $\pm\sigma$ (one standard deviation) yields a probability or confidence of 68.3 percent. Also, $W_x = \pm 1.966$ are the 95 percent confidence limits and $W_x = \pm 2.586$ are the 99 percent confidence limits for the population of items following the Gaussian distribution. The confidence limits and associated probability are illustrated in Fig. 3-34. This information is

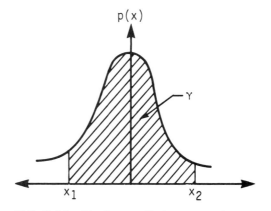

FIG. 3-34 Confidence limits on the Gaussian distribution.

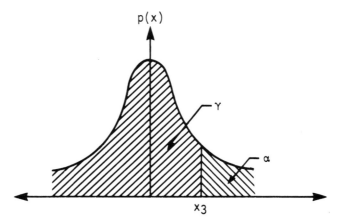

FIG. 3-35 Single-sided probabilistic statements.

often represented by the following probabilistic statement:

$$p(x_1 < x < x_2) = \gamma = 1 - \alpha \qquad (3\text{-}53)$$

where γ = the probability of the value of x from an observation to be between the values of x_1 and x_2. The value γ is known as the *confidence level,* whereas the value α is known as *significance level.* The meaning of the one-sided probabilistic statements

$$p(x < x_3) = \gamma \qquad \text{and} \qquad p(x > x_3) = \alpha = 1 - \gamma \qquad (3\text{-}54)$$

is illustrated in Fig. 3-35.

EXAMPLE 10. Certain strain gauges are manufactured with a resistance specification of $120 \pm 0.5 \ \Omega$. All gauges not meeting this specification are rejected. If all such strain gauges manufactured follow a Gaussian probability function, estimate the standard deviation of the manufacturing process if 2 percent are typically rejected (refer to Fig. 3-36 and Table A-4 of Ref. [3-7]).

Solution

$$p(119.5 < R < 120.5) = 0.98$$

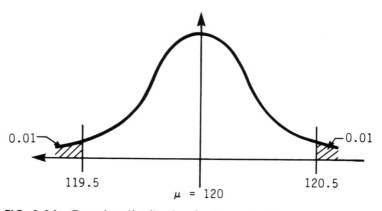

FIG. 3-36 Gaussian distribution for Example 10.

$$0.01 = \int_{z_1}^{\infty} f(z) \, dz = 0.500 - \int_{0}^{z_1} f(z) \, dz$$

$$\int_{0}^{z_1} f(z) \, dz = 0.490 \qquad z_1 = 2.323$$

$$z = \frac{x - \mu}{\sigma} = \frac{120.5 - 120.0}{\sigma} = 2.323$$

$$\sigma = \frac{0.5}{2.323} = 0.215 \; \Omega$$

3-10-1 Confidence Limits on Means

The confidence limits on establishment of the mean μ of a population from sample data are established [3-13] by the probabilistic statement

$$P \left[-t(\nu, \gamma) < \frac{\overline{x} - \mu}{\sigma/\sqrt{n}} < t(\nu, \gamma) \right] = \gamma \qquad (3\text{-}55)$$

where $t(\nu, \gamma)$ is the well-known t statistic. Rearrangement of Eq. (3-55) yields the probabilistic statement showing how to establish confidence limits on μ:

$$P \left[\left(\overline{x} - t \frac{\sigma}{\sqrt{n}} \right) < \mu < \left(\overline{x} + \frac{t\sigma}{\sqrt{n}} \right) \right] = \gamma \qquad (3\text{-}56)$$

The effects of measurement resolution and significant digits can be included in the expression to yield Eq. (3-57). This equation shows that even if the random error is zero, the uncertainty on μ cannot be less than the resolution and truncation uncertainties:

$$P \left[\left(\overline{x} - \frac{t\sigma}{\sqrt{n}} - R - \frac{5}{10^m} \right) < \mu < \left(\overline{x} + \frac{t\sigma}{\sqrt{n}} + R + \frac{5}{10^m} \right) \right] = \gamma \qquad (3\text{-}57)$$

POOLING OR COMBINING DATA. If one has several samples (perhaps obtained by different instrument systems) for estimating a population mean μ and variance σ^2, these data can be formally combined to obtain better estimates of these entities. If each data set comes from a normal population of mean μ and variance σ^2, the maximum-likelihood technique can be used to show how the means and variances of the samples are combined to provide the better estimates:

$$\hat{\mu}_c = \frac{\sum n_j \overline{x}_j / \hat{\sigma}_j^2}{\sum n_j / \hat{\sigma}_j^2} = \frac{n_1 \overline{x}_1 / \hat{\sigma}_1^2 + n_2 \overline{x}_2 / \hat{\sigma}_2^2 + \cdots}{n_1 / \hat{\sigma}_1^2 + n_2 / \hat{\sigma}_2^2 + \cdots} \qquad (3\text{-}58)$$

$$\hat{\sigma}_c^2 = \frac{\sum n_j}{\sum n_j / \hat{\sigma}_j^2} = \frac{n_1 + n_2 + \cdots}{n_1 / \hat{\sigma}_1^2 + n_2 / \hat{\sigma}_2^2 + \cdots} \qquad (3\text{-}59)$$

The reason for pooling data is to obtain more precise estimates of μ and σ^2 than any sample alone can provide. The intuitive thought to use the more precise data and to discard the less precise data *is not* the appropriate thing to do. Instead, the uncertainty intervals on the estimate of population mean μ and variance σ^2 are considerably reduced by pooling the data.

EXAMPLE 11. The data in the sample table below represent shear strengths in pounds per square inch (psi) of an adhesive. To market this adhesive, what should its guaranteed shear strength be with a confidence level of 99.5 percent?

Sample 1	Sample 2	Sample 3	Sample 4
3566	3180	3470	3520
3630	3080	3620	3960
3800	3400	3466	4040
3880	3820	3460	3600
3840	3480	3760	3899

Solution $\hat{\mu}_1 = 3742.2$ $\hat{\mu}_2 = 3392.0$ $\hat{\mu}_3 = 3555.2$ $\hat{\mu}_4 = 3803.8$

$\hat{\sigma}_1^2 = 18\ 880$ $\hat{\sigma}_2^2 = 83\ 334$ $\hat{\sigma}_3^2 = 17\ 612$ $\hat{\sigma}_4^2 = 70\ 567$

$\hat{\mu}_c = 3639.7$ psi $\hat{\sigma}_c^2 = 29\ 431$ (psi)^2 $\hat{\sigma}_c = 171.3$ psi

$$\mu = \hat{\mu} \pm \left(t\frac{\hat{\sigma}}{\sqrt{n}} + \frac{5}{10^m} + R \right) = 3639.7 \pm 2.921 \frac{(171.3)}{\sqrt{20}}$$

$$= 3640 \pm 108$$

where $t = t(\nu, \gamma) = t(16, 0.99) = 2.921$ from Ref. [3-7], Table A-8. The strength should be guaranteed to $3640 - 108 = 3532$ psi.

3-10-2 Confidence Limits on Variance

To establish the confidence limits on variance the chi-square statistic $\chi^2 = [\Sigma(x_i - \bar{x})^2]/\sigma^2$ is used [3-13], and the probabilistic statement becomes

$$P\left[\chi_L^2 < \frac{\Sigma(x_i - \bar{x})^2}{\sigma^2} < \chi_R^2 \right] = \gamma \qquad (3\text{-}60)$$

Rearranging yields the probabilistic statement showing how to determine confidence limits on variance:

$$P\left[\frac{\Sigma(x_i - \bar{x})^2}{\chi_R^2} < \sigma^2 < \frac{\Sigma(x_i - \bar{x})^2}{\chi_L^2} \right] = \gamma \qquad (3\text{-}61)$$

EXAMPLE 12. The standard deviation of the lifetimes of a sample of 200 high-pressure seals is 100 h. What are the 95 percent confidence limits on the standard deviation of all such seals? (See Ref. [3-7], Table A-7, for $\nu > 30$.)

Solution

$$\sqrt{2\chi^2} - \sqrt{2\nu - 1} \sim N(0, 1)$$

$$\therefore \quad \sqrt{2\chi^2} - \sqrt{2\nu - 1} = z \quad \text{or} \quad \chi^2 = \tfrac{1}{2}(z + \sqrt{2\nu - 1})^2$$

$$\chi_R^2 = \chi^2(0.025, 199)$$

$$= \tfrac{1}{2}(+z_{0.025} + \sqrt{2(199) - 1})^2$$

$$= \tfrac{1}{2}(+1.96 + 19.92)^2 = 239$$

$$\chi_R = \sqrt{239} = 15.4$$

$$\chi_L^2 = \tfrac{1}{2}(+z_{0.975} + \sqrt{2(199) - 1})^2$$

$$= \tfrac{1}{2}(-1.96 + 19.92)^2 = 161$$

$$\chi_L = \sqrt{161} = 12.7$$

$$P\left(\frac{\hat{\sigma}\sqrt{n-1}}{\chi_R} < \sigma < \frac{\hat{\sigma}\sqrt{n-1}}{\chi_L}\right) = \gamma$$

$$\therefore \quad P(91.2 < \sigma < 111.3) = 0.95$$

3-11 PROPAGATION OF ERROR OR UNCERTAINTY

In many cases the desired quantity and its uncertainty cannot be measured directly but must be calculated from the data of two or more measured variables. This is represented mathematically by

$$R = R(x_1, x_2, x_3, \ldots, x_n) \tag{3-62}$$

where the x's = measured variables, and R = the dependent or calculated quantity. To determine the most representative value and uncertainty of the calculated quantity, the following equations can be used [3-15]:

$$\mu_R = R(\mu_{x1}, \mu_{x2}, \mu_{x3}, \ldots, \mu_{xn}) + \frac{1}{2}\Sigma\left(\frac{\partial^2 R}{\partial x_i^2}\right)\sigma_{xi}^2 \tag{3-63}$$

$$\sigma_R^2 = \Sigma\left(\frac{\partial R}{\partial x_i}\right)_\mu^2\sigma_{xi}^2 + \frac{1}{2}\Sigma\left(\frac{\partial^2 R}{\partial x_i^2}\right)_\mu^2\sigma_{xi}^4 + \cdots \tag{3-64}$$

EXAMPLE 13. If $r = x^n$, then μ_R and σ_R^2 become

$$\mu_R = (\mu_x)^n\left[1 + \tfrac{1}{2}(n)(n-1)\left(\frac{\sigma_x}{\mu_x}\right)^2\right] \tag{3-65}$$

$$\sigma_R^2 = n^2(\mu_x)^n\left[1 + \tfrac{1}{2}(n-1)^2\left(\frac{\sigma_x}{\mu_x}\right)^2\right] \tag{3-66}$$

The role of the coefficient of variation σ_x/μ_x should be noted. If σ_x/μ_x is small, the first terms in each of Eqs. (3-63) and (3-64) are all that need be evaluated to yield the desired results. The results for several other functions are given by Mischke [3-15].

The variances in Eqs. (3-63) and (3-64) can be replaced with confidence limits according to the equation

$$W_x = k\sigma_x \tag{3-67}$$

Notes ▪ Drawings ▪ Ideas

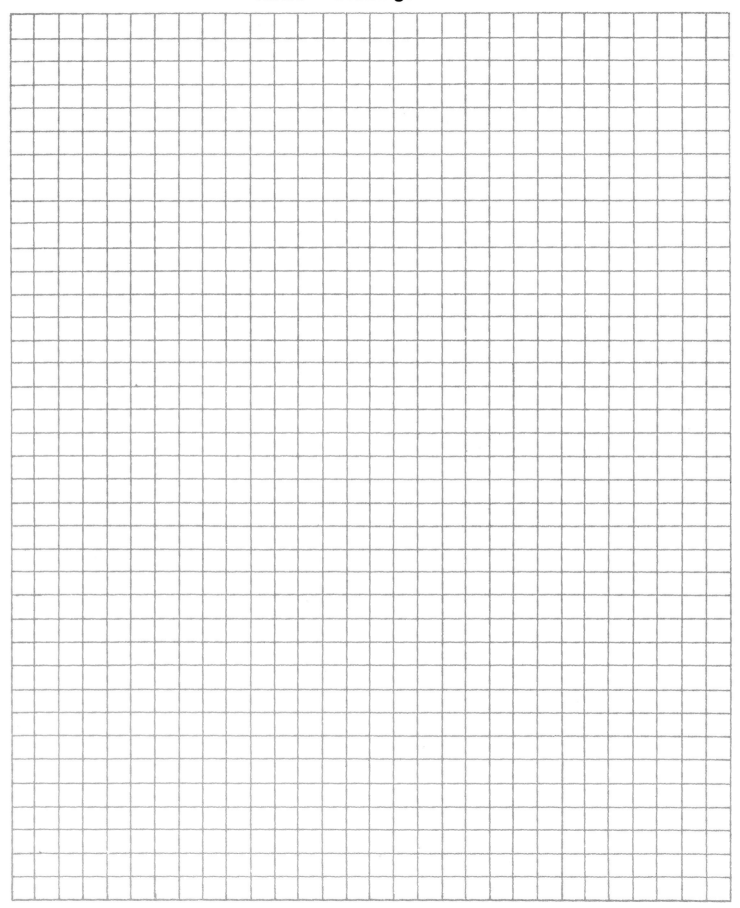

where k = a constant depending on the type of data distribution. The propagation-of-variance equation becomes the following propagation-of-uncertainty formula:

$$W_R^2 = \Sigma \left(\frac{\partial R}{\partial x_i}\right)_\mu^2 W_{x_i}^2 \qquad (3\text{-}68)$$

Use of this equation requires that all the x_i's be independently measured, that the k values be the same for each x_i distribution, and that all W_{x_i}'s represent the same level of uncertainty or confidence.

EXAMPLE 14. The strain and its uncertainty a distance L from the load F on the top surface of the cantilever beam shown in Fig. 3-32 is to be determined subject to the following measured data:

$$b = 0.500 \pm 0.001 \text{ in}$$
$$h = 0.250 \pm 0.001 \text{ in}$$
$$L = 20.00 \pm 0.01 \text{ in}$$
$$F = 10.00 \pm 0.01 \text{ lbf}$$
$$E = (30.0 \pm 0.01) \times 10^6 \text{ psi}$$

Solution. The strain is determined by $\epsilon = 6FL/(Ebh^2) = 1280 \times 10^{-6}$ in/in, or ϵ = 1280 microstrain. The uncertainty in the strain is determined by

$$W_\epsilon^2 = \left(\frac{\partial \epsilon}{\partial F}\right)_\mu^2 W_F^2 + \left(\frac{\partial \epsilon}{\partial L}\right)_\mu^2 W_L^2 + \left(\frac{\partial \epsilon}{\partial E}\right)_\mu^2 W_E^2 + \left(\frac{\partial \epsilon}{\partial b}\right)_\mu^2 W_b^2 + \left(\frac{\partial E}{\partial h}\right)_\mu^2 W_h^2 \quad (3\text{-}69)$$

This simplifies to the following equation when all the coefficients of variation are small:

$$\left(\frac{W_\epsilon}{\bar{\epsilon}}\right)^2 = \left(\frac{W_F}{\bar{F}}\right)^2 + \left(\frac{W_L}{\bar{L}}\right)^2 + \left(\frac{W_E}{\bar{E}}\right)^2 + \left(\frac{W_b}{\bar{b}}\right)^2 + 4\left(\frac{W_h}{\bar{h}}\right)^2 \qquad (3\text{-}70)$$

Substitution of the data in Eq. (3-70) yields $W_\epsilon = \pm 11$ microstrain. When the second terms in Eqs. (3-63) and (3-64) are used, the results are ϵ = 1280.1 microstrain and $W_\epsilon = \pm 11.3$ microstrain, which illustrates that when the coefficients of variation are small, the additional terms do not contribute significantly to ϵ and W_ϵ.

A simplified form of the preceding propagation-of-uncertainty equation results if the function R has the special form

$$R = (X_1^a X_2^b \cdots X_n^m)K \qquad (3\text{-}71)$$

where K = any constant and the exponents a, b, and m may be positive or negative, integer or noninteger. Substitution of Eq. (3-71) into Eq. (3-68) yields

$$\left(\frac{W_R}{\bar{R}}\right)^2 = a^2 \left(\frac{W_{x_i}}{\bar{x}_1}\right)^2 + b^2 \left(\frac{W_{x_2}}{\bar{x}_2}\right)^2 + \cdots + m^2 \left(\frac{W_{x_n}}{\bar{x}_n}\right)^2 \qquad (3\text{-}72)$$

The equation for uncertainty in the calculated quantity allows one to see the effect of the exponents a, b, $\ldots$, m in propagation of the measured variable uncertainties to the uncertainty in the calculated quantity. For example, a squared variable x_i^2 has four times the effect on the propagation of uncertainty in the result than if the variable had a unity exponent. It should also be noted that all terms are dimensionless in Eq. (3-72) and that the ratios $W_{x_i}/\bar{x}_i$, called *relative error,* are proportional to coefficients of variation by the factor k, since $W_x = k\sigma_x$.

If the experimental data are "single sample," the values of W_{x_i} must be estimated by the experimentor, as indicated by Kline and McClintock [3-14]. It is suggested that with single-sample data the W_{x_i} be estimated as the maximum error (which corresponds approximately to the 99 percent confidence level).

The propagation-of-uncertainty equation is extremely valuable in planning experiments. If one desires a certain precision on the calculated result R, the precision of the measured variables can be determined from this equation. Because instrument precision is directly related to its cost, one also has a method of estimating costs of a proposed measuring system by use of the propagation equation.

REFERENCES

3-1 E. A. Mechtly, *The International System of Units, Physical Constants and Conversion Factors,* 2d rev. ed., NASA sp-7012, 1973.

3-2 Anon., "Units, Standards and References," *Measurements and Control,* March–April 1970, pp. 49–80.

3-3 J. F. Swindells (ed.), *Precision Measurement and Calibration, Temperature,* vol. 2, National Bureau of Standards Special Publication 300, 1968.

3-4 P. K. Stein, *Measurement Engineering,* Stein Engineering Services, Inc., Phoenix, Arizona, 1974.

3-5 T. G. Beckwith, N. L. Buck, and R. D. Marangoni, *Mechanical Measurement,* 3d ed., Addison-Wesley Publishing Co., Inc., Reading, Mass., 1982.

3-6 E. Doebelin, *Measurement Systems: Application and Design,* 3d ed., McGraw-Hill Book Company, Inc., New York, 1983.

3-7 N. H. Cook, and F. Rabinowicz, *Physical Measurement and Analysis,* Addison-Wesley Publishing Co., Inc., Reading, Mass., 1963.

3-8 H. L. Harrison and J. G. Bollinger, *Introduction to Automatic Controls,* 2d ed., Harper and Row, Publishers, New York, 1969.

3-9 Anon., *Piezoelectric Accelerometer User's Handbook,* Bulletin 4200-96, Consolidated Electrodynamics Corp., Data Instruments Division, Pasadena, Calif.

3-10 S. D. Prensky, *Electronic Instrumentation,* 2d ed., Prentice-Hall Inc., Englewood Cliffs, N.J., 1971.

3-11 Headquarters Staff, *The Radio Amateur's Handbook,* 40th ed., American Radio Relay League, 1963.

3-12 M. R. Cereijo, "Shields and Grounds: The 'Other' Circuit Elements," *Machine Design,* August 22, 1974, pp. 88–91.

3-13 J. B. Kennedy and A. M. Neville, *Basic Statistical Methods for Engineers and Scientists,* 2d ed., Harper and Row, Publishers, New York, 1976.

3-14 S. J. Kline, and F. McClintock, "Describing Uncertainty in Single Sample Experiments," *Mechanical Engineering,* vol. 75, 1953, pp. 3–8.

3-15 C. R. Mischke, "Mathematical Model Building," in *An Introduction to Engineering,* 2d rev. ed., Iowa State University Press, Ames, Iowa, 1980.

3-16 C. Lipson, and N. J. Sheth, *Statistical Design and Analysis of Engineering Experiments,* McGraw-Hill Book Company, Inc., New York, 1973.

ADDITIONAL REFERENCES

Bartee, E. M.: *Statistical Methods in Engineering Experiments,* Charles E. Merril Books, Inc., Columbus, Ohio, 1966.

Cannon, R. H., Jr.: *Dynamics of Physical Systems,* McGraw-Hill Book Company, Inc., New York, 1967.

Dally, J. W., Riley, W. F., and McConnell, K. G.: *Instrumentation for Engineering Measurements,* John Wiley and Sons, Inc., New York, 1984.

Dove, R., and Adams, P.: *Experimental Stress Analysis and Morton Measurement,* Charles E. Merril Books, Inc., Columbus, Ohio, 1964.

Holman, J. P.: *Experimental Methods for Engineers,* 4th ed., McGraw-Hill Book Company, Inc., New York, 1984.

Ku, H. H. (ed.): *Precision Measurement and Calibration,* vol. 1, National Bureau of Standards Special Publication 300, Feb. 1969.

Natrella, M. G.: *Experimental Statistics,* National Bureau of Standards Handbook 91, Aug. 1, 1963.

Nilsson, J. W.: *Introduction to Circuits, Instruments and Electronics,* Harcourt, Brace and World, Inc., New York, 1968.

Snedecor, G. W., and Cochran, W. G.: *Statistical Methods,* 6th ed., Iowa State University Press, Ames, Iowa, 1967.

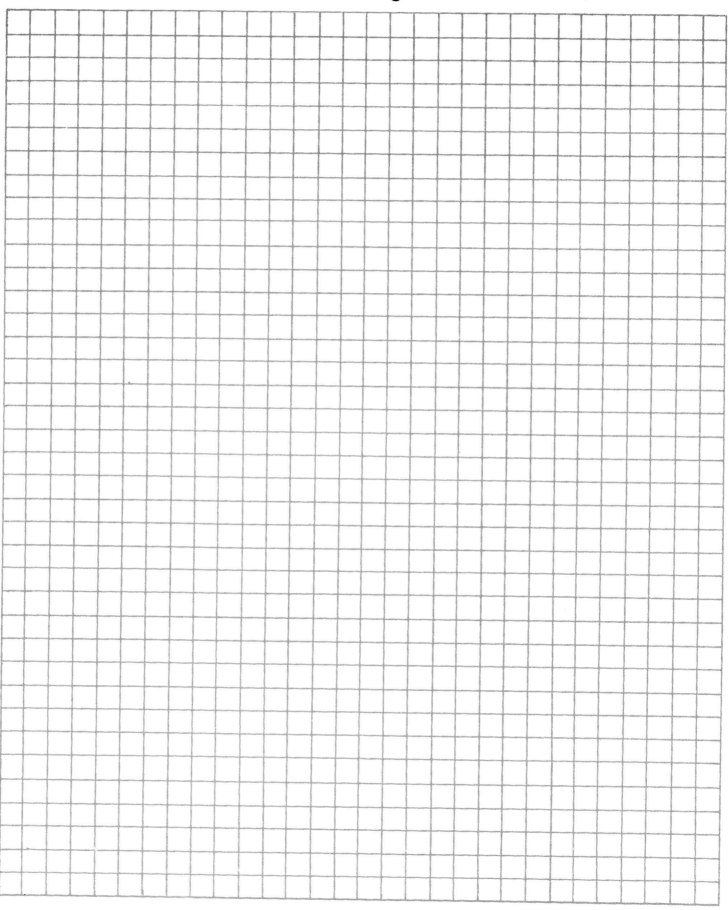

chapter 4
NUMERICAL METHODS

RAY C. JOHNSON, Ph.D.
Higgins Professor of Mechanical Engineering
Worcester Polytechnic Institute
Worcester, Massachusetts

In this chapter some numerical techniques particularly useful in the field of machine design are briefly summarized. The presentations are directed toward automated calculation applications using electronic calculators and digital computers. The sequence of presentation is logically organized in accordance with the preceding table of contents, and emphasis is placed on useful equations and methods rather than on the derivation of theory.

4-1 NUMBERS

In the design and analysis of machines it is necessary to obtain quantities for various items of interest, such as dimensions, material properties, area, volume, weight, stress, and deflection. Quantities for such items are expressed by numbers accompanied by the units of measure for a meaningful perspective. Also, numbers always have an algebraic sign, which is assumed to be positive unless clearly designated as negative by a minus sign preceding the number. The various kinds of numbers are briefly summarized as follows.

4-1-1 Integers

Integers are whole numbers without a fractional part, such as 1, 2, 3, 4, ... They are used for measuring discrete quantities of items, such as the number of holes in a part, the number of parts to be manufactured, the number of teeth in a gear, and the number of rollers in a bearing. Also, integers are used as parts of equations and series. Integers by themselves are exact, but they may be used for approximating a quantity of measurement.

4-1-2 Rational Numbers

Rational numbers are ones that are expressed by quotients of integers, such as m/n for $n \neq 0$. For example, the angular velocity ratio for a gearset is expressed as a quotient of tooth numbers, N_1/N_2. Expressed as a quotient of integers, the rational numbers are exact. However, the number obtained by actually dividing the integers may be approximated for practical purposes. Thus we may desire to approximate an angular velocity ratio $N_1/N_2 = 40/30$ by 1.333, using only four significant digits.

4-1-3   Irrational Numbers

Integers and rational numbers are often inadequate for defining quantities of interest in machine design, necessitating the use of approximated irrational numbers. *Irrational numbers* are precisely expressed by infinite decimal expansions, which for practical calculations are approximated by a finite number of significant digits. For example, the square root of 2 is precisely expressed by an infinite decimal expansion 1.414 213 . . . which in calculation applications is expressed by a finite number of digits, such as 1.414. As another example, the calculated deflection of a beam is generally an irrational number which is approximated by a finite number of digits, such as .0376 in. Most calculated quantities of analysis in machine design are irrational numbers which are approximated by a finite number of digits. However, if a specified quantity is expressed by a definite number, such as a dimension of 2.3875 in, it may be considered as an approximated irrational number as it stands.

4-1-4   Real Numbers, Precision, and Rounding

Any numerical quantity is expressed by a *real number* which may be classified as an integer, a rational number, or an irrational number. For practical purposes of calculation or manufacturing, it is often necessary to approximate a real number by a specified number of significant digits. For such cases, the number of significant digits used is related to the obtainable degree of precision, which will be discussed next.

DEGREE OF PRECISION. In machine design, real numbers are expressed by significant digits as related to practical considerations of accuracy in manufacturing and operation. For example, a dimension of a part may be expressed by four significant digits as 3.876 in, indicating for this number that the dimension will be controlled in manufacturing by a tolerance expressed in thousandths of an inch. As another example, the weight density of steel may be used as 0.283 lbm/in^3, indicating a level of accuracy associated with control in the manufacturing of steel stock. Both these examples illustrate numbers as basic terms in a design specification.

However, it is often necessary to analyze a design for quantities of interest using equations of various types. Generally, we wish to evaluate a dependent variable by an equation expressed in terms of independent variables. The degree of precision obtained for the dependent variable depends on the accuracy of the predominant term in the particular equation, as related to algebraic operations. In what follows, we will assume that the accuracy of the computational device is better than the number of significant figures in a determined value.

For addition and subtraction, the predominant term is the one with the least number of significant decimals. For example, suppose a dimension D in a part is determined by three machined dimensions A, B, and C using the equation $D = A + B - C$. Specifically, if the accuracy of each dimension is indicated by the significant digits in $A = 12.50$ in, $B = 1.062$ in, and $C = 12.375$ in, the predominant term is A, since it has the least number of significant decimals with only two. Thus D would be accurate to only two decimals, and we would calculate $D = A + B - C = 12.50 + 1.062 - 12.375 = 1.187$ in. We should then round this value to two decimals, giving $D = 1.19$ in as the determined value. Also, we note that D is accu-

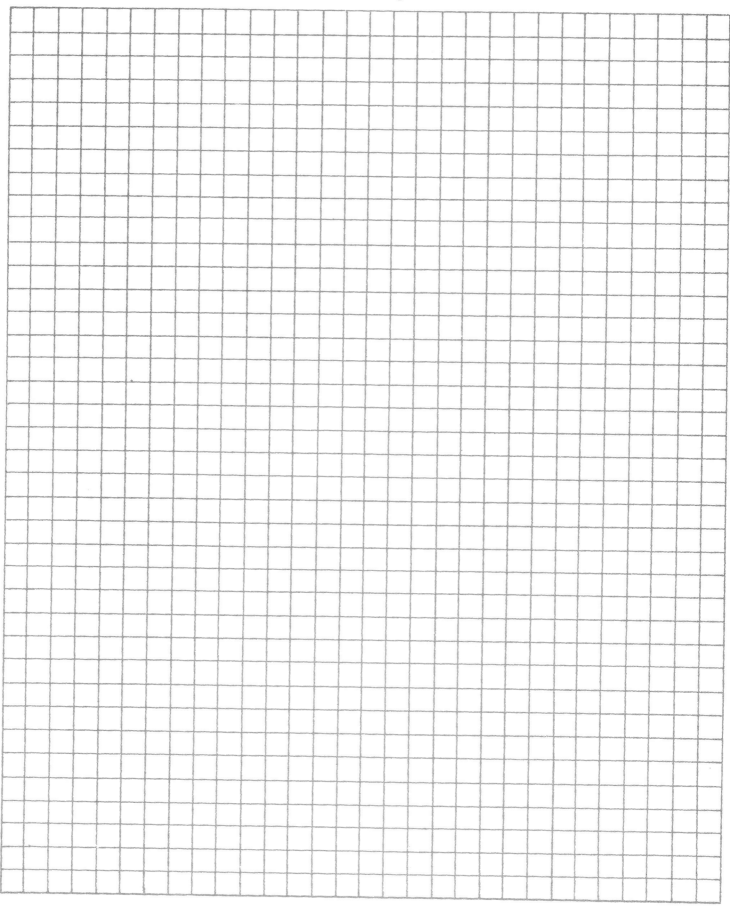

rate to only three significant figures, although *A* and *B* were accurate to four and *C* was accurate to five.

For multiplication and division, the predominant term is simply defined as the one with the least number of significant digits. For example, suppose tensile stress σ is to be calculated in a rectangular tensile bar of cross section *b* by *h* using the equation $\sigma = P/(bh)$. Specifically, if $P = 15\,000$ lb, and as controlled by manufacturing accuracy $b = 0.375$ in and $h = 1.438$ in, the predominant term is *b*, since it has only three significant digits. Incidentally, we have also assumed that *P* is accurate to at least three significant digits. Thus we would calculate $\sigma = P/(bh) = 15\,000/[0.375(1.438)] = 27\,816$ psi. We should then round this value to three significant digits, giving $\sigma = 27\,800$ psi as the determined value.

For a more rigorous approach to accuracy of dependent variables as related to error in independent variables, the theory of relative change may be applied, as explained in Sec. 4-4.

ROUNDING. In the preceding examples, we note that determined values are rounded to a certain number of significant decimals or digits. For any case, the calculations are initially made to a higher level of accuracy, but rounding is made to give a more meaningful answer. Hence we will briefly summarize the rules for rounding as follows:

1. If the least significant digit is immediately followed by any digit between 5 and 9, the least significant digit is increased in magnitude by 1. (An exception to this rule is the case where the least significant digit is even and it is immediately followed by the digit 5 with all trailing zeros. In that event, the least significant digit is left unchanged.)
2. If the least significant digit is immediately followed by any digit between 0 and 4, the least significant digit is left unchanged.

For example, with three significant digits desired, 2.765 01 becomes 2.77, 2.765 becomes 2.76, -1.8743 becomes -1.87, -0.4926 becomes -0.493, and 0.003 792 8 becomes 0.003 79.

4-1-5 Complex Numbers

Complex numbers are ones that contain two independent parts, which may be represented graphically along two independent coordinate axes. The independent components are separated by introduction of the operator $j = \sqrt{-1}$. Thus we express complex number $c = a + bj$, where *a* and *b* by themselves are either integers, rational numbers, or irrational numbers. Often *a* is called the *real component* and *bj* is called the *imaginary component*. The magnitude for *c* is $\sqrt{a^2 + b^2}$. For example, if $c = 3.152 + 2.683j$, its magnitude is

$$|c| = \sqrt{(3.152)^2 + (2.683)^2} = 4.139$$

Algebraically, the values for *a* and *b* may be positive or negative, but the magnitude of *c* is always positive.

4-2 FUNCTIONS

Functions are mathematical means for expressing a definite relationship between variables. In numerical applications, generally the value of a dependent variable is determined for a set of values of the independent variables using an appropriate functional expression. Functions may be expressed in various ways, by means of tables, curves, and equations.

4-2-1 Tables

Tables are particularly useful for expressing discrete value relations in machine design. For example, a catalog may use a table to summarize the dimensions, weight, basic dynamic capacity, and limiting speed for a series of standard roller bearings. In such a case, the dimensions would be the independent variables, whereas the weight, basic dynamic capacity, and limiting speed would be the dependent variables.

For many applications of machine design, a table as it stands is sufficient for giving the numerical information needed. However, for many other applications requiring automated calculations, it may be appropriate to transform at least some of the tabular data into equations by curve-fitting techniques. For example, from the tabular data of a roller-bearing series, equations could be derived for weight, basic dynamic capacity, and limiting speed as functions of bearing dimensions. The equations would then be used as part of a total equation system in an automated design procedure.

4-2-2 Curves

Curves are particularly useful in machine design for graphically expressing continuous relations between variables over a certain range of practical interest. For the case of more than one independent variable, families of curves may be presented on a single graph. In many cases, the graph may be simplified by the use of dimensionless ratios for the independent variables. In general, curves present a valuable picture of how a dependent variable changes as a function of the independent variables.

For example, for a stepped shaft in pure torsion, the stress concentration factor K_{ts} is generally presented as a family of curves, showing how it varies with respect to the independent dimensionless variables r/d and D/d. For the stepped shaft, r is the fillet radius, d is the smaller diameter, and D is the larger diameter.

For many applications of machine design, a graph as it stands may be sufficient for giving the numerical data needed. However, for many other applications requiring automated calculations, equations valid over the range of interest may be necessary. The given graph would then be transformed to an equation by curve-fitting techniques. For example, for the stepped shaft previously mentioned, stress concentration factor K_{ts} would be expressed by an equation as a function of r, d, and D derived from the curves of the given graph. The equation would then be used as part of a total equation system in the decision-making process of an automated design procedure.

4-2-3 Equations

Equations are the most powerful means of function expression in machine design, especially when automated calculations are to be made in a decision-making procedure. Generally, equations express continuous relations between variables, where a dependent variable y is to be numerically determined from values of independent variables x_1, x_2, x_3, etc. Some commonly used types of equations in machine design are summarized next.

LINEAR EQUATIONS. The general form of a linear equation is expressed as follows:

$$y = b + c_1x_1 + c_2x_2 + \cdots + c_nx_n \qquad (4\text{-}1)$$

Constant b and coefficient $c_1, c_2, \ldots, c_n$ may be either positive or negative real numbers, and in a special case, any one of these may be zero.

For the case of one independent variable x, the linear equation $y = b + cx$ is graphically a straight line. In the case of two independent variables x_1 and x_2, the linear equation $y = b + c_1x_1 + c_2x_2$ is a plane on a three-dimensional coordinate system having orthogonal axes x_1, x_2, and y.

POLYNOMIAL EQUATIONS. The general form of a polynomial equation in two variables is expressed as follows:

$$y = b + c_1x + c_2x^2 + \cdots + c_nx^n \qquad (4\text{-}2)$$

Constant b and coefficients $c_1, c_2, \ldots, c_n$ may be either positive or negative real numbers, and in a special case, any one of these may be zero.

For the special case of $n = 1$, the equation $y = b + c_1x$ is linear in x. For the special case of $n = 2$, the equation $y = b + c_1x + c_2x^2$ is known as a *quadratic equation.* For the special case of $n = 3$, the equation $y = b + c_1x + c_2x^2 + c_3x^3$ is known as a *cubic equation.* In general, for $n > 3$, Eq. (4-2) is known as a *polynomial of degree n.*

SIMPLE EXPONENTIAL EQUATIONS. The general form for a type of simple exponential equation commonly used in machine design is expressed as follows:

$$y = bx_1^{c1}x_2^{c2} \cdots x_n^{cn} \qquad (4\text{-}3)$$

Coefficient b and exponents $c_1, c_2, \ldots, c_n$ may be either positive or negative real numbers. However, except for the special case of any c_i being an integer, the corresponding values of x_i must be positive.

For the special case of $n = 1$ with $c_1 = 1$, the equation $y = bx$ is a simple straight line. For $n = 1$ with $c_1 = 2$, the equation $y = bx^2$ is a simple parabola. For $n = 1$ with $c_1 = 3$, the equation $y = bx^3$ is a simple cubic equation.

As a specific example of the more general case expressed by Eq. (4-3), a simple exponential equation might be as follows:

$$y = 38.69 \frac{x_1^{2.670}x_4^2}{x_2^{0.092}x_3^{1.07}}$$

For this example, $n = 4$, $b = 38.69$, $c_1 = 2.670$, $c_2 = -0.092$, $c_3 = -1.07$, and $c_4 = 2$. Also, if at a specific point we have $x_1 = 4.321$, $x_2 = 3.972$, $x_3 = 8.706$, and $x_4 = 0.0321$, the equation would give the value of $y = 0.1725$.

The general form for another type of simple exponential equation occasionally used in machine design is expressed as follows:

$$y = bc_1^{x1}c_2^{x2} \cdots c_n^{xn} \qquad (4\text{-}4)$$

Coefficient b and independent variables $x_1, x_2, \ldots, x_n$ may be either positive or negative real numbers. However, except for the special case of any x_i being an integer, the corresponding values of c_i must be positive.

Notes · Drawings · Ideas

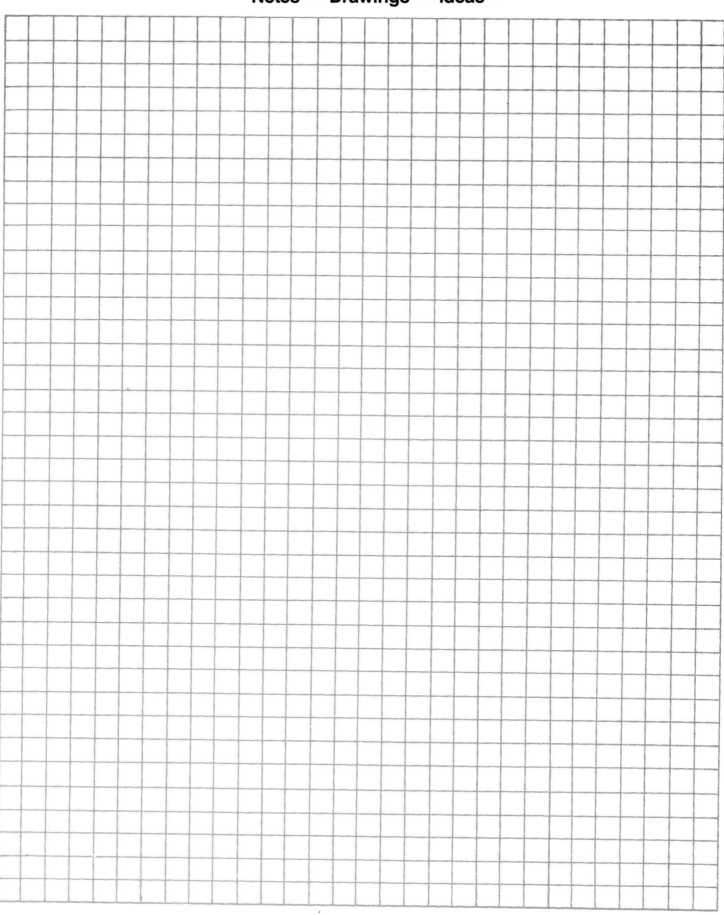

TRANSCENDENTAL EQUATIONS. The most commonly encountered types of transcendental equations are classified as being either trigonometric or logarithmic. For either case, inverse operations may be desired. In general, *transcendental equations* determine a dependent variable y from the value of an independent variable x as the argument.

The basic *trigonometric equations* are $y = \sin x$, $y = \cos x$, and $y = \tan x$. The argument x may be any real number, but it should carry angular units of radians or degrees. For electronic calculators, the units for x are generally degrees. However, for microcomputers or larger electronic computers, the units for x are generally radians.

The basic *logarithmic equation* is $y = \log x$. However, in numerical applications, care must be exercised in recognizing the base for the logarithmic system used. For natural logarithms, the Napierian base $e = 2.718\ 281\ 8\ldots$ is used, and the inverse operation would be $x = e^y$. For common logarithms, the base 10 is used, and the inverse operation would be $x = 10^y$.

A special relationship of importance is recognized by taking the logarithm of both sides in the simple exponential Eq. (4-3), resulting in the following equation:

$$\log y = \log b + c_1 \log x_1 + c_2 \log x_2 + \cdots + c_n \log x_n \qquad (4\text{-}5)$$

We see that this equation is analogous to linear Eq. (4-1) by replacing y, b, x_1, x_2, $\ldots$, x_n of Eq. (4-1) with $\log y$, $\log b$, $\log x_1$, $\log x_2$, $\ldots$, $\log x_n$, respectively. Thus the equation $y = bx^c$ will plot as a straight line on log-log graph paper, regardless of the values for constants b and c.

COMBINED EQUATIONS. Some basic types of equations have now been summarized, and they will be applied later in techniques of curve fitting. However, any of the more complicated equations found in machine design may be considered as special combinations of the basic equations, with the terms related by algebraic operations. Such equations might be placed in the general classification of combined equations. As a specific example of a combined equation, a *polynomial equation* is merely the sum of positive simple exponential terms, each of which has the general form of the right side of Eq. (4-3).

4-3 SERIES

A *series* is an ordered set of sequential terms generally connected by the algebraic operations of addition and subtraction. The number of terms can be either finite or infinite in scope. If the terms contain independent variables, the series is really an equation for calculating a dependent variable, such as the polynomial Eq. (4-2).

If a series is lengthy, it is often possible to approximate the series with a finite number of terms. The criterion for determining how many terms of the sequence are necessary is based on a consideration of convergence. The number of terms used must be sufficient for convergence of the determined value to an acceptable level of accuracy when compared with the entire series evaluation. This will be considered specifically in Sec. 4-4 on approximations and error.

Some commonly used series in machine design will be briefly summarized next. A more complete coverage can be found in any handbook on mathematics, and what follows is just a small sample.

4-3-1 Binomial Series

Consider the combined equation $y = (x_1 + x_2)^n$, where x_1 and x_2 are independent variables and n is an integer. The binomial series expansion of this equation is as follows:

$$y = (x_1 + x_2)^n$$
$$= x_1^n + nx_1^{n-1}x_2 + \frac{n(n-1)}{2!}x_1^{n-2}x_2^2 + \frac{n(n-1)(n-2)}{3!}x_1^{n-3}x_2^3 + \cdots \qquad (4\text{-}6)$$

In Eq. (4-6), if integer n is positive, the series consists of $n + 1$ terms. However, if integer n is negative, in general the number of terms is infinite and the series converges if $x_2^2 < x_1^2$.

4-3-2 Trigonometric Series

Some trigonometric relations will be approximated in Sec. 4-4 based on the series expansions summarized as follows:

$$y = \sin x = x - \frac{x^3}{3!} + \frac{x^5}{5!} - \frac{x^7}{7!} + \cdots \qquad (4\text{-}7)$$

$$y = \cos x = 1 - \frac{x^2}{2!} + \frac{x^4}{4!} - \frac{x^6}{6!} + \cdots \qquad (4\text{-}8)$$

In Eqs. (4-7) and (4-8), angle x must be expressed in radians.

4-3-3 Taylor's Series

If any function $y = f(x)$ is differentiable, it may be expressed by a Taylor's series expansion as follows:

$$y = f(x) = f(a) + f'(a)\frac{(x-a)}{1!} + f''(a)\frac{(x-a)^2}{2!} + f'''(a)\frac{(x-a)^3}{3!} + \cdots \qquad (4\text{-}9)$$

In Eq. (4-9), a is any feasible real number value of x, $f'(a)$ is the value of dy/dx at $x = a$, $f''(a)$ is the value of d^2y/dx^2 at $x = a$, and $f'''(a)$ is the value of d^3y/dx^3 at $x = a$. If only the first two terms in the series of Eq. (4-9) are used, we have a first-order Taylor's series expansion of $f(x)$ about a. If only the first three terms in the series of Eq. (4-9) are used, we have a second-order Taylor's series expansion of $f(x)$ about a. If $a = 0$ in Eq. (4-9), we have the special case known as a *Maclaurin's series expansion of $f(x)$*.

4-3-4 Fourier Series

Any periodic function $y = f(x) = f(x + 2\pi)$ can generally be expressed as a Fourier series expansion as follows:

$$y = f(x) = \frac{a_0}{2} + \sum_{n=1}^{\infty} [a_n \cos(nx) + b_n \sin(nx)] \qquad (4\text{-}10)$$

where
$$a_n = \frac{1}{\pi} \int_{-\pi}^{\pi} f(x) \cos (nx)\, dx \qquad \text{for } n = 0, 1, 2, 3, \ldots \qquad (4\text{-}11)$$

and
$$b_n = \frac{1}{\pi} \int_{-\pi}^{\pi} f(x) \sin (nx)\, dx \qquad \text{for } n = 1, 2, 3, \ldots \qquad (4\text{-}12)$$

Coefficients a_n and b_n of Eq. (4-10) are determined by Eqs. (4-11) and (4-12).

For the Fourier series expansion of Eq. (4-10) to be valid, the Dirichlet conditions summarized as follows must be satisfied:

1. $f(x)$ must be periodic; i.e., $f(x) = f(x + 2\pi)$, or $f(x - \pi) = f(x + \pi)$.
2. $f(x)$ must have a single, finite value for any x.
3. $f(x)$ can have only a finite number of finite discontinuities and points of maxima and minima in the interval of one period of oscillation.

Techniques of numerical integration covered later can be applied to determine the significant Fourier coefficients a_n and b_n by Eqs. (4-11) and (4-12), respectively. A corresponding finite number of terms would then be used from the Fourier series of Eq. (4-10) for approximating $y = f(x)$. Fourier series are particularly valuable when complex periodic functions expressed graphically are to be approximated by an equation for automated calculation use.

4-4 APPROXIMATIONS AND ERROR

In many applications of machine design and analysis, it is advantageous to simplify equations by using approximations of various types. Such approximations are often obtained by using only the significant terms of a series expansion for the function. The approximation used must give an acceptable degree of accuracy for the dependent variable over the range of interest for the independent variables. After defining error next, we will summarize some approximations particularly useful in machine design. Some other techniques of approximation will be presented later, under curve fitting, interpolation, root finding, differentiation, and integration.

4-4-1 Error

Relative error is defined as the difference between an approximate value and the true value, divided by the true value of a variable, as in Eq. (4-13):

$$e = \frac{y_a - y_t}{y_t} \qquad (4\text{-}13)$$

From this equation, error e is determined as a dimensionless decimal, y_a is an approximate value for y, and y_t is the true value for y. If y_a and y_t are expressed by equations as functions of an independent variable x, Eq. (4-13) gives an error equation as a function of x.

Also, from Eq. (4-13) we see that error e carries an algebraic sign. For positive y_t, a positive value for e means that algebraically we have the relation $y_a > y_t$, whereas for negative e we would have $y_a < y_t$. The opposite relations are true if y_t is negative. Finally, the magnitude of error is its absolute value $|e|$.

For example, for $y_a = 1.003$ in and $y_t = 1.015$ in, by Eq. (4-13) we calculate $e =$

Notes ▪ Drawings ▪ Ideas

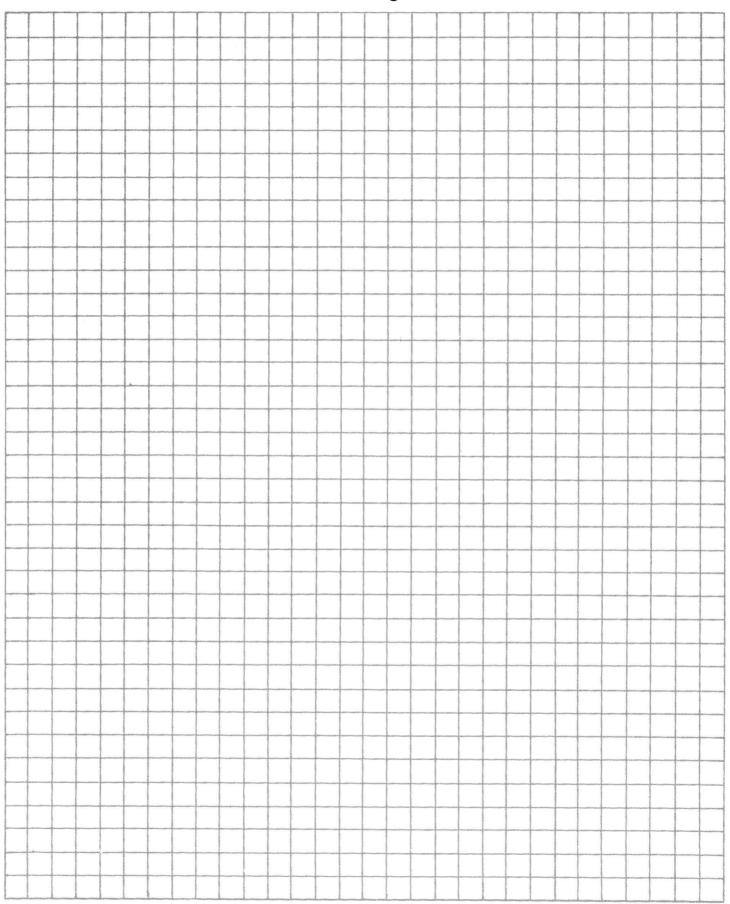

$(1.003 - 1.015)/1.015 = -0.0118$. This means that y_a is 1.18 percent less than its true value y_t. The magnitude of the error is $|e| = 0.0118$.

Incidentally, if error occurs at random on two or more independent variables, the accompanying error on a dependent variable may be determined statistically. This will be illustrated specifically by application of the theory of variance, as presented later under relative change.

4-4-2 Arc Sag Approximation

Consider a circular arc of radius of curvature ρ as shown in Fig. 4-1 with sag y accompanying a chordal length of $2x$. The true value for y can be calculated from the following equation [4-5], p. 60:

$$y_t = \rho\left[1 - \sqrt{1 - \left(\frac{x}{\rho}\right)^2}\right]$$

However, from the right triangle of Fig. 4-1, we obtain the following:

$$y_t = \frac{x^2 + y_t^2}{2\rho}$$

If in this equation we drop the term y_t^2, the following approximation is derived for y (its use would obviously simplify the calculation of either sag y or radius of curvature ρ):

$$y_a = \frac{x^2}{2\rho} \tag{4-14}$$

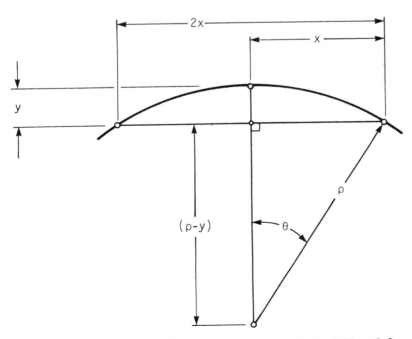

FIG. 4-1 Circular arc of radius ρ showing sag y and chordal length $2x$.

Applying Eq. (4-13), error e in using approximate Eq. (4-14) is as follows [4-5], p. 62:

$$e = \frac{-y_t}{2\rho} = -\sin^2 \frac{\theta}{2} \qquad (4\text{-}15)$$

In Eq. (4-15), angle θ is as shown in Fig. 4-1. As specific examples, from this equation we find that y_a by Eq. (4-14) has error $e = -0.005$ for $\theta = 8.11°$, $e = -0.010$ for $\theta = 11.48°$, and $e = -0.02$ for $\theta = 16.26°$. Hence using the simple Eq. (4-14) to calculate sag would be acceptably accurate in many practical applications of machine design.

4-4-3   Approximation for $1/(1 \pm x)$

In some equations of analysis we have a term of the form $(1 + x)$ in the denominator. For purposes of simplification, as in operations of differentiation or integration, it may be desired not to have such a term in the denominator. Hence consider the true term $y_t = 1/(1 + x)$, which can be expanded into an infinite series by simple division, giving the following:

$$y_t = \frac{1}{1 + x} = 1 - x + x^2 - x^3 + \cdots$$

By dropping all but the first two terms of the series, $1/(1 + x)$ may be approximated by $1 - x$, expressed as follows:

$$\frac{1}{1 + x} \approx y_a = 1 - x \qquad (4\text{-}16)$$

Applying Eq. (4-13), the error in using this approximation is derived as follows:

$$e = \frac{y_a - y_t}{y_t}$$

$$= \frac{(1 - x) - 1/(1 + x)}{1/(1 + x)} \qquad (4\text{-}17)$$

$$e = -x^2$$

As specific examples, for x within the range $-0.1 \le x \le 0.1$ we would have the corresponding error range of $-0.01 \le e \le 0$, whereas for $-0.02 \le x \le 0.2$ we would have $-0.04 \le e \le 0$.

Hence a denominator term of the form $1 + x$ could be replaced in an equation with a numerator term $1 - x$, providing the error is acceptably small over the anticipated range of variation for x. Similarly, a denominator term of the form $1 - x$ could be replaced with a numerator term $1 + x$ if the error is likewise acceptably small. The error equation in this case would still be Eq. (4-17).

4-4-4   Trigonometric Approximations

Approximations for some trigonometric functions will be summarized next, followed by the error function as derived by Eq. (4-13) in each case. For the summarized equations, angle x must be in radians. However, in the examples, ranges of angle x will be given in degrees, using the notation $x°$ in such cases.

An approximation for $\sin x$ is obtained by using only the first term in the Maclaurin's series of Eq. (4-7) as follows:

$$\sin x \approx x \tag{4-18}$$

$$e = \frac{x}{\sin x} - 1 \tag{4-19}$$

Hence for $-10° \le x° \le 10°$ we obtain positive error for e with $e \le 0.005\ 10$, whereas for $-20° \le x° \le 20°$ we have positive error $e \le 0.0206$.

A more accurate approximation for $\sin x$ is obtained by using the first two terms in the series of Eq. (4-7) as follows:

$$\sin x \approx x - \frac{x^3}{6} \tag{4-20}$$

$$e = \frac{x}{\sin x}\left(1 - \frac{x^2}{6}\right) - 1 \tag{4-21}$$

Hence for $-50° \le x° \le 50°$ we obtain negative error for e with its magnitude $|e| \le 0.005\ 41$.

An approximation for $\cos x$ is obtained by using only the first term in the Maclaurin's series of Eq. (4-8) as follows:

$$\cos x \approx 1 \tag{4-22}$$

$$e = \frac{1}{\cos x} - 1 \tag{4-23}$$

Hence for $-5° \le x° \le 5°$ we obtain positive error for e with $e \le 0.003\ 82$, whereas for $-15° \le x° \le 15°$ we have positive error $e \le 0.0353$.

A more accurate approximation for $\cos x$ is obtained by using the first two terms in the series of Eq. (4-8) as follows:

$$\cos x \approx 1 - \frac{x^2}{2} \tag{4-24}$$

$$e = \frac{1 - x^2/2}{\cos x} - 1 \tag{4-25}$$

Hence for $-30° \le x° \le 30°$ we obtain negative error for e with its magnitude $e \le 0.003\ 58$.

An approximation for $\tan x$ is obtained by using only the first term of its Maclaurin's series expansion which follows:

$$\tan x = x + \frac{x^3}{3} + \frac{2x^5}{15} + \cdots$$

Thus the approximation and error function are as follows:

$$\tan x \approx x \tag{4-26}$$

$$e = \frac{x}{\tan x} - 1 \tag{4-27}$$

Hence for $-10° \leq x° \leq 10°$ we obtain negative error for e with its magnitude $|e| \leq 0.0102$.

A more accurate approximation for $\tan x$ is obtained by using the first two terms in its series expansion as follows:

$$\tan x \approx x + \frac{x^3}{3} \tag{4-28}$$

$$e = \frac{x}{\tan x}\left(1 + \frac{x^2}{3}\right) - 1 \tag{4-29}$$

Hence for $-30° \leq x° \leq 30°$ we obtain negative error for e with its magnitude $|e| \leq 0.0103$.

4-4-5 Taylor's Series Approximations

Consider a general differentiable function $y = f(x)$. Its first-order Taylor's series approximation about $x = a$ is obtained by using only the first two terms of the Eq. (4-9) series, resulting in the following equation:

$$y = f(x) \approx f(a) + (x - a)f'(a) \tag{4-30}$$

In Eq. (4-30), a is any feasible real number value of x, and $f'(a)$ is the value of dy/dx at $x = a$.

The accuracy of Eq. (4-30) depends on the particular function $f(x)$ and the range anticipated for x about a. For this reason, a general error function is difficult to derive and impractical to apply. The clue for best accuracy is to choose a value for a such that $(x - a)$ will be small, resulting in negligible terms beyond the second in the Eq. (4-9) series.

For example, suppose we consider $f(x) = \sin x$ and anticipate a range of $-10° \leq x° \leq 10°$ for x. A good choice for a would be $a = 0$. Equation (4-30) would then give

$$\sin x \approx \sin 0 + x \cos 0 \qquad \therefore \sin x \approx x$$

This is merely Eq. (4-18), and the error analysis for the anticipated range of x has already been made after that equation.

However, if we still consider $f(x) = \sin x$ but anticipate a range of $45° \leq x° \leq 65°$ for x, Eq. (4-18) would be highly inaccurate. Hence Eq. (4-30) will be applied, and a good choice for a would be the midpoint of the x range, with $a = 55°\pi/180 = 0.9599$ radian. Equation (4-30) would then give the following approximation:

$$\sin x \approx \sin 0.9599 + (x - 0.9599) \cos 0.9599 \qquad \therefore \sin x \approx 0.2685 + 0.5736x$$

Hence for $x° = 45°$ we would have $y_t = \sin 45° = 0.7071$ and $y_a = 0.2685 + 0.5736(45\pi/180) = 0.7190$. For that value of x, the error by Eq. (4-13) is

$$e = \frac{0.7190 - 0.7071}{0.7071} = 0.0168$$

For $x = 55°$ we would have $y_t = \sin 55° = 0.8192$ and $y_a = 0.2685 + 0.5736(55\pi/180) = 0.8191$. For that value of x, by Eq. (4-13), the error is

$$e = \frac{0.8191 - 0.8192}{0.8192} = -0.0001$$

Finally, for $x = 65°$ we would have $y_t = \sin 65° = 0.9063$ and $y_a = 0.2685 + 0.5736(65\pi/180) = 0.9192$. For that value of x, by Eq. (4-13), the error is

$$e = \frac{0.9192 - 0.9063}{0.9063} = 0.0142$$

For any differentiable $f(x)$, a more accurate approximation can be obtained by using the first three terms of the Eq. (4-9) series, giving a second-order Taylor's series approximation about $x = a$. The technique is similar to what has been illustrated for a first-order Taylor's series approximation. An appreciably greater range of accuracy would be achieved at the expense of increased complexity for the approximation derived.

4-4-6 Fourier Series Approximation

The Fourier series of Eq. (4-10) involves an infinite number of terms, and for practical calculations, only the significant ones should be used. The clue for significance is the relative magnitude of a Fourier coefficient a_n or b_n, since the amplitudes of $\sin nx$ and $\cos nx$ in Eq. (4-10) are both unity regardless of n.

In establishing significance of a Fourier coefficient, Eqs. (4-11) and (4-12) are solved, perhaps automatically by a computer using numerical integration. The Fourier coefficients are determined for $n = 1, 2, 3, \ldots, N$, where generally a value of N equal to 10 or 12 is sufficient for the investigation. Only the coefficients of significant relative magnitude for a_n and b_n are retained. They determine the significant harmonic content of the periodic function $f(x)$, and only those coefficients are used in the Eq. (4-10) series for the approximation derived. An error analysis could then be made for the derived approximation, including perhaps a graphic presentation by a computer video display for comparative purposes.

As a final item of practical importance, a Fourier series approximation can be derived for many nonperiodic functions $f(x)$ if independent variable x is limited to a definite range corresponding to 2π. In such a case, the derived approximation is used for calculation purposes only within the confined range for x. Hence the derivation assumes hypothetical periodicity outside the confined x range. Of course, the Dirichlet conditions previously stated must be satisfied for $f(x)$ within that range.

4-4-7 Relative Change and Error Analysis

Consider a general differentiable function expressed as follows and used specifically for calculating dependent variable y in terms of independent variables $x_1, x_2, \ldots, x_n$:

$$y = f(x_1, x_2, \ldots, x_n) \tag{4-31}$$

By the theory of differentiation, we can write the following equation in terms of partial derivatives and differentials for the variables:

$$dy = \frac{\partial y}{\partial x_1} dx_1 + \frac{\partial y}{\partial x_2} dx_2 + \cdots + \frac{\partial y}{\partial x_n} dx_n \tag{4-32}$$

Small changes $\Delta x_1, \Delta x_2, \ldots, \Delta x_n$ in $x_1, x_2, \ldots, x_n$ can be substituted respectively for the differentials $dx_1, dx_2, \ldots, dx_n$ of Eq. (4-32). Thus we obtain an approximation for estimating the corresponding change in y, designated as Δy in the following equation:

$$\Delta y \approx \frac{\partial y}{\partial x_1} \Delta x_1 + \frac{\partial y}{\partial x_2} \Delta x_2 + \cdots + \frac{\partial y}{\partial x_n} \Delta x_n \qquad (4\text{-}33)$$

This equation can be used to estimate the change in y corresponding to small changes or errors in $x_1, x_2, \ldots, x_n$.

As an example of application for Eq. (4-33), consider the simple exponential Eq. (4-3), since many equations in machine design are of this general form. Application of Eq. (4-33) to Eq. (4-3) results in the following simple approximation [4-5], pp. 67–69:

$$\frac{\Delta y}{y} \approx c_1 \frac{\Delta x_1}{x_1} + c_2 \frac{\Delta x_2}{x_2} + \cdots + c_n \frac{\Delta x_n}{x_n} \qquad (4\text{-}34)$$

In this equation $\Delta y/y$, $\Delta x_1/x_1$, $\Delta x_2/x_2$, $\ldots$, $\Delta x_n/x_n$ are dimensionless ratios corresponding to relative changes in the variables of Eq. (4-3).

As a specific example of application for Eq. (4-34), suppose we are given the following simple exponential equation:

$$y = \frac{5.32 x_1^{1.62} x_3^2}{x_2^{2.86}} \qquad (4\text{-}35)$$

If at a point of interest we have the theoretical values $x_1 = 3.796$, $x_2 = 1.095$, and $x_3 = 2.543$. Then Eq. (4-35) results in a theoretical value of $y = 230.35$. Suppose that errors exist on the theoretical values of $x_1, x_2, \ldots, x_n$, specifically given as $\Delta x_1 = 0.005$, $\Delta x_2 = 0.010$, and $\Delta x_3 = -0.020$. By Eq. (4-34) we calculate the corresponding relative change in y of Eq. (4-35) as follows:

$$\frac{\Delta y}{y} \approx 1.62 \frac{0.005}{3.796} + -2.86 \frac{0.010}{1.095} + 2 \frac{-0.020}{2.543} = -0.0397$$

Thus the given errors $\Delta x_1, \Delta x_2, \ldots, \Delta x_n$ would result in a corresponding error of $\Delta y \approx -0.0397(230.35) = -9.14$ on the theoretical value of $y = 230.35$.

In the manner illustrated by the preceding example, by application of Eq. (4-34), accuracy estimates can quickly be made for simple exponential equations of the Eq. (4-3) form. The worst possible combination of errors for $\Delta x_1, \Delta x_2, \ldots, \Delta x_n$ can be used to estimate the corresponding error Δy on the theoretical value for y. However, for cases where random errors are anticipated on the independent variables, a statistical approach is more appropriate. This will be considered next.

A STATISTICAL APPROACH TO ERROR ANALYSIS. Consider a general differentiable function of several variables typically expressed by Eq. (4-31). Suppose that relatively small errors are anticipated on the theoretical values of the independent variables $x_1, x_2, \ldots, x_n$, with a normal distribution of relatively small spread on any theoretical value for each variable considered as the mean. Designate the standard deviation of the normal distribution for each variable respectively by $\sigma_{x_1}, \sigma_{x_2}, \ldots, \sigma_{x_n}$. Then, for most cases, dependent variable y would approximately have a corresponding normal distribution with standard deviation σy on its theoretical value.

$$(\sigma_y)^2 \approx \left(\frac{\partial y}{\partial x_1}\right)^2 (\sigma_{x_1})^2 + \left(\frac{\partial y}{\partial x_2}\right)^2 (\sigma_{x_2})^2 + \cdots + \left(\frac{\partial y}{\partial x_n}\right)^2 (\sigma_{x_n})^2 \qquad (4\text{-}36)$$

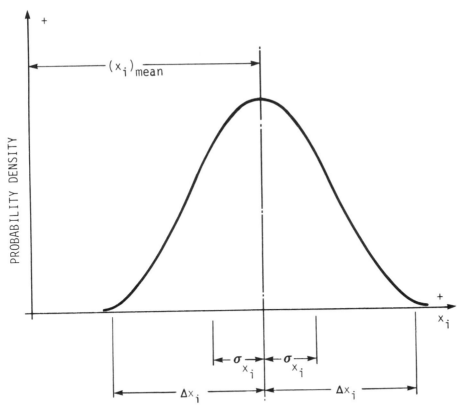

FIG. 4-2 Typical normal distribution curve for an independent variable x_i.

Suppose each of the independent variables $x_1, x_2, \ldots, x_n$ has a normal distribution typically shown in Fig. 4-2 with theoretical value corresponding to the mean value $\bar{x}_i$ for variable x_i. Let Δx_i represent a tolerance band, as shown in Fig. 4-2, corresponding to, say, three standard deviations. If the tolerance band Δx_i corresponds to three standard deviations, 99.73 percent of the total population for x_i values would be within the range $x_i - \Delta x_i \leq x_i + \Delta x_i$, and we would use the following relation:

$$\Delta x_i = 3\sigma_{xi} \qquad \text{for } i = 1, 2, \ldots, n \qquad (4\text{-}37)$$

Combining Eq. (4-37) with Eq. (4-36) by eliminating σ_{x_i} for $i = 1, 2, \ldots, n$, and using the corresponding relation $\Delta y = 3\sigma_y$, we obtain the following:

$$(\Delta y)^2 \approx \left(\frac{\partial y}{\partial x_1}\right)^2 (\Delta x_1)^2 + \left(\frac{\partial y}{\partial x_2}\right)^2 (\Delta x_2)^2 + \cdots + \left(\frac{\partial y}{\partial x_n}\right)^2 (\Delta x_n)^2 \qquad (4\text{-}38)$$

In this equation, all the tolerance bands $\Delta y, \Delta x_1, \Delta x_2, \ldots, \Delta x_n$ would correspond to three standard deviations and would encompass 99.73 percent of the total population for each variable.

As an example of application for Eq. (4-38), we will consider the general linear equation expressed by Eq. (4-1). Hence by calculus we obtain $\partial y/\partial x_1 = c_1, \partial y/\partial x_2 = c_2, \ldots, \partial y/\partial x_n = c_n$. Substituting these relations in Eq. (4-38), we obtain the following approximation for use in the case of linear Eq. (4-1):

$$(\Delta y)^2 \approx (c_1 \, \Delta x_1)^2 + (c_2 \, \Delta x_2)^2 + \cdots + (c_n \, \Delta x_n)^2 \qquad (4\text{-}39)$$

Notes ▪ Drawings ▪ Ideas

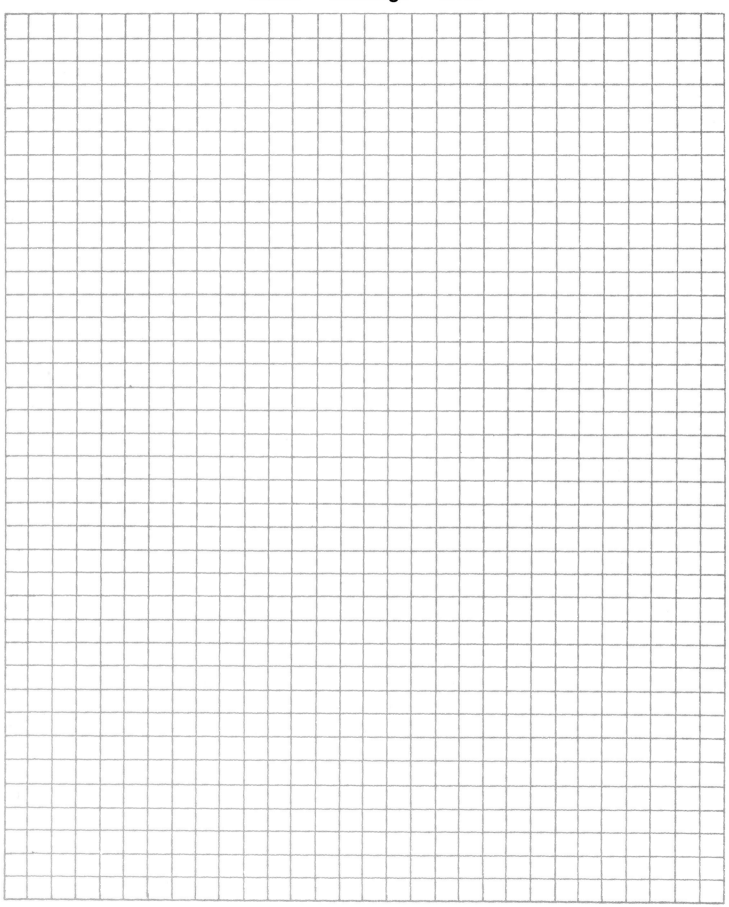

As a specific example, suppose we have the following linear equation:

$$y = 2.97x_1 - 3.42x_2 + 7.81x_3$$

If tolerances of $\Delta x_1 = \pm 0.005$, $\Delta x_2 = \pm 0.015$, and $\Delta x_3 = \pm 0.010$ exist on the theoretical values of x_1, x_2, and x_3, we calculate the corresponding tolerance Δy on the theoretical value of y statistically by Eq. (4-39) as follows:

$$(\Delta y)^2 \approx [2.97(0.005)]^2 + [-3.42(0.015)]^2 + [7.81(0.010)]^2 \quad \therefore \Delta y \approx \pm 0.0946$$

Thus the theoretical value of y calculated by the given linear equation would have a corresponding tolerance of $\Delta y \approx \pm 0.0946$. All the tolerances would correspond to, say, three standard deviations.

As another example of application for Eq. (4-38), we will consider the general simple exponential equation expressed by Eq. (4-3). By application of calculus to Eq. (4-3), we obtain the expressions for $\partial y/\partial x_1$, $\partial y/\partial x_2$, $\ldots$, $\partial y/\partial x_n$, which are then substituted into Eq. (4-38). Dividing the left and right sides of this equation, respectively, by the left and right sides of Eq. (4-3), we obtain the following approximation for use in the case of simple exponential Eq. (4-3):

$$\left(\frac{\Delta y}{y}\right)^2 \approx \left(\frac{c_1 \Delta x_1}{x_1}\right)^2 + \left(\frac{c_2 \Delta x_2}{x_2}\right)^2 + \cdots + \left(\frac{c_n \Delta x_n}{x_n}\right)^2 \tag{4-40}$$

As a specific example, suppose we are given the same simple exponential equation as before in Eq. (4-35). At a point of interest we have the same theoretical values as before for x_1, x_2, $\ldots$, x_n and y, and they are given following Eq. (4-35). However, the tolerance bands are now given as $\Delta x_1 = \pm 0.005$, $\Delta x_2 = \pm 0.010$, and $\Delta x_3 = \pm 0.020$, all corresponding to three standard deviations. Using the stated values following Eq. (4-40), we calculate statistically the corresponding tolerance Δy on the theoretical value of y as follows:

$$\left(\frac{\Delta y}{230.35}\right)^2 \approx \left[\frac{1.62(0.005)}{3.796}\right]^2 + \left[\frac{-2.86(0.010)}{1.095}\right]^2 + \left[\frac{2(0.020)}{2.543}\right]^2$$

$$\therefore \Delta y \approx \pm 7.04$$

Thus the theoretical value of y calculated by Eq. (4-35) as $y = 230.35$ would have a tolerance of $\Delta y \approx \pm 7.04$, corresponding to three standard deviations. As a final note, based on the given possibilities, we calculated $\Delta y \approx -9.47$ in the example following Eq. (4-35). However, based on probabilities, we have calculated $\Delta y \approx \pm 7.04$ in the present example.

4-5 FINITE DIFFERENCE APPROXIMATIONS

Consider the general differentiable function $y = f(x)$ graphically shown in Fig. 4-3. First and second derivatives can be approximated at a point k of interest by the application of finite difference equations. The simplest finite difference approximations are summarized as follows [4-5], pp. 28–35:

$$\left(\frac{dy}{dx}\right)_k \approx \frac{y_{k+1} - y_{k-1}}{2\,\Delta x} \tag{4-41}$$

$$\left(\frac{d^2y}{dx^2}\right)_k \approx \frac{y_{k-1} + y_{k+1} - 2y_k}{(\Delta x)^2} \tag{4-42}$$

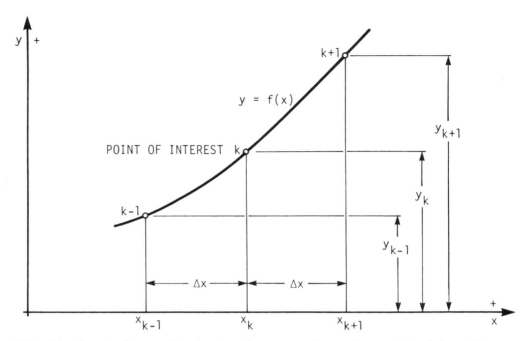

FIG. 4-3   Graph of $y = f(x)$ showing three successive points used in finite difference equations.

Equations (4-41) and (4-42) approximate the first and second derivatives of y with respect to x, respectively, at $x = x_k$. For both equations, the point of interest at x_k is surrounded by two equally spaced points, at x_{k-1} and x_{k+1}. The equal increment of spacing is Δx. The values of $y = f(x)$ at the three successive points x_{k-1}, x_k, and x_{k+1} are y_{k-1}, y_k, and y_{k+1}, respectively.

For most differentiable functions $y = f(x)$, the given finite difference equations are reasonably accurate if the following two conditions are satisfied:

1. Spacing increment Δx, in general, should be reasonably small.
2. The values for y_{k-1}, y_k, and y_{k+1} must carry enough significant figures to give acceptable accuracy in the difference terms of Eqs. (4-41) and (4-42).

Adequate smallness of Δx can be determined by trial, that is, by successively decreasing Δx until no significant difference is determined in the calculated derivatives.

As a very simple test example, consider the function $y = \sin x$. Suppose we wish to calculate first and second derivatives at $x_k^\circ = 35°$ using Eqs. (4-41) and (4-42). We arbitrarily choose the increment $\Delta x^\circ = 2°$, giving $x_{k-1}^\circ = 33°$ and $x_{k+1}^\circ = 37°$. Thus $y_{k-1} = \sin 33° = 0.544\,639$, $y_k = \sin 35° = 0.573\,576$, and $y_{k+1} = \sin 37° = 0.601\,815$. However, for Eqs. (4-41) and (4-42), increment Δx must be expressed in radians, giving $\Delta x = 2(\pi/180) = 0.034\,906\,6$ radian. Hence by Eq. (4-41) we calculate

$$\left(\frac{dy}{dx}\right)_k \approx \frac{0.601\,815 - 0.544\,639}{2\,\Delta x}$$

$$= \frac{0.057\,176}{2(0.034\,906\,6)}$$

$$= 0.818\,99$$

Also, by Eq. (4-42), we calculate

$$\left(\frac{d^2y}{dx^2}\right)_k \approx \frac{0.544\ 639 + 0.601\ 815 - 2(0.573\ 576)}{(\Delta x)^2}$$

$$= \frac{0.000\ 698}{(0.034\ 906\ 6)^2}$$

$$= -0.573$$

To check the accuracy of the approximations, for $y = \sin x$ we know by calculus that $dy/dx = \cos x$ and $d^2y/dx^2 = -\sin x$. Therefore, the theoretically correct derivatives are calculated as $(dy/dx)_k = \cos x = \cos 35° = 0.819\ 15$ and $(d^2y/dx^2)_k = -\sin x = -\sin 35° = -0.5736$. We see that the finite difference approximations were reasonably accurate, which could be further improved by reducing $\Delta x°$ to, say, $1°$.

Finite difference approximations can also be used for solving differential equations. Equations (4-41) and (4-42) can be used to substitute for derivatives in such differential equations, also substituting $x = x_k$ where encountered. The range of interest for x is divided into small increments Δx. At each net point so obtained, the finite difference–transformed differential equation is evaluated to determine the discrepancies of satisfaction, known as *residuals*. An iterative procedure is logically developed for successively relaxing the residuals by changing x values at the net points until the differential equation is approximately satisfied at each net point. Thus the solution function $y = f(x)$ is approximated at each net point by such a numerical technique. The iterative procedure of relaxation is greatly facilitated by using a digital computer.

As a final item, finite difference Eqs. (4-41) and (4-42) may be applied to calculate partial derivatives for the case of a differentiable function of several variables. Hence, for the equation $y = f(x_1, x_2, \ldots, x_i, \ldots, x_n)$, the first and second partial derivatives may be approximated as follows:

$$\left(\frac{\partial y}{\partial x_i}\right)_k \approx \frac{(y_{k+1} - y_{k-1})_i}{2\ \Delta x_i} \tag{4-43}$$

$$\left(\frac{\partial^2 y}{\partial x_i^2}\right)_k \approx \frac{(y_{k-1} + y_{k+1} - 2y_k)_i}{(\Delta x_i)^2} \tag{4-44}$$

In these equations, the difference terms are subscripted by i, indicating that only x_i is incremented by Δx_i for calculating y_{k-1} and y_{k+1}, holding the other independent variables $x_1, x_2, \ldots, x_n$ constant at their k point values.

4-6 NUMERICAL INTEGRATION

Often it is necessary to evaluate a definite integral of the following form, where $y = f(x)$ is a general integrand function:

$$I = \int_{x_0}^{x_n} y\, dx \tag{4-45}$$

For the case where $y = f(x)$ is a complicated function, numerical integration will greatly facilitate obtaining the solution. If software is available for a particular computational device, the program should be directly applied. However, a commonly used numerical technique will be described next as the basis for writing a special program if necessary.

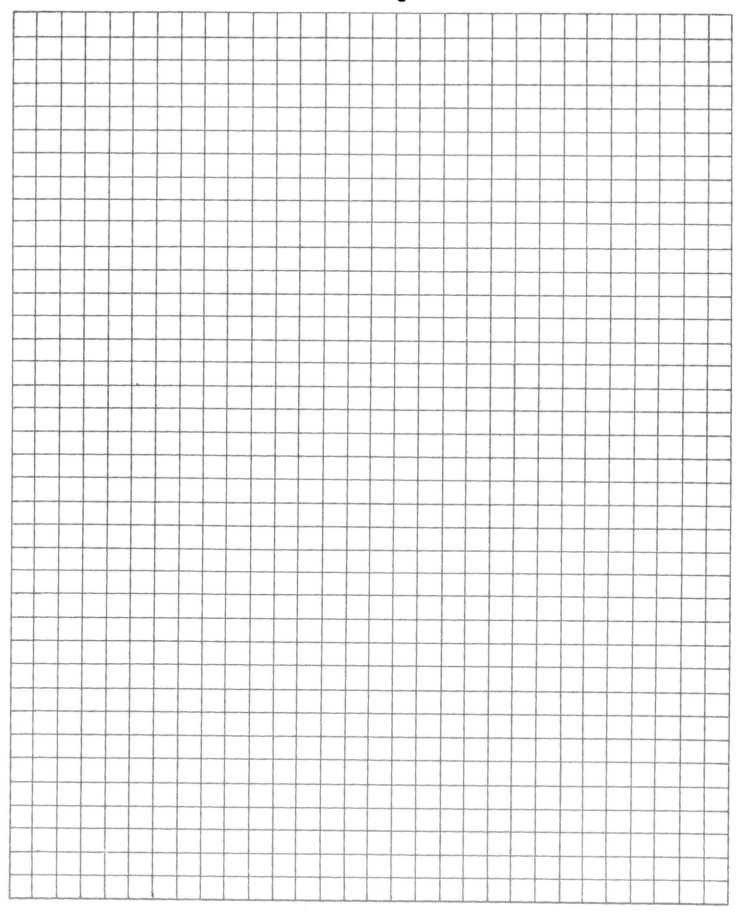

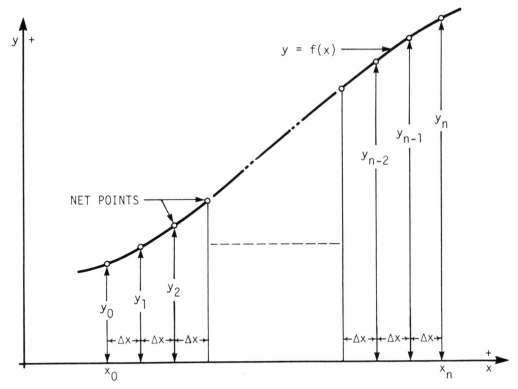

FIG. 4-4 Graph of $y = f(x)$ divided into equal increments for numerical integration between x_0 and x_n by Simpson's rule.

A simple and generally very accurate technique for numerical integration is based on Simpson's rule, referring to Fig. 4-4 for what follows. First, the limit range for x, between x_0 and x_n, is divided into n equal intervals by Eq. (4-46), where n must be an even number:

$$\Delta x = \frac{x_n - x_0}{n} \qquad (4\text{-}46)$$

The values of y are then calculated at each of the net points so determined, giving $y_0, y_1, y_2, \ldots, y_{n-2}, y_{n-1}, y_n$. Simpson's rule, given by Eq. (4-47), is then used to approximate the definite integral I of Eq. (4-45):

$$I \approx \frac{\Delta x}{3} [(y_0 + y_n) + 4(y_1 + y_3 + \cdots + y_{n-1})$$

$$+ 2(y_2 + y_4 + \cdots + y_{n-2})] \qquad (4\text{-}47)$$

With automated computation being used, probably the simplest way for determining adequacy of smallness for Δx is by trial. Hence even integer n is successively increased until the difference between successive I calculations is found to be negligible.

As a very simple test example, consider the following definite integral:

$$I = \int_{x_0}^{x_n} \sin x \, dx$$

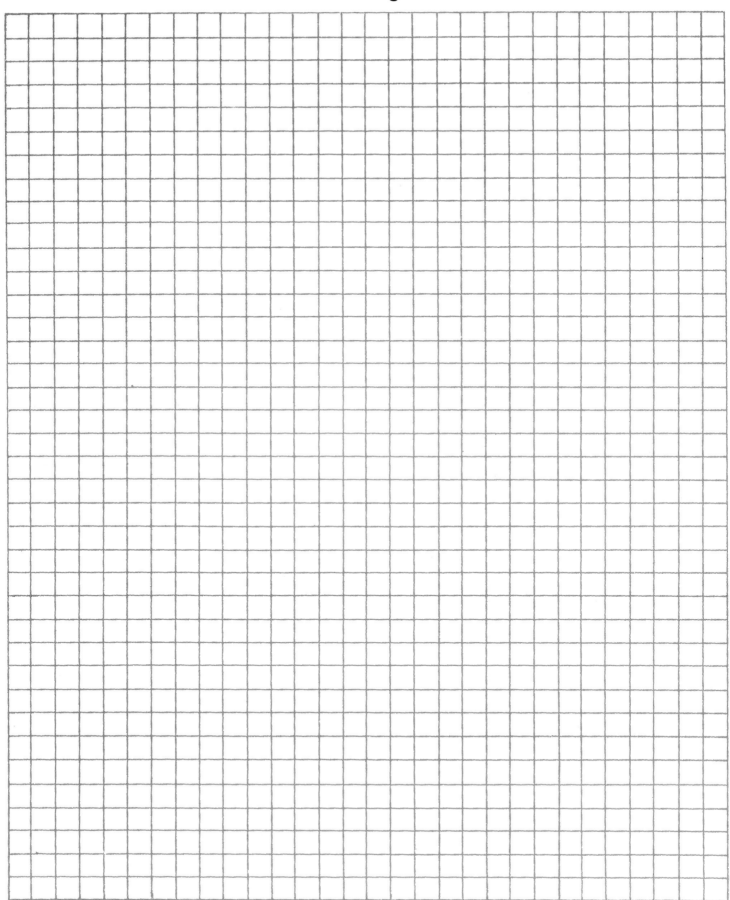

Suppose the limits of integration are $x_0^\circ = 30^\circ$ and $x_n^\circ = 60^\circ$, giving $y_0 = \sin 30^\circ$ and $y_n = \sin 60^\circ$. For the test example, a value of $n = 20$ is arbitrarily chosen. Equation (4-46) is used to calculate Δx as follows, which must be expressed in radians for use in Eq. (4-47):

$$\Delta x = \frac{(60 - 30)(\pi/180)}{20} = 0.026\ 179\ 938\ 8$$

In degrees, the increment is $\Delta x^\circ = (60 - 30)/20 = 1.5^\circ$. The y values at the remaining net points are then calculated as $y_1 = \sin 31.5^\circ$, $y_2 = \sin 33^\circ, \ldots, y_{n-2} = \sin 57^\circ$, and $y_{n-1} = \sin 58.5^\circ$. Simpson's rule is then applied using Eq. (4-47) to calculate the approximate value of $I = 0.366\ 025\ 404\ 7$. The described procedure, of course, is programmed for automatic calculation, and specifically the TI-59 Master Library Program ML-09 was used for the test example [4-11]. To check the accuracy of the approximation, from elementary calculus we know that $\int \sin x\ dx$ is $-\cos x$. Hence, theoretically, we obtain $I = [(-\cos 60^\circ) - (-\cos 30^\circ)] = 0.366\ 025\ 403\ 8$, and we see that the approximation for I by Simpson's rule was extremely accurate.

4-7 CURVE FITTING FOR PRECISION POINTS

Consider the situation where we have corresponding values of x and y available for a finite number of data points. Suppose we wish to derive an equation which passes precisely through some or all of these given data sets, and these we will call *precision points*. Some techniques of curve fitting for precision points will now be presented. In each case, accuracy checks could be made for the derived equation relative to all the given data points. Validity of the equation over the range of interest could then be established.

4-7-1 Simple Exponential Equation Curve Fit

In many cases of machine design, given graphs or tabular data would plot approximately as a straight line on log-log graph paper. Stress concentration factor graphs and a table of tensile strength versus wire diameter for spring steel are good examples. In such cases, a simple exponential equation of the following form can readily be derived for passing through two precision points (it is assumed that both x and y are positive):

$$y = bx^c \tag{4-48}$$

General curve shapes which are compatible with Eq. (4-48) are summarized graphically in Fig. 2-4 of Ref. [4-5]. Taking the logarithm of both sides in Eq. (4-48) results in the following, which reveals that a straight line would be the plot on log-log graph paper:

$$\log y = c \log x + \log b \tag{4-49}$$

Suppose two precision points (x_1, y_1) and (x_2, y_2) are chosen from the given data sets. The algebraic order for x is $x_1 < x_2$. If we use these precision points in Eq. (4-49), we obtain the following:

$$\log y_1 = c \log x_1 + \log b$$

$$\log y_2 = c \log x_2 + \log b$$

Subtracting the preceding two equations gives the following relation for calculating exponent c:

$$c = \frac{\log (y_2/y_1)}{\log (x_2/x_1)} \qquad (4\text{-}50)$$

Either one of the two precision points can then be used to calculate coefficient b as follows, as derived from Eq. (4-48):

$$b = \frac{y_1}{x_1^c} = \frac{y_2}{x_2^c} \qquad (4\text{-}51)$$

With values of c and b so determined, the simple exponential equation is uniquely defined.

As a simple example, suppose we have available the following data for two precision points:

x	y
0.1	8.5
0.25	5.3

Equation (4-50) would then yield the following value for exponent c:

$$c = \frac{\log (5.3/8.5)}{\log (0.25/0.1)} \qquad \therefore c = -0.516$$

Equation (4-51) would then give the following value for coefficient b:

$$b = \frac{8.5}{(0.1)^{-0.516}} = 2.591$$

Therefore, the derived equation passing through the given precision points is as follows:

$$y = \frac{2.591}{x^{0.516}}$$

Accuracy checks could then be made using Eq. (4-13) for all known data points to determine the validity of the derived equation over the range of interest.

4-7-2 Polynomial Equation Curve Fit

A polynomial equation of the following form can be derived to pass through $(n + 1)$ given precision points:

$$y = b + c_1 x + c_2 x^2 + \cdots + c_n x^n \qquad (4\text{-}2)$$

The $(n + 1)$ given data sets are substituted into Eq. (4-2), giving $(n + 1)$ linear equations in terms of $b, c_1, c_2, \ldots, c_n$. These $(n + 1)$ linear equations are then solved simultaneously for the $(n + 1)$ unknowns $b, c_1, c_2, \ldots, c_n$, which uniquely defines the polynomial equation.

As a simple example, suppose we wish to derive a polynomial equation through the following four precision points. With $(n + 1) = 4$, we will obtain a polynomial equation of the third degree, since $n = 3$.

x	y
0.0	2.0
0.1	1.65
0.2	1.50
0.3	1.41

Substituting these data sets into Eq. (4-2), we obtain the following:

$$2.0 = b$$

$$\therefore 1.65 = 2.0 + c_1(0.1) + c_2(0.1)^2 + c_3(0.1)^3$$

$$1.50 = 2.0 + c_1(0.2) + c_2(0.2)^2 + c_3(0.2)^3$$

$$1.41 = 2.0 + c_1(0.3) + c_2(0.3)^2 + c_3(0.3)^3$$

Simultaneous solution of these linear equations gives $b = 2.0$, $c_1 = -4.97$, $c_2 = 17.0$, and $c_3 = -23.3$. Therefore, the derived polynomial equation passing through the four precision points is as follows:

$$y = 2.0 - 4.97x + 17.0x^2 - 23.3x^3$$

Accuracy checks could then be made using Eq. (4-13) for all known data points to determine the validity of the derived equation over the range of interest.

4-8 CURVE FITTING BY LEAST SQUARES

In many cases of machine design we wish to derive a simple equation $y = f(x)$ which approximates a large number of given data points (x_k, y_k) for $k = 1, 2, \ldots, M$, as illustrated in the following table:

x	y
x_1	y_1
x_2	y_2
$\vdots$	$\vdots$
x_k	y_k
$\vdots$	$\vdots$
x_M	y_M

The given data points are illustrated by + symbols in Fig. 4-5, which also shows the curve of the equation $y = f(x)$ to be derived. For any x_k, the difference between the

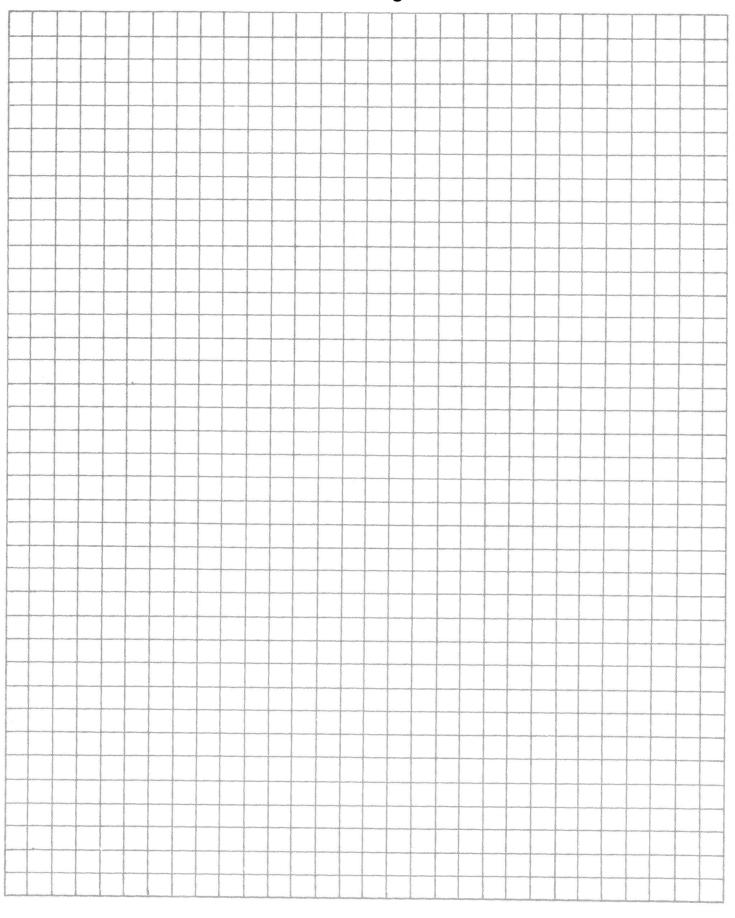

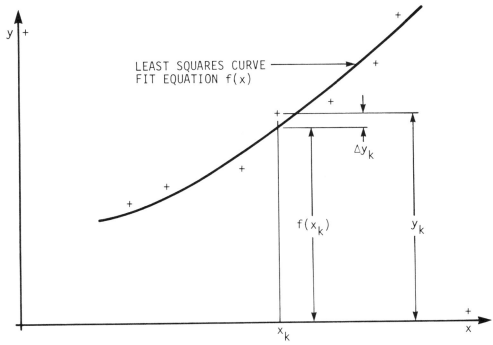

FIG. 4-5   Least-squares curves $y = f(x)$ for given data points indicated by $+$.

given point value y_k and the corresponding equation value $f(x_k)$ is Δy_k, defined as follows:

$$\Delta y_k = y_k - f(x_k) \qquad (4\text{-}52)$$

The equation $y = f(x)$ which minimizes the summation of $(\Delta y_k)^2$ terms for $k = 1$ to M of the given data set is known as the *least-squares fit*. A measure of accuracy for the derived equation is given by the dimensionless correlation coefficient r, which will have a value close to unity for the case of a "good" fit. Some simple examples will now be summarized for use in special cases of programming, although software programs are often already available for direct application [4-11].

4-8-1   Linear Equation Fitt

Consider the equation of a straight line as follows, which is to be used for curve fitting in the case where the given set of data points approximates a straight line on a graph:

$$y = b + cx \qquad (4\text{-}53)$$

Such an equation can be made to pass through only two precision points. However, if many data points (x_k, y_k) are given, the least-squares fit is determined as follows: First, we calculate the values of five summations as follows for S_1 through S_5. In each

---

†Ref. [4-5], pp. 55–56.

case, the summations are made for $k = 1$ to M, corresponding to the given data points:

$$S_1 = \Sigma x_k \tag{4-54}$$

$$S_2 = \Sigma y_k \tag{4-55}$$

$$S_3 = \Sigma(x_k y_k) \tag{4-56}$$

$$S_4 = \Sigma(x_k^2) \tag{4.57}$$

$$S_5 = \Sigma(y_k^2) \tag{4-58}$$

Then we calculate c and b for Eq. (4-53) by Eqs. (4-59) and (4-60), respectively:

$$c = \frac{MS_3 - S_1 S_2}{MS_4 - S_1^2} \tag{4-59}$$

$$b = \frac{S_2 - cS_1}{M} \tag{4-60}$$

Finally, we calculate the correlation coefficient r as follows:

$$r = \frac{MS_3 - S_1 S_2}{[(MS_4 - S_1^2)(MS_5 - S_2^2)]^{1/2}} \tag{4-61}$$

4-8-2 Simple Exponential Equation Fitt

Consider the simple exponential equation as follows, which is to be used for curve fitting in the case where the given set of data points approximates a straight line on a log-log graph:

$$y = bx^c \tag{4-48}$$

By taking the logarithm of both sides of this equation, we obtain the following:

$$\log y = \log b + c \log x \tag{4-49}$$

Hence, Eq. (4-48) would be a straight line on a log-log graph, and the least-squares fit is accomplished as follows: First, we calculate the values of three summations for S_1 through S_3 by Eqs. (4-62) to (4-64). In each case, the summations are made for $k = 1$ to M, corresponding to the given data points:

$$S_1 = \Sigma(\log x_k) \tag{4-62}$$

$$S_2 = \Sigma(\log y_k) \tag{4-63}$$

$$S_3 = \Sigma[(\log x_k)(\log y_k)] \tag{4-64}$$

Then we calculate c and b for Eq. (4-48) by Eqs. (4-65) and (4-66), respectively:

$$c = \frac{MS_3 - S_1 S_2}{2MS_1 - S_1^2} \tag{4-65}$$

†Ref. [4-5], pp. 56–57.

$$\log b = \frac{S_2 - cS_1}{M} \qquad (4\text{-}66)$$

Finally, we calculate the correlation coefficient r as follows:

$$r = \frac{MS_3 - S_1S_2}{[(2MS_1 - S_1^2)(2MS_2 - S_2^2)]^{1/2}} \qquad (4\text{-}67)$$

As a specific example, suppose we are given the following set of data points:

k	x_k	y_k
1	0.05	1.78
2	0.10	1.65
3	0.15	1.57
4	0.20	1.50
5	0.25	1.45
6	0.30	1.41

These data fall nearly as a straight line on a log-log graph, and Eq. (4-48) should be appropriate for a least-squares fit. Hence by Eqs. (4-62) to (4-67) we calculate the following values (we use $M = 6$, corresponding to the number of given data points):

$$c = -0.1305 \qquad b = 1.2138 \qquad r = 0.9929$$

Therefore, the derived equation for the least-squares fit is as follows:

$$y = \frac{1.2138}{x^{0.1305}}$$

We note that the correlation coefficient r is close to unity, so we conclude that the derived equation is a "good" fit.

4-8-3 Polynomial Equation Fit

Polynomial Eq. (4-1) may be used for a least-squares fit, but the derivation of such an equation is appreciably more complicated than the preceding examples. If interested, the designer should consult the literature for the details of derivation [4-2], pp. 19–21.

4-9 CURVE FITTING FOR SEVERAL VARIABLES†

Occasionally in machine design we wish to derive a simple equation $y = f(x_1, x_2, \ldots, x_i, \ldots, x_n)$ for the case where we have n independent variables. In such cases, the problem of curve fitting can be very difficult. However, the following simple approach is often of acceptable accuracy in practical problems.

---

†Ref. [4-5], pp. 57–59.

Notes · Drawings · Ideas

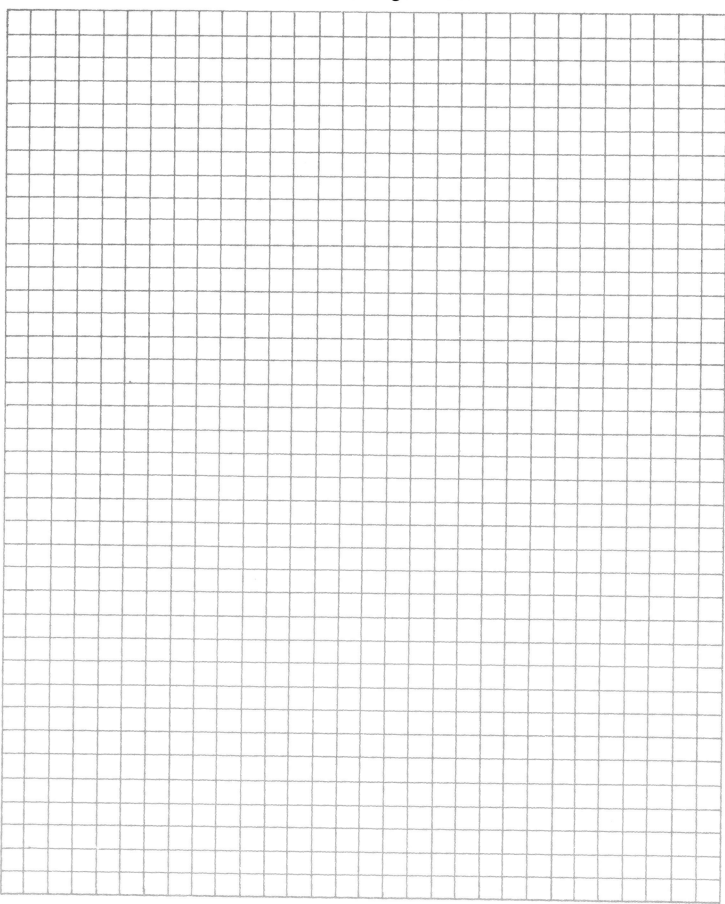

To start, consider the case of two independent variables x_1 and x_2, and we wish to derive an equation $y = f(x_1, x_2)$ to match approximately a given set of data points. Then the function $y = f(x_1, x_2)$ represents a three-dimensional surface using the orthogonal coordinate axes x_1, x_2, and y. The simple technique requires a common precision point for the given data, designated by subscript p in what follows. First, we derive an equation $y = f_1(x_1)$ by holding x_2 constant at $(x_2)p$. Next, we derive an equation $y = f_2(x_2)$ by holding x_1 constant at $(x_1)p$. The final equation is derived using $f_1(x_1)$ and $f_2(x_2)$ satisfying the y_p, $(x_1)_p$, and $(x_2)_p$ values of the given data.

As a simple specific example, consider the problem of deriving an equation $y = f(x_1, x_2)$ for given data-point values as follows:

For $x_2 = 4.5$		For $x_1 = 3.0$	
x_1	y	x_2	y
2.0	3.0	2.5	5.4
3.0	4.2	4.5	4.2
5.0	6.4	7.0	3.5

The common precision points in these data are $(x_1)_p = 3.0$, $(x_2)_p = 4.5$, and $y_p = 4.2$. Plots of these data for y versus x_1 and y versus x_2 fall nearly as a straight line on log-log graphs. Hence Eq. (4-3) should be appropriate for the curve fit, giving the following form for the equation to be derived:

$$y = bx_1^{c1}x_2^{c2}$$

Thus the first and last data points are used for both parts of the table to calculate exponents c_1 and c_2 using Eq. (4-50) as follows:

$$c_1 = \frac{\log(6.4/3.0)}{\log(5.0/2.0)} = 0.8269$$

$$c_2 = \frac{\log(3.5/5.4)}{\log(7.0/2.5)} = -0.4212$$

Coefficient b for the equation is then calculated using the common precision-point values as follows:

$$4.2 = b(3.0)^{0.8269}(4.5)^{-0.4212} \qquad \therefore b = 3.190$$

Therefore, the derived equation for the curve fit is as follows:

$$y = 3.190 \frac{x_1^{0.8269}}{x_2^{0.4212}}$$

Finally, accuracy checks could be made to see if the equation is acceptable for the intended use.

The simple technique as now illustrated can be applied to curve fitting for the case of more than two independent variables. Surprisingly, often a reasonably accurate equation is derived. As a specific example in machine design, see [4-5], pp. 383–388, for the derivation of an equation for helical gears having six independent variables. Accuracy checks are also presented in that example.

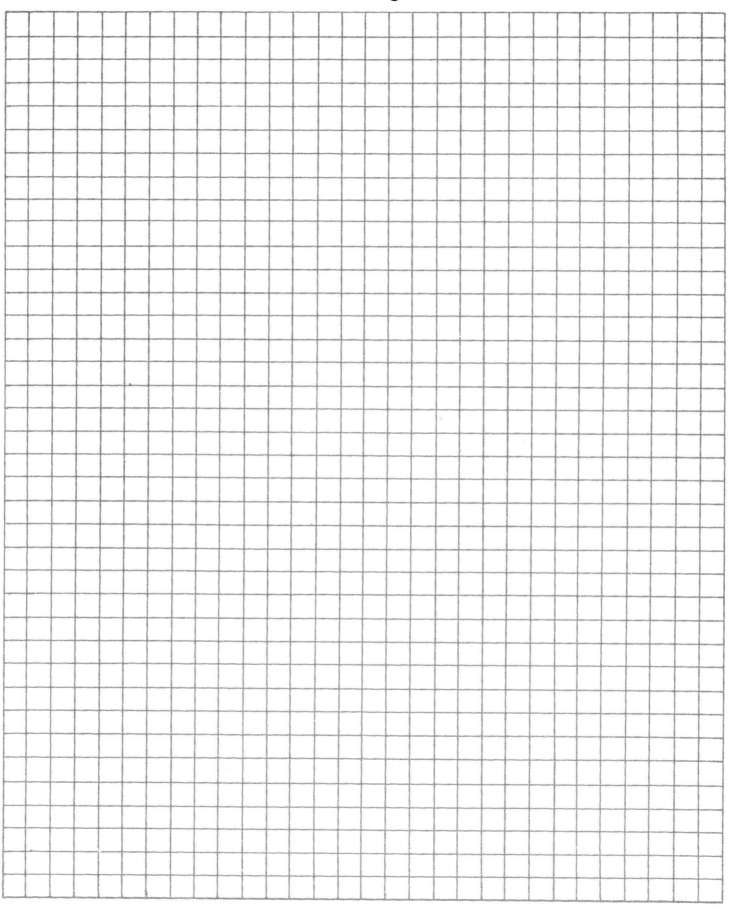

4-10 INTERPOLATION

Interpolation is generally of concern when we wish to estimate the value of a variable between two known data points. Suppose the values for x and y are known at two points k and $k + 1$ in Fig. 4-6. At some intermediate point j we wish to estimate either y_j for a specified value x_j or x_j for a specified value of y_j. The problem is really an application of curve fitting by using an equation $y = f(x)$ passing through the two precision points k and $k + 1$ for obtaining the estimate. Some specific techniques will be considered next.

4-10-1 Linear Interpolation

Consider passing a straight line between given points k and $k + 1$ in Fig. 4-6, with the assumed algebraic order for x being $x_k < x_j < x_{k+1}$. The equation for estimating y_j if x_j is specified would then be as follows:

$$y_j = y_k + \frac{y_{k+1} - y_k}{x_{k+1} - x_k}(x_j - x_k) \tag{4-68}$$

However, the equation for estimating x_j if y_j is specified would be as follows:

$$x_j = x_k + \frac{x_{k+1} - x_k}{y_{k+1} - y_k}(y_j - y_k) \tag{4-69}$$

In Eq. (4-69) it is assumed that y_k does not equal y_{k+1}, and y_j must be algebraically between y_k and y_{k+1}.

As a specific example, suppose we have the following values for x and y at two points:

Point	x	y
k	2.693	1.876
$k + 1$	2.981	2.210

For given $x_j = 2.729$, we would estimate y_j by Eq. (4-68) as follows:

$$y_j = 1.876 + \frac{2.210 - 1.876}{2.981 - 2.693}(2.729 - 2.693) \quad \therefore y_j = 1.918$$

However, for given $y_j = 2.107$, we would estimate x_j by Eq. (4-69) as follows:

$$x_j = 2.693 + \frac{2.981 - 2.693}{2.210 - 1.876}(2.107 - 1.876) \quad \therefore x_j = 2.892$$

4-10-2 Exponential Interpolation

If we believe that the given set of data points is curved and that it is compatible with a simple exponential type curve in the vicinity of precision points k and $k + 1$, we

Notes · Drawings · Ideas

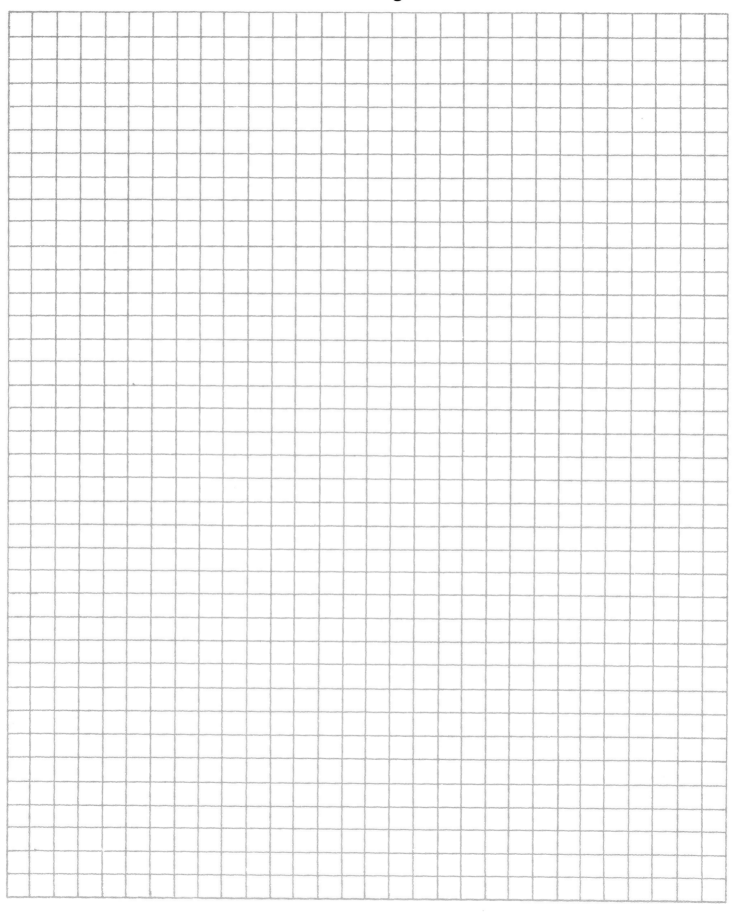

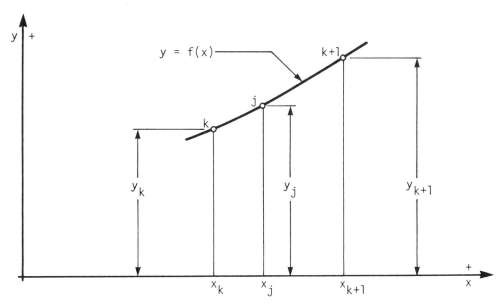

FIG. 4-6 Curve $y = f(x)$ for interpolation at j between two data points k and $k + 1$.

can apply Eqs. (4-50), (4-51), and (4-48) to derive Eqs. (4-70), (4-71), and (4-72), respectively, for use in the interpolation:

$$c = \frac{\log (y_{k+1}/y_k)}{\log (x_{k+1}/x_k)} \tag{4-70}$$

$$b = \frac{y_k}{x_k^c} \tag{4-71}$$

$$y_j = bx_j^c \tag{4-72}$$

It is assumed that x and y are both positive, with the algebraic order being $x_k < x_j < x_{k+1}$.

As a specific example we will use the preceding tabulated data for the points k and $k + 1$, and again we wish to estimate the value of y_j for given $x_j = 2.729$. Applying Eqs. (4-70), (4-71), and (4-72) we calculate the following values for c, b, and y_j, respectively:

$$c = \frac{\log (2.210/1.876)}{\log (2.981/2.693)} = 1.613$$

$$b = \frac{1.876}{(2.693)^{1.613}} = 0.3795$$

$$y_j = 0.3795(2.729)^{1.613} = 1.916$$

We see that this value of y_j is very close to the value of 1.918 previously calculated by linear interpolation.

4-11 ROOT FINDING

Given a function in the form $y = f(x)$, the problem is to find the values of x for which $y = 0$. For very simple functions, the roots can be found precisely. For example, for the given linear equation $y = b + cx$ we can choose any two values x_k and x_{k+1} and calculate the corresponding values y_k and y_{k+1}. Then, setting $y_j = 0$ in Eq. (4-69) we calculate the singular root x_j precisely. As another example, for the given parabolic equation $y = b + c_1 x + c_2 x^2$ we can find the two roots precisely using the quadratic equation as follows:

$$x = \frac{-c_1 \pm \sqrt{c_1^2 - 4bc_2}}{2c_2}$$

For more complicated functions $y = f(x)$, the problem of finding the roots becomes more difficult. Numerical methods may then be employed in an iterative procedure of automated calculation to approximate the values of x for which $y = 0$. For practical cases, to start, it is generally desired to determine the general characteristics of the complicated function $y = f(x)$, and this can be accomplished by execution of an exploratory search. From this initial stage, each root x_j will be bracketed in an interval $x_k \le x_j \le x_{k+1}$, with x and y values known at points k and $k + 1$. If only an approximate value for root x_j is needed, linear interpolation can be used by applying Eq. (4-69) directly and setting $y_j = 0$. However, if the root x_j is to be determined very accurately, an iterative numerical technique may be applied, such as by interval halving or by the Newton-Raphson method. The various procedures now mentioned will be outlined as follows.

4-11-1 Exploratory Search Stage

For complicated functions $y = f(x)$, it is advantageous to locate the approximate neighborhoods of the roots x_j before a more accurate determination is made for each. This is accomplished by an exploratory search stage, which calculates the y values at successive step points of the range of interest $x_{min} \le x \le x_{max}$. The exploratory search stage can be programmed in accordance with the flowchart in Fig. 4-7. Values of x_{min} and x_{max} are initially specified, as is the step increment Δx, which may require some trial. The increment Δx is chosen relatively large to save on computation time, but

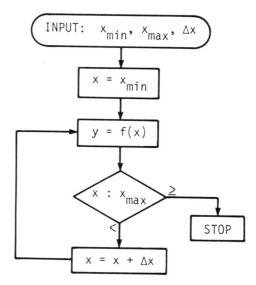

FIG. 4-7 Exploratory search program for given equation $y = f(x)$.

it must be small enough to identify the neighborhoods of the roots. These are recognized by an algebraic sign change in y for successive step points of the search. In this way, the roots are bracketed by known x and y values for step points which we will designate by subscripts k and $k + 1$ in what follows. First, we will consider a specific example for the exploratory search stage.

EXAMPLE. Consider the problem of finding the roots of the following equation:

$$y = \sqrt{x} - 3x^{1.53} + 7.656 \qquad (4\text{-}73)$$

Suppose the range of interest is $0.2 \le x \le 3.8$, and we choose $\Delta x = 0.2$ for the exploratory search to be made in accordance with Fig. 4-7. The results are tabulated as follows:

x	y	x	y
0.2	7.848	2.0	0.407
0.4	7.550	2.2	−0.884
0.6	7.058	2.4	−2.246
0.8	6.418	2.6	−3.674
1.0	5.656	2.8	−5.168
1.2	4.786	3.0	−6.723
1.4	3.819	3.2	−8.338
1.6	2.763	3.4	−10.011
1.8	1.624	3.6	−11.741
		3.8	−13.525

Hence by the sign change in y we recognize that there is only one root to the given equation in the range of interest, and it will be located between $x_k = 2.0$ and $x_{k+1} = 2.2$. We now have the problem of determining more accurately the value of this root x_j.

4-11-2 Approximate Roots by Linear Interpolation

In many practical applications of machine design, it is only necessary to determine approximate values for the roots of an equation. In such cases, the roots are first bracketed by an exploratory search, and linear interpolation is then made between the bracketed points k and $k + 1$ for each root using Eq. (4-69) with $y_j = 0$. As a specific illustration, consider the preceding example where we found from the exploratory search that the root of Eq. (4-73) lies between $x_k = 2.0$ and $x_{k+1} = 2.2$. The corresponding values for y are calculated accurately by Eq. (4-73), giving $y_k = 0.406$ 638 and $y_{k+1} = -0.884\ 458$. These values are substituted in Eq. (4-69) with $y_j = 0$, giving the approximate root as $x_j = 2.063$.

4-11-3 Roots by Interval Halving

From the exploratory search for $y = f(x)$, each root is bracketed within an original interval of uncertainty $[x_k, x_{k+1}]$, as shown in Fig. 4-8. The midpoint of this interval is then determined with respect to x, and y is calculated at that point by the given function $f(x)$. Thus a new interval of uncertainty is determined based on the sign of the calculated y, as shown in the figure. Its size is one-half the original interval. The process is successively repeated until the interval of uncertainty is reduced to a size Δx which is equal to or less than a specified accuracy ε on x. The described calculation strategy is summarized in the flowchart in Fig. 4-9. In general, as the search progresses, the values of x_j and y_j are known at point A in Fig. 4-8 for an interval of uncertainty, the midpoint value x_{j+1} is determined for point C in the figure, and y_{j+1} is calculated for that point by $f(x_{j+1})$. If the product $y_j y_{j+1}$ is positive, the new interval of uncertainty is as shown in Fig. 4-8. However, if the product $y_j y_{j+1}$ is negative, the new interval of uncertainty would be within the range $[x_j, x_{j+1}]$ of the figure. For each new interval of uncertainty, its span Δx is one-half of what it was previously, and only one function evaluation is necessary for its determination, in accordance with the flowchart in Fig. 4-9.

As a specific example, consider the problem of finding the root of Eq. (4-73) with the previously tabulated results from the exploratory search now available. Therefore, for the input of Fig. 4-9, we would use $x_k = 2.0$ and $x_{k+1} = 2.2$, and we choose an accuracy specification of $\varepsilon = 10^{-6}$ for the root to be determined. The Fig. 4-9 calculation process was programmed on a TI-59 calculator, resulting in the following root value at the conclusion of the search (which took approximately 60 seconds for the execution time):

$$\text{Root} \approx x_{j+1} = 2.064\ 209\ 747$$

Incidentally, the corresponding value for y_{j+1} is $-7.125\ 32 \times 10^{-7}$, which we see is very close to zero, as it should be for the root.

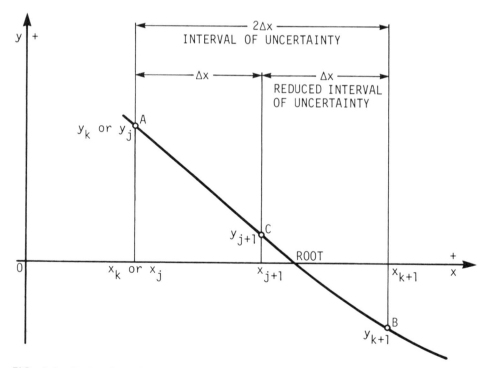

FIG. 4-8 Reduction of interval of uncertainty by interval halving for root finding.

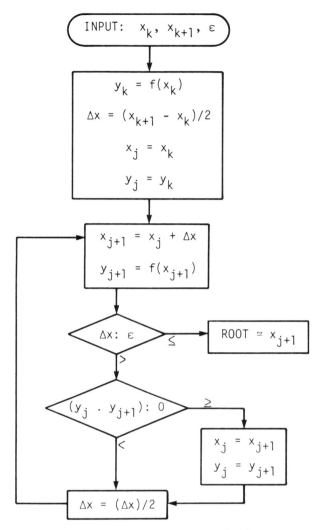

FIG. 4-9 Interval-halving flowchart for finding root of $y = f(x)$ within bracketed interval $[x_k, x_{k+1}]$.

4-11-4 Roots by the Newton-Raphson Method

The Newton-Raphson method is generally a highly efficient iterative technique for very accurately finding the roots of a given complicated function $y = f(x)$. For the method to work with some given functions it is necessary to start the search process at a point not too far from the root. The exploratory search stage will give the function characteristics necessary for choosing a good starting point.

If in the iterative search process of the Newton-Raphson method we are at some point j in Fig. 4-10, we determine an improved estimate x_{j+1} for the root by extrapolation as follows:

$$\left(\frac{dy}{dx}\right)_j = f'(x_j) = \frac{y_j}{x_j - x_{j-1}} \qquad \therefore \; x_{j+1} = x_j - \frac{y_j}{f'(x_j)} \qquad (4\text{-}74)$$

However, for complicated functions, the equation for $f'(x)$ is generally difficult to derive, and we circumvent this problem by resorting to a finite difference approximation instead. Thus consider an adjacent point A separated from j by a small increment δ, as shown in Fig. 4-10. Therefore, the finite difference approximation for $f'(x_j)$ is as follows:

$$f'(x_j) \approx \frac{y_A - y_j}{\delta}$$

where $y_A = f(x_j + \delta)$ and $y_j = f(x_j)$. Substituting this finite difference approximation into Eq. (4-74), we obtain Eq. (4-75) for estimating x_{j+1}:

$$x_{j+1} \approx x_j - \frac{\delta y_j}{y_A - y_j} \qquad (4\text{-}75)$$

For use of this approximation, two function evaluations are necessary for y_j and y_A as explained. The iterative calculation procedure for finding the root is summarized in the flowchart in Fig. 4-11, where start point x_k is initially specified. Also, solution accuracy ε and finite difference increment δ are generally specified as relatively small numbers compared with x_k.

As a specific example, consider the problem of finding the root of Eq. (4-73), with the previously tabulated results from the exploratory search now available. Therefore, for the input in Fig. 4-11 we could use $x_k = 2.0$ as a good start point. Also, we choose the accuracy specification for the root as $\varepsilon = 10^{-6}$ and finite difference increment as $\delta = 10^{-6}$. The Fig. 4-11 calculation process was programmed on a TI-59

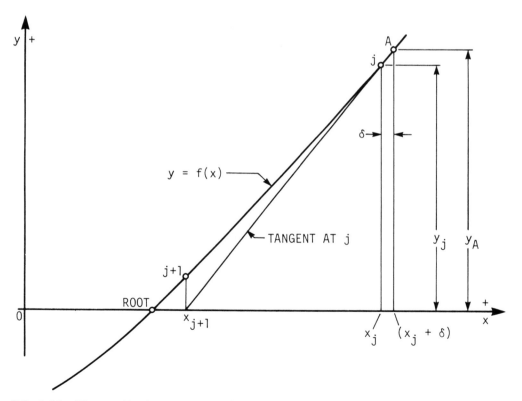

FIG. 4-10 Newton-Raphson method of root finding.

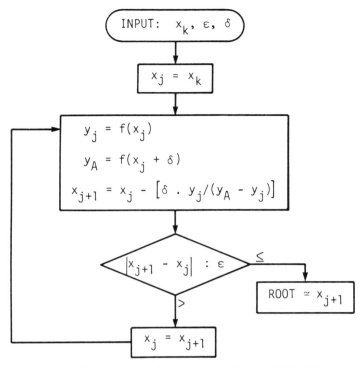

FIG. 4-11 Flowchart for finding root of $y = f(x)$ by Newton-Raphson method.

calculator, resulting in the following root value at the conclusion of the search (which took approximately 15 seconds for the execution time):

$$\text{Root} \approx x_{j+1} = 2.064\ 209\ 636$$

Incidentally, the corresponding value for y_{j+1} is -1.054×10^{-9}, which we see is extremely close to zero, as it should be for the root. Finally, it should be mentioned that exactly the same root was found by the Fig. 4-11 program using other start points of $x_k = 0.2$, $x_k = 2.2$, and $x_k = 3.8$.

4-11-5 Summary of Roots Found for Eq. (4-73)

A comparison of the root findings for Eq. (4-73) from the preceding examples is given in Table 4-1. We see that linear interpolation was extremely fast, but the root was

TABLE 4-1 Root for Eq. (4-73)

Method	Root found	TI-59 execution time, s
Linear interpolation	2.063	2
Interval halving	2.064 209 747	60
Newton-Raphson	2.064 209 636	15

Notes ▪ Drawings ▪ Ideas

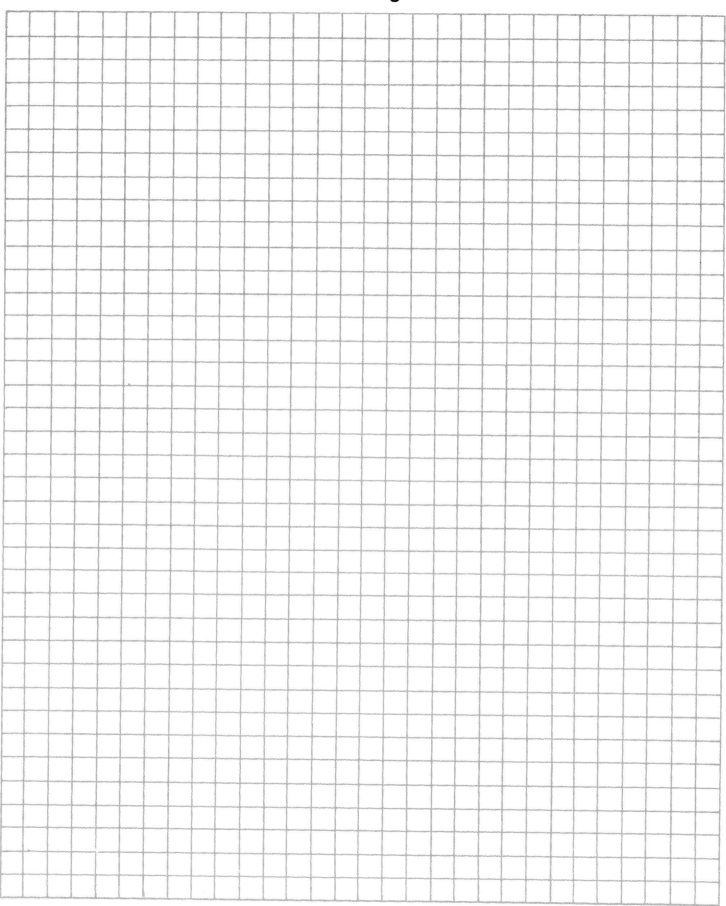

only determined approximately. The last two methods were extremely accurate, but more time-consuming for the solution. As indicated by the summary, the Newton-Raphson method is generally very accurate and appreciably faster than the interval-halving approach.

4-12 SYSTEMS OF EQUATIONS

The simultaneous solution of two or more equations can be a very difficult problem. In general, the number of unknowns cannot exceed the number of equations. We wish to find the common solution to the equation system, and some simple techniques will now be outlined.

4-12-1 Two Equations with Two Unknowns

Case 1. Consider the problem where y is expressed by two given functions of x as follows:

$$y = f_1(x) \tag{4-76}$$

$$y = f_2(x) \tag{4-77}$$

We wish to find the common values of x and y at which the two curves cross in Fig. 4-12. To start, we could display the two curves graphically, to be sure that they do

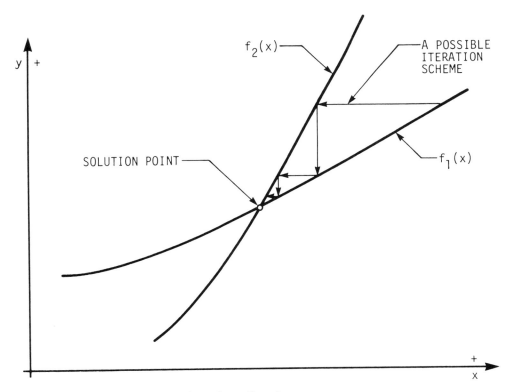

FIG. 4-12 Simultaneous solution of two functions.

cross in the range of interest for x. Depending on the general characteristics of the functions, we could devise an iterative scheme for converging to the neighborhood of the solution point as schematically shown in Fig. 4-12. However, a more direct approach might be to equate the functions, defining $g(x)$ and giving the following single equation to work with:

$$g(x) = f_1(x) - f_2(x) = 0 \qquad (4\text{-}78)$$

In this way, the problem has been simplified to one of merely finding the root of $g(x)$ expressed by Eq. (4-78).

As a specific example, suppose we are given the following two equations expressing y as a function of x:

$$y = \sqrt{x} + 4.302 \qquad (4\text{-}79)$$

$$y = 3x^{1.53} - 3.354 \qquad (4\text{-}80)$$

By equating the two functions of x, we derive the following relation for obtaining the solution:

$$g(x) = \sqrt{x} - 3x^{1.53} + 7.656 = 0 \qquad (4\text{-}81)$$

The solution value for x is merely the root of this equation, and a root-finding technique would be applied as previously explained. Since $g(x)$ of Eq. (4-81) is specifically the same as the right side of Eq. (4-73), from Table 4-1 the root is as follows:

$$x = 2.064\ 210$$

The corresponding value for y can then be calculated by either Eq. (4-79) or Eq. (4-80), giving the following specifically by Eq. (4-79):

$$y = \sqrt{2.064\ 210} + 4.302 = 5.739$$

The same value for y is obtained by Eq. (4-80).

Case 2. Consider the problem where we have two given functions of two variables x_1 and x_2 expressed in the following form:

$$f_1(x_1, x_2) = 0 \qquad (4\text{-}82)$$

$$f_2(x_1, x_2) = 0 \qquad (4\text{-}83)$$

As is often feasible, combine the two given equations by eliminating either x_1 or x_2. Thereby, a single equation in one variable is obtained, such as $g(x_1) = 0$ or $h(x_2) = 0$, which is solved by a root-finding technique as previously described. The corresponding remaining value for x_1 or x_2 is then readily calculated by reversing the equation-combination procedure.

As a specific example, suppose we are given the following two functions of x_1 and x_2:

$$\sqrt{x_1} + 3x_2 + 1.053 = 0 \qquad (4\text{-}84)$$

$$x_1^{1.53} + x_2 - 2.201 = 0 \qquad (4\text{-}85)$$

If we multiply Eq. (4-85) by 3 and subtract what is obtained from Eq. (4-84), we eliminate x_2 and obtain the following relationship for $g(x)$:

$$g(x) = \sqrt{x_1} - 3x_1^{1.53} + 7.656 = 0 \qquad (4\text{-}86)$$

A root-finding technique would then be applied to Eq. (4-86), and since $g(x)$ is specifically the same as the right side of Eq. (4-73), we may use the results from Table 4-1 in this example. Thus we have found for the solution point the following value for x_1:

$$x_1 = 2.064\ 210$$

The corresponding value for x_2 can then be calculated by either Eq. (4-84) or Eq. (4-85), giving the following specifically by Eq. (4-84):

$$x_2 = \frac{-(\sqrt{2.064\ 210} + 1.053)}{3} = -0.829\ 9$$

The same value for x_2 is obtained by Eq. (4-85).

For the situation where Eqs. (4-82) and (4-83) cannot readily be combined by eliminating either x_1 or x_2, curve-fitting techniques can generally be applied to either one of the equations, giving an explicit equation for either x_1 or x_2 expressed in terms of the other variable. This transformed equation is then substituted in the described equation-combination procedure for obtaining the solution.

4-12-2 Several Equations with Several Unknowns

The described procedures can generally be extended to solve several equations with several unknowns. For either the case 1 or case 2 type of problems previously described, the given equation system, now several in number, is reduced by equation combination to a single function of a single variable whose solution is found by a root-finding technique. The equation-combination procedure is then reversed to find the values of the other variables. If necessary, curve-fitting techniques may be employed to facilitate the equation-combination process.

4-13 OPTIMIZATION TECHNIQUES

In critical problems of design, the engineer wishes to make decisions which are as favorable as possible for the particular application at hand. In such cases, optimization of design is often worth striving for in the decision-making process. Based on the most critical aspects of the particular problem, an appropriate optimization objective must be chosen and mathematically formulated. Also, constraints of various types must be satisfied in almost all practical problems of design optimization, and these must be mathematically formulated. Hence the engineer must simultaneously address a complicated equation system of the following general form for arriving at decisions of optimal design:

$$Q^i = f(x_1, x_2, \ldots, x_i, \ldots, x_n) \tag{4-87}$$

subjected to

$$y_j = g_j(x_1, x_2 \ldots, x_i, \ldots, x_n) \quad \text{for } j = 1, 2, \ldots, J \tag{4-88}$$

and

$$x_i \gtrless c_i \quad y_j \gtrless c_j \tag{4-89}$$

In this compact representation of a complicated equation system, Q^i of Eq. (4-87) is the optimization quantity to be either minimized or maximized, and $x_1, x_2, \ldots, x_i$,

Notes ▪ Drawings ▪ Ideas

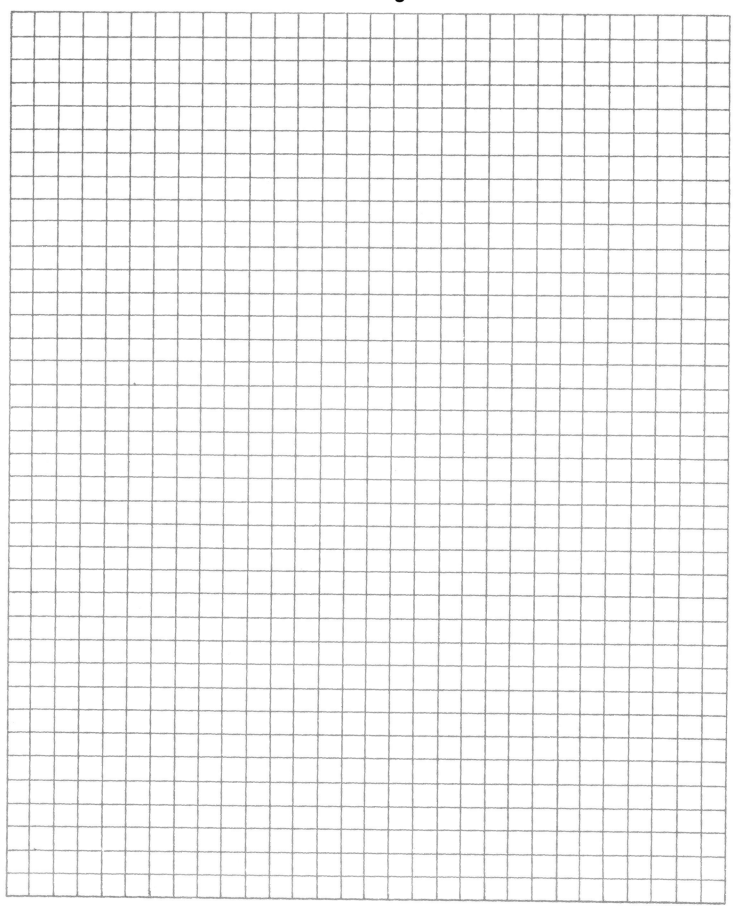

..., x_n are the independent variables. In Eq. (4-88), y_j represents a dependent variable, and there are J such equations in the system. Finally, the constraints of Eq. (4-89) are on the independent variables x_i and the dependent variables y_j. The general symbol $\gtreqless$ means that the required relation is one of the following, for any of the variables: $>$, $\geq$, $=$, $\leq$, or $<$. Specified constants c_i and c_j are the numerical limits imposed on the associated variables for an acceptable design, and any one may be zero in value.

Optimization of design is too large a subject area to describe in detail in this section. An explicit *method of optimal design* has been developed and applied to many practical examples of machine design, and it is particularly suited to mechanical elements and devices of various types (see Refs. [4-4] and [4-5]). By this technique, a calculation flowchart is derived for explicitly solving the optimization problem in numerical application. Many algorithms have also been developed based on techniques of nonlinear programming for iterative solutions to optimization problems by automated optimal design (see Refs. [4-3], [4-8], and [4-9]). Some specific examples of design optimization are also presented in Chap. 5 of this handbook.

REFERENCES

4-1 R. L. Burden, J. D. Faires, and A. C. Reynolds, *Numerical Analysis,* Prindle, Weber and Schmidt, 1978.

4-2 T. T. Furman, *Approximate Methods in Engineering Design,* Academic Press, 1981.

4-3 D. M. Himmelblau, *Applied Nonlinear Programming,* McGraw-Hill, 1972.

4-4 R. C. Johnson, *Mechanical Design Synthesis,* 2d ed., R. E. Krieger Co., 1978.

4-5 R. C. Johnson, *Optimum Design of Mechanical Elements,* 2d ed., Wiley-Interscience, 1980.

4-6 D. W. Kroeber, and R. L. LaForge, *Statistics and Quantitative Methods,* McGraw-Hill, 1980.

4-7 H. J. Larson, *Statistics: An Introduction,* Wiley, 1975.

4-8 C. R. Mischke, *Mathematical Model Building,* Iowa State University Press, 1980.

4-9 J. N. Siddall, *Analytical Decision-Making in Engineering Design,* Prentice-Hall, 1972.

4-10 J. M. Smith, *Scientific Analysis on the Pocket Calculator,* Wiley, 1975.

4-11 *TI Programmable 58C/59 Master Library,* Texas Instruments, Inc., 1979.

Notes ▪ Drawings ▪ Ideas

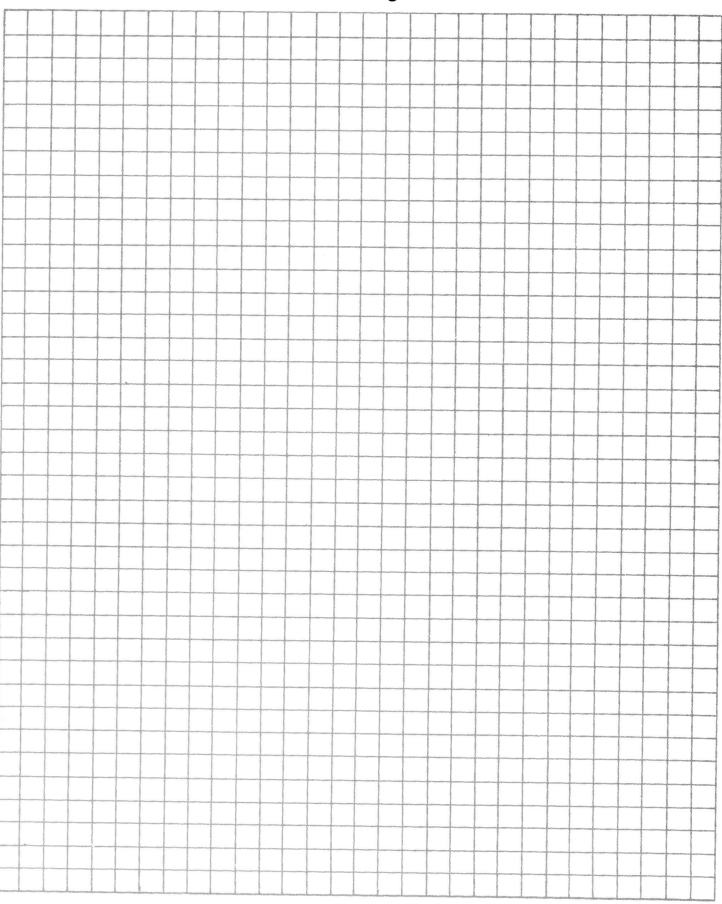

chapter **5**
COMPUTATIONAL CONSIDERATIONS IN DESIGN

CHARLES R. MISCHKE, Ph.D., P.E.
Professor of Mechanical Engineering
Iowa State University
Ames, Iowa

NOMENCLATURE

A	Spring wire strength constant; cross-sectional area; Jakobian matrix
b	Weibull distribution shape factor
c	Distance to outer fiber
C	Spring index, D/d
d	Wire diameter
d_{rod}	Diameter of rod over which spring operates
D	Spring helix diameter
e	Load eccentricity
E	Tensile modulus of elasticity
E_i	Error in Simpson's rule integration with i panels, $i/2$ applications
$f(x)$	Function of x, also $F(x)$
F_1	Spring working load
F_s	Spring load at closure
$g(x)$	Function of x
G	Shear modulus of elasticity
h	Interval between function evaluations for Simpson's rule
H_0	Statistical null hypothesis
H_1	Alternative to the null hypothesis
i	Subscript
Inv	Involute operator
I	Second-area moment; value of an integral by Simpson's rule
k	Spring rate; successive substitution convergence parameter
K_s	Spring factor $(1 + 0.5/C)$
ℓ	Length
ℓ_f	Free length of spring
ℓ_s	Solid height of spring

m	Spring wire-strength parameter; number of equality (functional) constraints
M	Figure of merit
n	Design factor, rpm
n_s	Design factor at soliding
$\sim N$	Gaussian- or normal-distributed
N_1, N_2	Number of panels in Simpson's rule application
N_i, N_j	Number of panels
OD	Outside diameter of spring
p	Parameter
P	Load
Q	Spring dead-coil number
Q'	Spring dead-coil augmentation for solid height determination
r	Residual; radius
R	Richardson's correction to Simpson's rule estimate
S_u	Engineering ultimate strength in tension
S_{su}	Engineering ultimate strength in shear
S_y	Engineering yield strength (0.2 percent) in tension
S_{sy}	Engineering yield strength (0.2 percent) in shear
t	Time
T	Total number of helical-spring turns; torque
$\sim W$	Weibull-distributed
x, y	Variables
$\hat{y}$	Ordinate to regression line
y_1	Spring end deflection under working load
y_s	Spring end deflection to solid
y_o	Weibull distribution parameter
z	Random variable; bound
Z	Bound
Δ	An increment
ϵ	Allowable difference between successive estimates
η	Factor of safety
θ	Angle
λ	Index
μ	Population mean
ξ	Fractional overrun to closure, $y_s = y_1 + \xi y_1$
ρ	Link length
σ	Population standard deviation
τ	Shear stress at wire surface
τ_s	Shear stress at wire surface at closure
ϕ	Angle
ω	Angular velocity

5-1 INTRODUCTION

Machine design is the decision-making process by which specifications for machines are created. It is from these specifications that materials are selected and machines are manufactured. The process includes

- Inventing the concept and connectivity
- Decisions of size, material, and method of manufacture
- Secondary decisions
- Adequacy assessment
- Documentation of the design
- Construction and testing of prototype(s)
- Final design

Computer-aided engineering (CAE) means computer assistance in the major decision-making process. *Computer-aided drafting* (CAD), often confused with CAE when called *computer-aided design,* means computer assistance in creating plans and can include geometric property estimates such as of volume, weight, centroidal coordinates, and various moments about the centroid. Three-dimensional depictions and their manipulations are often routinely available. *Computer-aided analysis* (CAA) involves use of the computer in an "if this then that" mode.

Computer-aided manufacturing (CAM) includes preparing tool passes for manufacture, including generating codes for executing complicated tool paths for numerically controlled machine tools. All kinds of auxiliary accounting associated with material and parts flow in a manufacturing line is also done by computer. The data base created during computer-aided drafting can be used by computer-aided manufacturing. This is often called *CAD/CAM.*

Some of these computer aids are commercially available and use proprietary programming. They are sometimes called "turnkey" systems. They may be used interactively by technically competent people without programming knowledge after only modest instruction. The programming detail is not important to the users. They react to displays, make decisions on the task to be accomplished, and proceed by entering appropriate system commands. Such systems are available for a number of highly repetitive tasks found in analysis, drawing, detailing, and manufacturing.

"Turnkey" systems are available from vendors to do some important work. A designer faced with a large problem may wish to inquire of the following nonexhaustive list of suppliers.†

COMPUTER-AIDED DRAFTING

Keuffel and Esser Company, 20 Whippany Road, Morristown, New Jersey 07960

Graftek, 616 Enterprise Drive, Oakbrook, Illinois 60521

California Computer Products, Inc., 2950 Metro Drive, Bloomington, Minnesota 55420

Vector Automation Inc., Village of Cross Keys, Baltimore, Maryland 21210

COMPUTER-AIDED ENGINEERING

Hewlett Packard Company, 3000 Hanover Street, Palo Alto, California 94304

McAuto, McDonnell Douglas Automation C., Box 516, St. Louis, Missouri 63166

General Electric CAE International Inc., 300 Technical Center Drive, Milford, Ohio 45150

---

†See also Ref. [5-1], pp. 36–38, for further information on software sources.

COMPUTER-AIDED ANALYSIS

Structural Dynamics Research Corporation, 2000 Eastman Drive, Milford, Ohio 45150

CAD/CAM

Computer Vision Corporation, 201 Burlington Road, Bedford, Massachusetts 01730

Prime Computer, Prime Park, Natick, Massachusetts 01760

Control Data Corporation, P. O. Box O, Minneapolis, Minnesota 55440

IBM, Box 2750, Irvine, Texas 75061

INFORMATION DISPLAY

Tektronix, Inc., Box 500, Beaverton, Oregon 97077

Intergraph Corporation, 30800 Telegraph Road, Birmingham, Michigan 48010

Chromatics, Inc., 2558 Mountain Industrial Boulevard, Tucker, Georgia 30084

The machine designer's effort, however, is composed of problem-specific tasks for many of which no commercial programming is available. The designer or his or her assistants may have to create or supervise the creation of such programs. The basis for this programming must come from their understanding of the problem. This section will view computer methods of direct use to the designer in making decisions using personal or corporate resources.

It is well to keep in mind what the computer can do:

- It can remember data as well as programs.
- It can calculate.
- It can branch unconditionally.
- It can branch conditionally based on whether a quantity is negative, zero, or positive, or whether a quantity is true or false, or whether a quantity is larger or smaller than something else. This capability can be described as *decision making.*
- It can do a repetitive task or series of tasks a fixed number of times or an appropriate number of times based on calculations it performs. This can be called *iteration.*
- It can read and write alphabetical and numerical information.
- It can draw.
- It can pause, interact, and wait for external decisions or thoughtful input.
- It does not tire.

Humans can

- Understand the problem
- Judge what is important and unimportant
- Plan strategies and modify them as they gain experience
- Weigh intangibles
- Be skeptical, suspicious, or unconvinced
- Program computers

The designer should try to delegate to the computer those things which the computer can do well and reserve for humans those things which they do well.

Notes ▪ Drawings ▪ Ideas

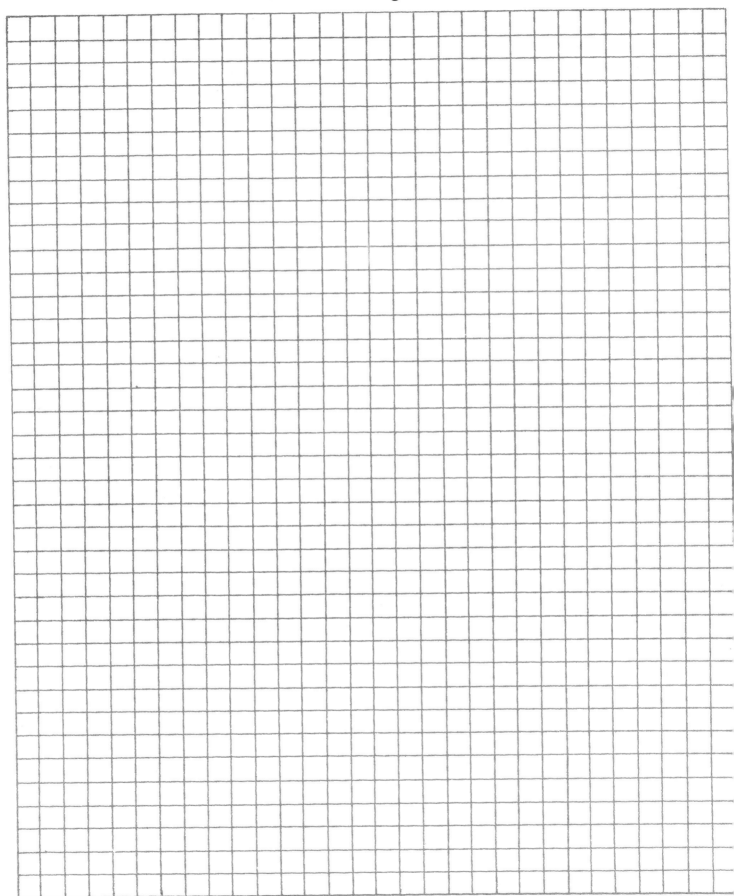

5-2 AN ALGORITHMIC APPROACH

An algorithm is a step-by-step process for accomplishing a task. A designer contemplating using the computer to help make decisions undertakes a series of tasks which can include

1. Identifying the specification set
2. Quantifying the adequacy assessment
3. Examining the needs to be met and identifying the a priori decisions
4. Identifying the design variables
5. Converting a priori and design decisions into a specification set
6. Quantifying a figure of merit
7. Choosing an optimization algorithm
8. Assembling the programs

These ideas can be illuminated best by example.

THE SPECIFICATION SET. The set of parameters which describes a part or assembly of parts so that it can be manufactured is called a *specification set*. One quick way to identify such a set is to examine the specification set of a manufacturer. If a helical-coil compression spring is to be manufactured, the springmaker needs to know

- Material and its condition
- Wire size (integral gauge numbers or preferred sizes [5-2], p. 20)
- End treatment
- Total number of turns or coils
- Coil diameter (OD or ID)
- Free length

and the associated tolerances. For purposes of illustration, we will assume that the tolerances are functions of the specification set and independently deducible from these six specifications.

THE ADEQUACY ASSESSMENT. The designer must quantify the basis for accepting or rejecting a specification set. A designer confronted with these six spring specifications might deem a spring satisfactory for static service if the

- Spring index $C = D/d$ lies between 4 and 16, that is, $4 \le C \le 16$.
- Number of active turns lies between 3 and 15, that is, $3 \le N \le 15$.
- Overrun to closure exceeds 10 percent, that is, $\xi \ge 0.1$.
- Factor of safety at closure exceeds 1.2, that is, $\eta_s \ge 1.2$.

In a mathematical sense, this sequence is a (Boolean) function. The independent variables are C, N, ξ, and η_s, and the dependent variable is the yes/no answer concerning adequacy. The FORTRAN coding for these tests might be as simple as

```
NOGOOD =0
IF(C.LT.4..OR.C.GT.16.) NOGOOD=NOGOOD + 1
IF(EN.LT.3..OR.EN.GT.15.) NOGOOD=NOGOOD + 10
IF(XI.LT.0.1) NOGOOD=NOGOOD + 100
IF(FOS.LT.1.2) NOGOOD=NOGOOD + 1000
```

If after executing these steps the variable NOGOOD is zero, the specification set is adequate. If not, the variable NOGOOD has a value other than zero. A value of NOGOOD of 101 means the spring index constraint has been violated (the ones place contains a 1), the turns constraint is satisfactory (the tens place contains a 0), the overrun constraint has been violated (the hundreds place contain a 1), and the factor of safety is satisfactory (the thousands place contains a 0).

In order to carry out the assessment task, given the following specification set:

Material and condition:	Hard-drawn spring wire; G, A, m [5-3], p. 452
Wire size:	d
End treatment:	Number of inactive coils, Q
Total turns:	Sum of inactive turns, Q, and active turns, N, $T = N + Q$
Coil diameter:	OD
Free length:	ℓ_f

the designer might proceed as follows, noting F_1 is the intended operating load (see Fig. 5-1). Estimate

Shearing yield strength:	$S_{sy} = 0.577(0.75)S_u = 0.577(0.75)A/d^m$
Active turns:	$N = T - Q$
Helix diameter:	$D = \mathrm{OD} - d$
Spring index:	$C = D/d$
Curvature factor:	$K_s = 1 + 0.5/C$
Solid height:	$\ell_s = (T - 1)d$ (for ground and squared ends)
Deflection to closure:	$y_s = \ell_f - \ell_s$
Spring rate:	$k = d^4 G/(8D^3 N)$
Force at closure:	$F_s = ky_s$
Shear stress at closure:	$\tau_s = 8K_s F_s D/\pi d^3$
Working end deflection:	$y_1 = F_1/k$
Overrun at closure:	$\xi = y_s/y_1 - 1$
Factor of safety at closure:	$\eta_s = S_{sy}/\tau_s$

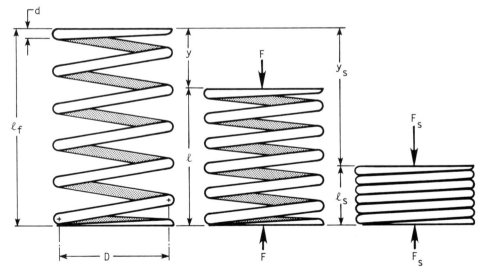

FIG. 5-1 Nomenclature of a helical-coil compression spring with ground and squared ends.

Is $4 \leq C \leq 16$?

Is $3 \leq N \leq 15$?

Is $\xi \geq 0.1$?

Is $\eta_s \geq 1.2$?

This entire string of computational and comparative steps is a mathematical function with independent variables represented by the six specifications and the intended working load, and the dependent variable is the yes/no determination of adequacy. The sequence can be programmed and serve to answer the question, "Given the six specifications and the working load, is the spring adequate?

IDENTIFY THE A PRIORI DECISIONS. This task involves identification of the needs to be met by the spring design and the a priori decisions. A designer might make these a priori decisions:

Meet the load-deflection requirement:	F_1, y_1
Use ground and squared ends:	Q
Use hard-drawn spring wire:	A, m, G
Ten percent overrun to closure:	ξ
Spring works over a rod:	d_{rod}

These decisions are five in number and do not agree completely with the entries in the springmaker's list. Nevertheless, five specifications have been made, and only one remains for the designer to make. With this decision he or she may choose to minimize cost or weight, for example. This remaining decision is called the *design decision* and its parametric representation is the *decision variable* or *design variable.*

IDENTIFY THE DESIGN VARIABLE(S). The task is to identify the parameter(s) the designer wishes to use as the design variable(s). In this case, the designer chooses the wire diameter d.

CONVERT TO A SPECIFICATION SET. The task is to construct a computational path from the a priori decisions plus the design decision to the springmaker's six specifications. For example, if the designer chooses the wire diameter, d, the path might be

Choose d

$D = d_{rod} + d + \text{allowance}$

$OD = D + d$

$k = F_1/y_1$

$N = d^4 G/(8D^3 k)$

$T = N + Q$

$y_s = (1 + \xi)y_1$

$\ell_s = (T - 1)d$

$\ell_f = \ell_s + y_s$

With the five a priori decisions and the wire size, the designer has converted to a specification set and can execute the adequacy analysis and obtain a yes/no answer. With several wire sizes producing adequate springs, which shall he or she choose?

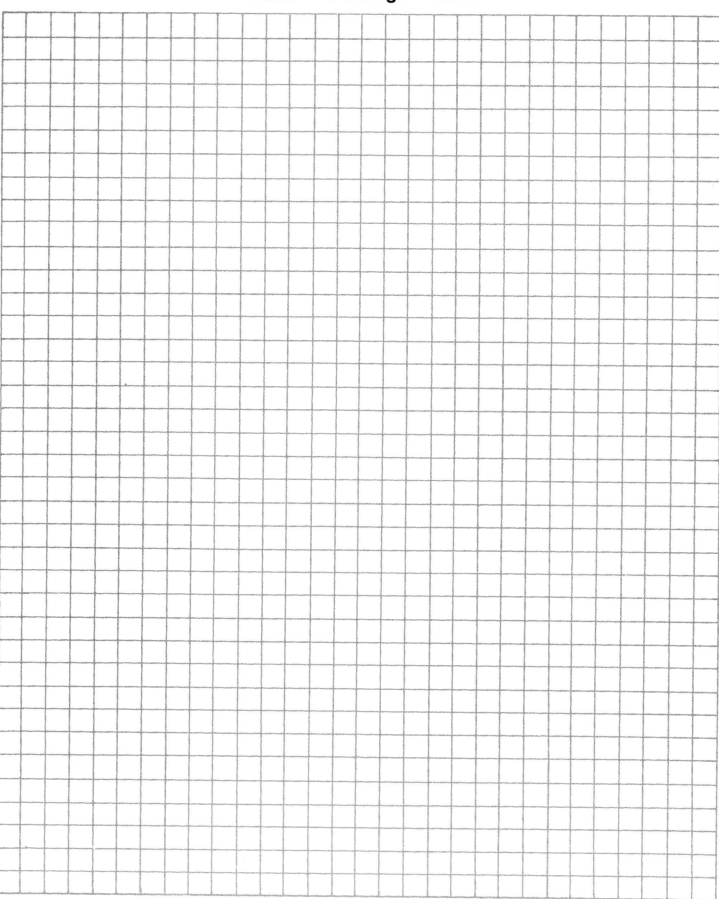

QUANTIFY A FIGURE OF MERIT. This task is to make a quantitative statement of merit so that the designer may distinguish between two satisfactory specification sets and choose the better. A *figure of merit* (FOM) is a number that increases monotonically with improving merit [5-4]. Such a number might be the negative of cost or the volume of material from which the spring is made. For the helical compression spring example, the figure of merit can be calculated from

$$FOM = (-\text{volume}) = -\frac{\pi^2 d^2 (N + Q)D}{4}$$

CHOOSE AN OPTIMIZATION ALGORITHM. The task is to devise or select a scheme for choosing wire diameters such that the merit increases until a maximum is attained. Such strategies are called *optimization algorithms* ([5-5], [5-6]). Skill and judgment are important here because in highly constrained problems certain algorithms can be defeated. The kinds of variables (continuous or discrete), their number, and the characters of the constraints play a role in a judicious selection of a useful optimization algorithm. In this case, the character of the design variable d is discrete. This is due to the practice of springmakers to draw wire in integral gauge-number sizes and other preferred sizes, and their stocks of wire may vary from time to time. The designer should not discard the pragmatic approach of marching through the available wire sizes and noting the specification set with the highest figure of merit.

5-3 ANALYSIS TASKS

In the discussion in the previous section of the adequacy-assessment task and the conversion to a specification set as illustrated by the static-service spring example, there occurred a number of routine computational chores. These were simple algebraic expressions representing mathematical models of the reality we call a spring. The expression for spring rate is either remembered or easily referenced. In a more complex problem the computational task may be more involved and harder to execute and program. However, it is of the same character. It is a calculation ritual that is known by the engineering community to be useful. It is an analysis-type "if this then that" algorithm that engineers instinctively reach for under appropriate circumstances. If this happens often, then once it is programmed it should be available for subsequent use by anyone. Computer languages created for algebraic computational use include a feature called the *subprogram capability.* The algorithm encoded is given a name and an argument list. In Fortran such a program can be a function subprogram or a subroutine subprogram. If the spring rate equation were to be coded as a Fortran subroutine with the name SPRNGK, then the coding could be

```
SUBROUTINE SPRNGK(DWIRE,DCOIL,G,EN,XK)
XK=DWIRE**4*G/8./DCOIL**3/EN
RETURN
END
```

and any program in which DWIRE, DCOIL, G, and EN have been defined can obtain XK by

```
.
.
.
CALL SPRNGK(DWIRE,DCOIL,G,EN,XK)
.
.
.
```

and XK is now defined in the calling program. This simplicity is welcome as the tasks becomes more complicated, such as finding the stress at the inner fiber of a curved beam of a tee cross section or locating the neutral axis of the cross section.

Such routine answers to computational chores can be added to a subroutine library to which the computer and user have access. Usage of programs by one designer written by another person depends on documentation, error messaging, and tests. At this point and for our purposes we will treat this as detail and retain the larger picture. A library of analysis subroutines can be created which the designer can manipulate in an executive manner simply by calling appropriate routines. Such subroutines are called *design subroutines* because through an inverse-analysis strategy they can be made to yield design decisions. Within them is the essence of the reality of the physical world. When decisions are made which completely describe a helical compression spring intended for static use, the computer can be used to examine important features. From decisions on

Material:	1085 music wire
Wire size:	0.071 in
Ends:	Ground and squared
Turns:	21.7 total
OD:	0.685 in
Length:	4.476 in

a large number of attributes can be viewed:

Ultimate strength estimate:	288 kpsi
Shearing yield strength:	125 kpsi
Spring rate:	8.01 lbf/in
Solid length:	1.47 in
Deflection to closure:	3.01 in
Working force:	7.8 lbf
Working deflection:	0.98 in
Working length:	3.5 in
Force at closure:	24.1 lbf
Spring index:	8.65
Shear stress at closure:	111 kpsi
Working shear stress:	36.1 kpsi
Static factor of safety:	3.5
Factor of safety at closure:	1.12
Critical frequency:	135 Hz
Buckling load:	9.6 lbf

Scanning these items, the designer can detect the need for a constraint to prevent buckling and observe the low factor of safety guarding against permanent set due to closure. This too can be assessed and the computer can assist routinely. The static factor of safety at closure is given by [see Ref. [5-3], Eqs. (10-3), (10-11), and (10-12)]:

$$\eta_s = \frac{S_{sy}}{\tau_s} = \frac{0.577(0.75)A}{d^m} \frac{\pi d^3}{[1 + (0.5d/D)]8F_sD}$$

Substituting for force to closure

$$F_s = ky_s = \frac{d^4G}{8D^3N}[\ell_f - (N + 1)d]$$

into the η_s equation yields

$$\eta_s = \frac{0.577(0.75)A\pi D^2 N}{[1 + (0.5d/D)]d^{1+m} G[\ell_f - (N + 1)d]}$$

for ground and squared ends. Tolerances on d, D, N, and ℓ_f give rise to variation in η_s, that tabulated above being a median value. The worst case of stacking of tolerance occurs when all deviations from the midrange values are such that

$$\Delta\eta_s = \left|\frac{\partial\eta_s}{\partial_d}\Delta d\right| + \left|\frac{\partial\eta_s}{\partial D}\Delta D\right| + \left|\frac{\partial\eta_s}{\partial N}\Delta N\right| + \left|\frac{\partial\eta_s}{\partial\ell_f}\Delta\ell_f\right|$$

In the case at hand with $A = 196$ kpsi (Ref. [5-3], Table 10-2), $m = 0.146$, $d = 0.071$ in, $D = 0.614$ in, $N = 19.7$, $\ell_f = 4.476$ in, and $G = 11.5 \times 10^6$ psi; $\eta_s = 1.121$:

$$\frac{\partial\eta_s}{\partial d} \doteq -11.03 \text{ in}^{-1} \qquad \frac{\partial\eta_s}{\partial D} \doteq 3.78 \text{ in}^{-1} \qquad \frac{\partial\eta_s}{\partial N} \doteq 0.083 \qquad \frac{\partial\eta_s}{\partial\ell_f} \doteq -0.372 \text{ in}^{-1}$$

where these values are obtained by taking partial derivatives in the η_s equation by numerical means. If the bilateral tolerances are

$$d = 0.071 \pm 0.001 \text{ in}$$

$$D = 0.614 \pm 0.010 \text{ in}$$

$$N = 19.7 \pm \tfrac{1}{4} \text{ turn}$$

$$\ell_f = 4.476 \pm 0.097 \text{ in}$$

we have

$$\Delta\eta_s = |-11.03(0.001)| + |3.78(0.010)| + |0.083(\tfrac{1}{4})| + |-0.372(0.097)|$$

$$= 0.011 + 0.038 + 0.021 + 0.036 = 0.106$$

The relative contribution of the various tolerances can be observed. The smallest possible value of η_s is

$$\eta_s(\text{min}) = \eta_s - \Delta\eta_s = 1.121 - 0.106 = 1.02$$

This is the worst-case stacking of tolerances.

To make a statistical statement as to the probability of observing a value of η_s of a particular magnitude, we need an estimate of the variance of η_s:

$$\sigma_{\eta_s}^2 = \left(\frac{\partial\eta_s}{\partial d}\right)^2 \sigma_d^2 + \left(\frac{\partial\eta_s}{\partial D}\right)^2 \sigma_D^2 + \left(\frac{\partial\eta_s}{\partial N}\right)^2 \sigma_N^2 + \left(\frac{\partial\eta_s}{\partial\ell_f}\right)^2 \sigma_{\ell_f}^2$$

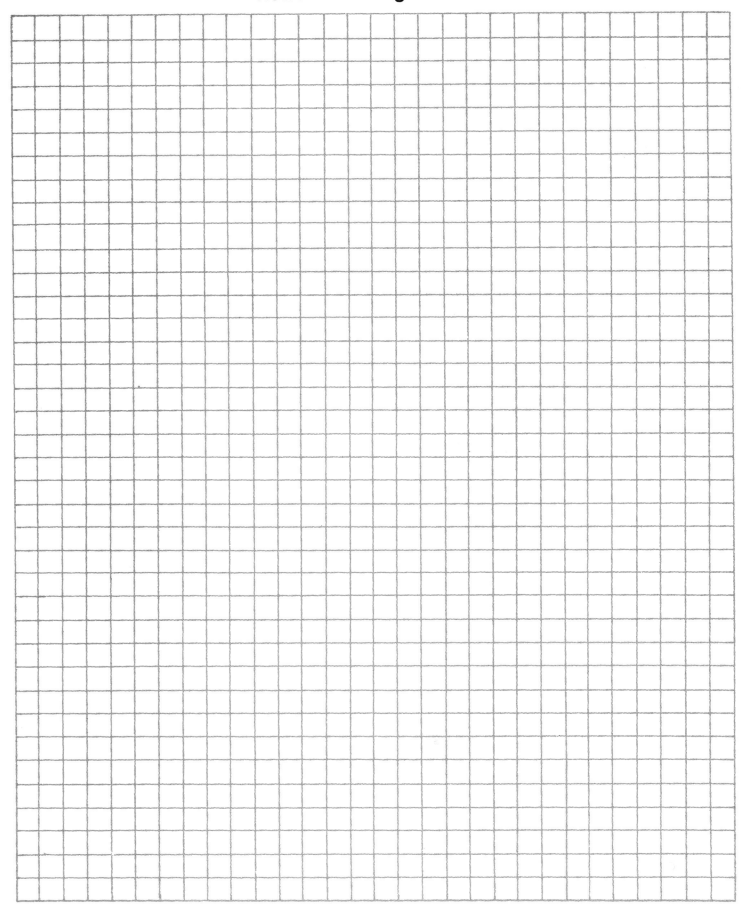

We can estimate the individual variances on the basis that the tolerance width represents six standard deviations as shown in Chap. 2:

$$\sigma_d = \frac{2(0.001)}{6} = 0.000\,333 \text{ in}$$

$$\sigma_D = \frac{2(0.010)}{6} = 0.003\,33 \text{ in}$$

$$\sigma_N = \frac{2(\frac{1}{4})}{6} = 0.0833$$

$$\sigma_{L_f} = \frac{2(0.097)}{6} = 0.032 \text{ in}$$

The estimate of the variance and standard deviation of η_s is

$$\sigma_{\eta_s}^2 = (-11.03)^2(0.000\,333)^2$$
$$+ (3.78)^2(0.003\,33)^2 + (0.083)^2(0.083)^2 + (0.372)^2(0.032)^2$$
$$= 0.000\,361$$
$$\sigma_{\eta_s} = \sqrt{0.000\,361} = 0.019$$

For a Gaussian distribution of η_s there are 3 chances in 1000 of observing a deviation from the mean of 3(0.019) = 0.057, or about $1\frac{1}{2}$ chances in 1000 of observing an instance of η_s less than 1.121 − 0.057 = 1.064. These kinds of analysis chores are easily built into a computer-adequacy display program. These are the kinds of quantitative information designers need before they commit themselves.

5-4 MATHEMATICAL TASKS

In problems which are coded for computer assistance a number of recurring mathematical tasks are encountered which can also be discharged by the computer as they are encountered. The procedure is to identify the pertinent algorithm and then code it as appropriate to your computer. Recurring tasks can be coded as subprograms which represent convenient building blocks for use in solving larger problems.

One frequently encountered task is that of finding a root or zero place of a function of a single independent variable. An effective algorithm for this task is the successive-substitution procedure with ensured convergence. The algorithm is as follows [5-7], p. 168:

Step 1. Express the problem in the form $f(x) = 0$. Establish the largest successive difference allowable in root estimates ϵ.

Step 2. Rewrite in the form $x = F(x)$, thereby defining $F(x)$.

Step 3. Establish convergence parameter $k = 1/[1 - F'(x)]$ or the finite-difference equivalent.

Step 4. Write the iteration equation [5-7], Eq. (3.25), that is,

$$x_{i+1} = [(1 - k)x + kF(x)]_i$$

and begin with root estimate x_0.

Step 5. If $|x_{i+1} - x_i| < \epsilon$, stop; otherwise go to step 4.

A simple example whose root is known is to find the root of $\ln x$:

Step 1. $f(x) = \ln x = 0$

Step 2. Solve for x by adding and subtracting x, to establish $F(x)$:

$$x - x + \ln x = 0$$
$$x = x - \ln x = F(x)$$

Step 3. Establish

$$k = \frac{1}{1 - F'(x)} = \frac{1}{1 - (1 - 1/x)} = x$$

Step 4. Write iteration equation:

$$x_{i+1} = [(1 - x)x + x(x - \ln x)]_i$$
$$= [x(1 - \ln x)]_i$$

With $x_0 = 2$, the following successive approximations are obtained:

$$2.000\ 000\ 000$$
$$0.613\ 705\ 639$$
$$0.913\ 341\ 207$$
$$0.996\ 131\ 704$$
$$0.999\ 992\ 508$$
$$1.000\ 000\ 000$$

In 5 iterations, 10 significant digits have been obtained. For a programmable hand-held calculator using reversed Polish notation, the problem-specific coding could be

| A | STO1 lnx CHS 1 + RCL1 × R/S

As an example of a problem with unknown answer consider a $2 \times \frac{1}{4}$ in tube of 1035 cold drawn steel ($S_y = 67$ kpsi) that is 48 in long and must support a column load with an eccentricity of $\frac{1}{8}$ in, as depicted in Fig. 5-2. For a design factor of 4 on the load, what allowable load is predicted by the secant column equation [5-3], Eq. (3-54)? The equation is

$$\frac{nP}{A} = S_y \left/ \left[1 + \frac{ec}{r^2} \sec \left(\frac{\ell}{r} \sqrt{\frac{nP}{A} \frac{1}{4E}} \right) \right] \right.$$

where $A = 1.374$ in^2, $r = 0.625$ in, $e = 0.125$ in, $c = 1$ in, $\ell = 48$ in, $E = 30 \times 10^6$

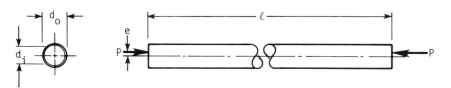

FIG. 5-2 An eccentrically loaded hollow column.

psi, $S_y = 67\,000$ psi. The secant equation is of the form $nP/A = F(nP/A)$. Choosing $\Delta = 0.001\, nP/A$, we can construct a finite-difference approximation to $F'(nP/A)$ for use in estimating the convergence parameter:

$$k = 1 \left/ \left[1 - \frac{F(1.001\,nP/A) - F(nP/A)}{0.001\,nP/A} \right] \right.$$

Using the iteration equation,

$$\left(\frac{nP}{A} \right)_{i+1} = \left[(1 - k)\frac{nP}{A} + kF\left(\frac{nP}{A} \right) \right]_i$$

Recalculating k every time and beginning with $(nP/A)_0 = 20\,000$ the successive approximations are

$$20\,000$$
$$34\,004$$
$$32\,548$$
$$32\,518$$
$$32\,518$$

It follows that

$$P = \frac{32\,518A}{n} = \frac{32\,518(1.374)}{4} = 11\,170 \text{ lbf}$$

The range over which convergence is prompt is shown by using three different estimates, that is, $(nP/A)_0 = 1, 10\,000,$ and $50\,000$:

1	10 000	50 000
39 967	36 353	38 322
33 367	32 726	33 015
32 528	32 519	32 521
32 518	32 518	32 518

Such an effective algorithm as successive substitution deserves coding on all kinds of computers. The designer should be able to perform the algorithm manually if required.

For finding the zero place of a function of more than one variable, a somewhat different formulation is useful. If a function of x is expanded about the point x_0 in the neighborhood of the root as a Taylor series (Ref. [5-8], p. 579), we obtain

$$f(x) = f(x_0) + f'(x_0)(x - x_0) + \frac{1}{2!}f''(x_0)(x - x_0)^2 + \cdots$$

If x is the root, then $f(x) = 0$, and if the series is truncated after two terms, solution for x is a better estimate of the root than is x_0. Denoting $x - x_0$ as Δx, then

$$\Delta x = -\frac{f(x_0)}{f'(x_0)}$$

and the better estimate of the root is $x_1 = x_0 + \Delta x$. Using this pair of equations iteratively will result in finding the root. For example, if the involute of ϕ is 0.01, what is the value of ϕ? Recalling (Ref. [5-9], p. 266), that inv $\phi = \tan \phi - \phi$, we write

$$f(\phi) = \tan \phi - \phi - 0.01 = 0$$

$$f'(\phi) = \sec^2 \phi - 1 = \frac{1}{\cos^2 \phi} - 1$$

$$\Delta \phi = -\frac{f(\phi)}{f'(\phi)} = -\frac{\tan \phi - \phi - 0.01}{(1/\cos^2 \phi) - 1}$$

$$\phi_{i+1} = \phi_i + \Delta \phi_i$$

For an initial estimate of $\phi_0 = 0.35$ we obtain

$$0.350\,000\,000$$
$$0.312\,261\,514$$
$$0.306\,874\,838$$
$$0.306\,772\,584$$
$$0.306\,772\,547$$
$$0.306\,772\,547$$

observing convergence to be rapid. For details, see any textbook on numerical methods, such as Carnahan et al. [5-7], p. 171.

For the problem of two functions of two independent variables, namely, $f_1(x, y)$ and $f_2(x, y)$, the Taylor-series expansions are (Ref. [5-8], p. 580):

$$f_1(x, y) = f_1(x_0, y_0) + \frac{\partial f_1(x_0, y_0)}{\partial x} (x - x_0) + \frac{\partial f_1(x_0, y_0)}{\partial y} (y - y_0) + \cdots$$

$$f_2(x, y) = f_2(x_0, y_0) + \frac{\partial f_2(x_0, y_0)}{\partial x} (x - x_0) + \frac{\partial f_2(x_0, y_0)}{\partial y} (y - y_0) + \cdots$$

If x and y represent the roots of $f_1(x, y) = 0$ and $f_2(x, y) = 0$, and identifying $(x - x_0) = \Delta x$ and $(y - y_0) = \Delta y$, then the preceding equations can be written as

$$\frac{\partial f_1}{\partial x} \Delta x + \frac{\partial f_1}{\partial y} \Delta y = -f_1 = r_1$$

$$\frac{\partial f_2}{\partial x} \Delta x + \frac{\partial f_2}{\partial y} \Delta y = -f_2 = r_2$$

where r_1 and r_2 are called *residuals*. Solving the preceding equations simultaneously for Δx and Δy, we obtain

$$\Delta x = \frac{1}{A} \left(r_1 \frac{\partial f_2}{\partial y} - r_2 \frac{\partial f_1}{\partial y} \right)$$

$$\Delta y = \frac{1}{A} \left(r_2 \frac{\partial f_1}{\partial x} - r_1 \frac{\partial f_2}{\partial x} \right)$$

where

$$A = \frac{\partial f_1}{\partial x} \frac{\partial f_2}{\partial y} - \frac{\partial f_2}{\partial x} \frac{\partial f_1}{\partial y}$$

Better estimates of x and y than x_0 and y_0 are

$$x_{i+1} = x_i + \Delta x_i \qquad y_{i+1} = y_i + \Delta y_i$$

The solution algorithm is

Step 1. Decide what value of ϵ that $|\Delta x|$ and $|\Delta y|$ must not exceed. Then write equations in the form

$$f_1(x, y) = 0 \qquad f_2(x, y) = 0$$

Step 2. Calculate the residuals using starting estimates $x = x_0$ and $y = y_0$ for first evaluation:

$$r_1 = -f_1(x, y) \qquad r_2 = -f_2(x, y)$$

Step 3. Evaluate the Jacobian:

$$A = \frac{\partial f_1}{\partial x}\frac{\partial f_2}{\partial y} - \frac{\partial f_2}{\partial x}\frac{\partial f_1}{\partial y}$$

Step 4.

$$\Delta x = \frac{1}{A}\left(r_1 \frac{\partial f_2}{\partial y} - r_2 \frac{\partial f_1}{\partial y}\right)$$

$$\Delta y = \frac{1}{A}\left(r_2 \frac{\partial f_1}{\partial x} - r_1 \frac{\partial f_2}{\partial x}\right)$$

Step 5. Estimate

$$x \leftarrow x + \Delta x \qquad y \leftarrow y + \Delta y$$

Step 6. If $|\Delta x| < \epsilon$ and $|\Delta y| < \epsilon$, stop; otherwise go to step 2 with new estimates of x and y.

As an example of the use of the Newton-Raphson method, consider a position analysis of the four-bar linkage depicted in Fig. 5-3, wherein $\rho_1 = 2$ in, $\rho_2 = 1$ in, $\rho_3 = 2.5$ in, and $\rho_4 = 3$ in. For a crank angle of $\theta_2 = 90°$, what are the abscissa angles θ_3 and θ_4? The vector equation

$$\rho_2 + \rho_3 = \rho_1 + \rho_4$$

gives rise to the pair of scalar equations

$$\rho_3 \cos \theta_3 = \rho_4 \cos \theta_4 - \rho_2 \cos \theta_2 + \rho_1$$

$$\rho_3 \sin \theta_3 = \rho_4 \sin \theta_4 - \rho_2 \sin \theta_2$$

Rewrite the equations in the form $f_1(\theta_3, \theta_4) = 0$ and $f_2(\theta_3, \theta_4) = 0$:

$$f_1(\theta_3, \theta_4) = \rho_4 \cos \theta_4 - \rho_2 \cos \theta_2 + \rho_1 - \rho_3 \cos \theta_3$$

$$f_2(\theta_3, \theta_4) = \rho_4 \sin \theta_4 - \rho_2 \sin \theta_2 - \rho_3 \sin \theta_3$$

The residuals are

$$r_1 = -f_1 = -\rho_4 \cos \theta_4 + \rho_2 \cos \theta_2 - \rho_1 + \rho_3 \cos \theta_3$$

$$r_2 = -f_2 = -\rho_4 \sin \theta_4 + \rho_2 \sin \theta_2 + \rho_3 \sin \theta_3$$

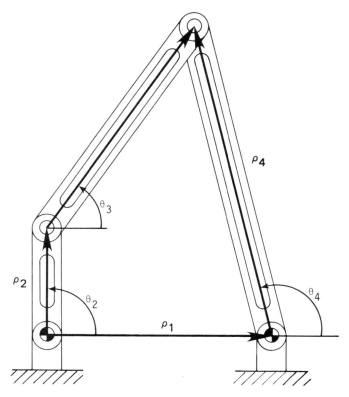

FIG. 5-3 A vector model of a four-bar linkage with link 1 grounded, link 2 as a crank, link 3 as a coupler, and link 4 as a follower.

The value of A is determined:

$$\frac{\partial f_1}{\partial \theta_3} = \rho_3 \sin \theta_3 \qquad \frac{\partial f_1}{\partial \theta_4} = -\rho_4 \sin \theta_4$$

$$\frac{\partial f_2}{\partial \theta_3} = -\rho_3 \cos \theta_3 \qquad \frac{\partial f_2}{\partial \theta_4} = \rho_4 \cos \theta_4$$

$$A = (\rho_3 \sin \theta_3)(\rho_4 \cos \theta_4) - (-\rho_3 \cos \theta_3)(-\rho_4 \sin \theta_4)$$

$$= \rho_3 \rho_4 \sin (\theta_3 - \theta_4)$$

Find $\Delta\theta_3$ and $\Delta\theta_4$:

$$\Delta\theta_3 = \frac{1}{A}(r_1 \rho_4 \cos \theta_4 + r_2 \rho_4 \sin \theta_4)$$

$$= \frac{\rho_4}{A}(r_1 \cos \theta_4 + r_2 \sin \theta_4)$$

$$\Delta\theta_4 = \frac{1}{A}[r_2 \rho_3 \sin \theta_3 - r_1(-\rho_3 \cos \theta_3)]$$

$$= \frac{\rho_3}{A}(r_2 \sin \theta_3 + r_1 \cos \theta_3)$$

Improve the estimate of θ_3 and θ_4:

$$\theta_3 \leftarrow \theta_3 + \Delta\theta_3 \qquad \theta_4 \leftarrow \theta_4 + \Delta\theta_4$$

For initial values $(\theta_3)_0 = 0.8$ and $(\theta_4)_0 = 1.6$, we obtain in four iterations

θ_3	θ_4
0.800 000	1.600 000
0.911 666	1.723 684
0.904 495	1.722 968
0.904 519	1.722 977
0.904 519	1.722 977

converging on $\theta_3 = 0.904\ 519$ rad or $51.83°$ and $\theta_4 = 1.722\ 977$ rad or $98.72°$. For initial values $(\theta_3)_0 = 5$ and $(\theta_4)_0 = 4$, we obtain in five iterations

θ_3	θ_4
5.000 000	4.000 000
4.477 696	3.743 041
4.440 784	3.626 671
4.451 343	3.632 940
4.451 371	3.632 893
4.451 371	3.632 893

identifying θ_3 as $255.0°$ and θ_4 as $208.1°$, which represents the configuration where the coupler crosses the grounded link.

Such a solution algorithm for simultaneous equations can be generalized to n equations. The previous kinematic problem can be coded for a handheld calculator in approximately a hundred steps.

Another recurring task is that of integration. A powerful numerical tool is Simpson's first rule:

$$\int_{x_0}^{x_2} f(x)\,dx = \frac{h}{3}\,[f(x_0) + 4f(x_1) + f(x_2)] - \frac{h^5}{90}\,f''''(\xi) \qquad x_0 \le \xi \le x_2$$

The error term is exact for some (generally unavailable) value of ξ. If the number of repetitions of this rule made in an interval a, b is n, then the number of panels is $N = 2n$. Richardson (Ref. [5-7], p. 78) showed that if an integration is performed in interval a, b with N_2 panels and then repeated with $N_1 = N_2/2$ panels (using every other ordinate), then the value of the integral is given by

$$I = I_{N_2} + \frac{I_{N_2} - I_{N_1}}{15} = I_{N_2} + R_{N_2}$$

where the last term is called *Richardson's error estimate*. The number of panels N_2 must be divisible by 4. The approximate relation between the number of panels and the error is

$$N_j \doteq N_i \left| \frac{E_i}{E_j} \right|^{1/4} = N_i \left| \frac{I_{N_2} - I_{N_1}}{15E_j} \right|^{1/4} = N_i \left| \frac{R_i}{E_j} \right|^{1/4}$$

Notes · Drawings · Ideas

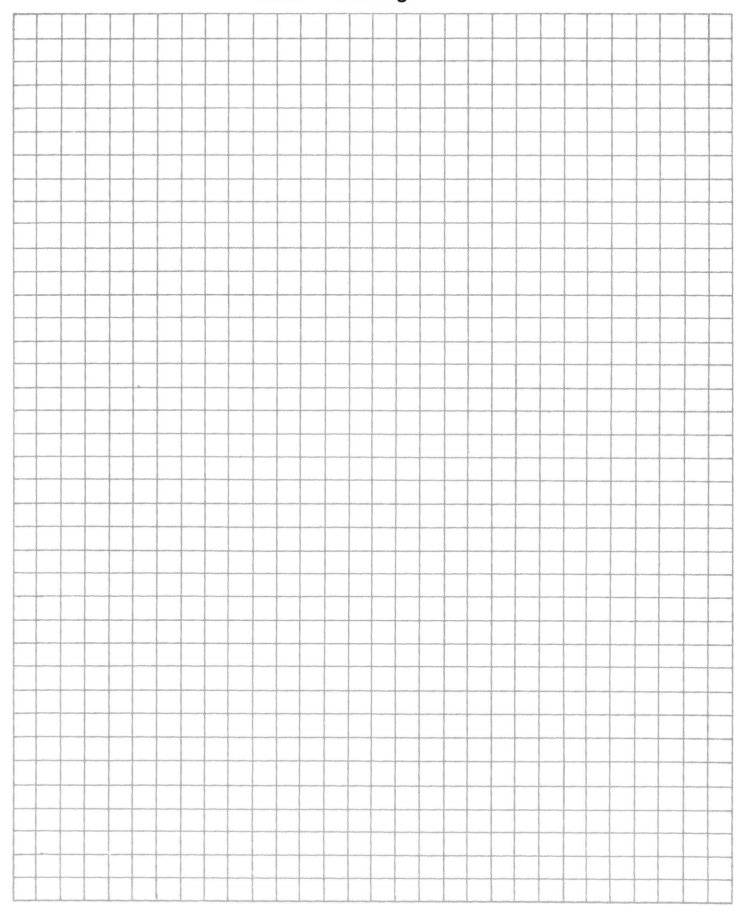

EXAMPLE. Estimate the value of $\int_0^\pi \sin x \, dx$ to five significant digits to the right of the decimal point.

Step 1. Perform the integration with 2 panels, obtaining $I_2 = 2.0944$.

Step 2. Perform the integration with 4 panels obtaining $I_4 = 2.00456$.

Step 3. Estimate the error in I_4 as

$$R_i = \frac{I_4 - I_2}{15} = \frac{2.004\ 56 - 2.0944}{15} = -0.005\ 989$$

Step 4. Estimate the number of panels necessary to attain requisite accuracy:

$$N_j \doteq N_i \left| \frac{R_i}{E_j} \right|^{1/4} = 4 \left| \frac{0.005\ 989}{0.5 \times 10^{-5}} \right|^{1/4}$$

$$= 23.5$$

say, 24 panels.

Step 5. Integrate using 24 panels, obtaining $I_{24} = 2.000\ 003\ 269$.

This result is high, as indicated by the sign of Richardson's correction and by an estimated amount of $-0.000\ 003\ 290$. Note that the objective has been achieved. An improved estimate of the value of the integral might be $I_{24} + R_{24} = 1.999\ 999\ 979$, which rounded to five significant digits to the right of the decimal point is still 2.000 00.

EXAMPLE. An electric motor has a torque-rpm characteristic of $36\ (1 - n/1800)$ ft · lbf and a moment of inertia of 1 slug ft². Estimate within a tenth of a second the time to come up to a speed of 1600 rpm from rest in the absence of load.

The expression for the time estimate is in the form of an integral:

$$t = \int \frac{I}{T} d\omega = \frac{2\pi}{60} \int_0^{1600} \frac{dn}{36(1 - n/1800)}$$

Integrating with four panels using Simpson's rule, the Richardson correction is $R_4 = -0.094\ 561\ 754$. The estimated number of panels to assess the starting time to within a tenth of a second ($E = 0.05$ s) is

$$N_j \doteq N_i \left| \frac{R_i}{E_j} \right|^{1/4} = 4 \left| \frac{0.094\ 561\ 754}{0.05} \right|^{1/4} = 4.69$$

This is rounded to the next larger integer divisible by 4 using eight panels:

$$I = I_8 + R_8 = 11.571\ 809\ 98 - 0.023\ 455\ 747$$

$$= 11.548\ 354\ 23$$

The result shows the objective achieved with a result of 11.5 s. Simpson's first rule should be coded and available to any user of a computer.

In computer-aided engineering, a number of routine mathematical tasks are encountered, and these should be available to the programmer in an executive fashion, discharged, if possible, by a one-line call statement (in Fortran).

5-5 STATISTICAL TASKS

There are innumerable statistical tasks to be performed incidental to engineering calculations, for example:

- Descriptive statistics such as means, medians, variances, and ranks have to be developed from data.
- Probabilities of observations from binomial, hypergeometric, Poisson, normal, lognormal, exponential, and Weibullian distributions need to be found.
- Inferential statistics must be developed for distributional parameters such as means, variances, and proportions.
- Data need to be fitted to distributional curves using least-square lines, polynomials, or distributional functions.
- Goodness-of-fit tests for conformity must be made.

There exist programs for large computational machines which can be imitated or approximated on smaller machines. An important thing to be remembered concerning statistical computations conducted with paper and pencil as compared to with a computer is that computer programs are executed out of sight and supervision of a human and there is no experienced eye monitoring intermediate results and exhibiting a healthy skepticism when the occasion warrants.

It is so easy to calculate a correlation coefficient, be impressed with its nearness of unity, have it indicate statistical significance of fit, and be wrong without a warning signal. The correlation coefficient has meaning *only* if the data fall randomly about the regression curve. When using the computer it is important to inspect a graphic presentation or to conduct a run test prior to testing for significance of fit. This test detects randomness or the lack of it in the case of dichotomous events (heads or tails, larger or smaller than the mean, above or below a regression curve). We can observe successes (above), failures (below), and runs (sequences of successes or failures). If n_1 is the number of successes, n_2 is the number of failures, and $n_1 \geq 10$ and $n_1 \geq 10$, then the sampling distribution of the number of runs n is approximately Gaussian, with (Ref. [5-10], p. 414)

$$\mu_n = \frac{2n_1 n_2}{n_1 + n_2} + 1$$

$$\sigma_n = \left[\frac{2n_1 n_2 (2n_1 n_2 - n_1 - n_2)}{(n_1 + n_2)^2 (n_1 + n_2 - 1)} \right]^{1/2}$$

The null hypothesis that the sample is random can be based on the statistic

$$z = \begin{cases} \dfrac{n + \frac{1}{2} - \mu_n}{\sigma_n} & n > \mu_n \\[3mm] \dfrac{n - \frac{1}{2} - \mu_n}{\sigma_n} & n < \mu_n \end{cases}$$

where the $\frac{1}{2}$ improves the Gaussian continuous fit to the discrete PDF of n.

If a regression line were determined from data and using a for above the line and b for below the line, then as we move along the abscissa we would observe

<u>bb</u> <u>aa</u> <u>baa</u> <u>bba</u> <u>ba</u> <u>bb</u> <u>ababa</u> <u>aa</u> <u>b</u> <u>a</u> <u>ba</u> <u>ba</u> <u>baa</u> <u>ba</u> <u>baa</u>

detecting $n = 27$ runs, $n_1 = 19$ above, $n_2 = 16$ below. The mean number of runs expected μ_n and the standard deviation expected σ_n are

$$\mu_n = \frac{2(19)16}{19 + 16} + 1 = 18.37$$

$$\sigma_n = \left[\frac{2(19)16[2(19)16 - 19 - 16]}{(19 + 16)^2(19 + 16 - 1)}\right]^{1/2} = 2.89$$

Since the number of runs, that is, 27, is greater than the mean of 18.37,

$$z = \frac{27 + \frac{1}{2} - 18.37}{2.89} = 3.16$$

If the null hypothesis is H_0: runs random, then under H_0, $z = 3.16$, and z (tabulated two-tailed) = 1.96, we can reject H_0 at 0.95 confidence level and embrace the alternative that the runs are not random. Similarly, if a straight line is fitted to parabolic data, the number of runs might be 3 or 4 or 5. If it is as much as 9, then

$$z = \frac{9 - \frac{1}{2} - 18.37}{2.89} = -3.42$$

and we can still reject randomness at the 0.95 confidence level. It is important that in as much as no one is looking we build in guardian sentinels such as this.

If the differences between y and $\hat{y}$ are ranked in the order of their corresponding abscissas and placed in the column vector DY, then the number of runs can be detected with the following Fortran coding:

```
          NUMBER=1
          DO 100 I=2,N
          A=DY(I)/ABS(DY(I))
          B=DY(I-1)/ABS(DY(I-1))
          IF(A/B.LT.0.)NUMBER=NUMBER+1
    100   CONTINUE
```

where the integer NUMBER has a magnitude equal to the number of runs.

5.6 OPTIMIZATION TASKS

The structure of the design-decision problem and that of the optimization problem are similar. Many ideas and techniques of the latter are applicable to the former. The optimization problem can be posed as

$$\text{Maximize (or minimize) } M(x_1, x_2, \ldots, x_n)$$

subject to

$$g_1(x_1, x_2, \ldots, x_n) = 0$$

$$g_2(x_1, x_2, \ldots, x_n) = 0$$

$$\ldots \ldots \ldots \ldots \ldots \ldots$$

$$g_m(x_1, x_2, \ldots, x_n) = 0$$

Notes · Drawings · Ideas

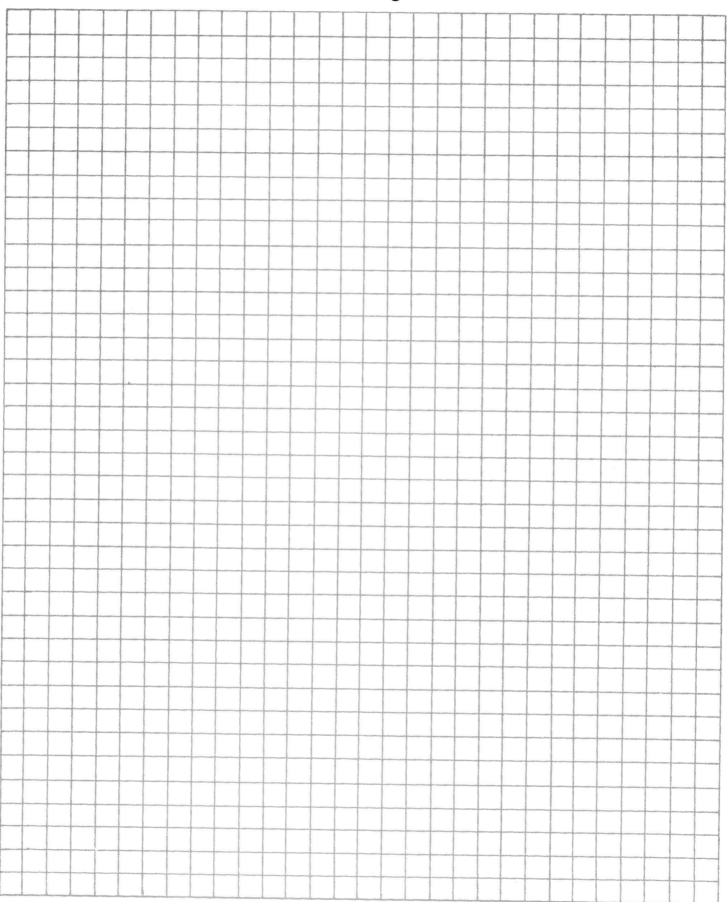

and

$$z_1 \le f_1(x_1, x_2 \ldots, x_n) \le Z_1$$

$$z_2 \le f_2(x_1, x_2, \ldots, x_n) \le Z_2$$

$$\cdots\cdots\cdots\cdots\cdots\cdots\cdots\cdots\cdots$$

$$z_\lambda \le f_\lambda(x_1, x_2, \ldots, x_n) \le Z_\lambda$$

The functions $g_i\{x_n\} = 0$ are called *equality* or *functional constraints*. The functions $z_i \le f_i\{x_n\} \le Z_i$ are called *inequality* or *regional constraints*. The set $\{x_n\}$ is called the *decision set*. In terms of the ideas in Sec. 5-2 the *specification set* consists of

$$P_1, P_2, \ldots, P_k$$

which for a helical-coil compression spring can consist of (1) material and its condition, that is, A, m, G, E, (2) wire size d, (3) end treatment, that is, Q, Q', (4) total number of turns T, (5) coil outside diameter OD, and (6) free length l_f. The adequacy assessment can be performed by a Fortran subroutine:

```
ADEQ(A,m,G,E,d,Q,Q',T,OD,d,l_f,J)
```

where J is returned as $\ne 0$ if inadequate and as 0 if adequate. If the a priori decisions are (1) material and condition, (2) end treatment, (3) total turns, (4) coil outside diameter, and (5) free length and the wire diameter is chosen as the sole decision variable, then the tasks are

1. Choose d. (This completes the decision set.)
2. Call CONVERT. (Change the decision set into equivalent specification set.)
3. Call ADEQ. (Establish the adequacy of decision set.)
4. Call FOM. (Evaluate figure of merit if decision set is adequate.)

The choice of d is provided either manually (interactively) or by an appropriate optimization algorithm which makes successive choices of d which have superior merit. The program CONVERT might be problem-specific and need to be created for each type of design problem. The program ADEQ is durable and once programmed can be used. The program FOM is durable as long as the merit criterion (say spring cost) is unchanged.

Figure 5-4 shows the interrelationships of programs FOM, CONVERT, ADEQ, OPT, and the executive program for the helical-spring example.

Optimization programs have to be chosen with care because highly constrained problems can defeat classical strategies. The issue is further complicated by the mixture of discrete and continuous variables. In a spring design the wire size, end treatment, and material parameters are discrete, whereas the others are usually continuous. The user is solving a problem to which the answer is not known and cannot be sure of having attained the global extreme of the figure-of-merit function. Since multidimensional optimization strategies involve some gradient sensitivity, it is judicious to ensure that discrete variables in a problem are among the a priori decisions and the decision set and not buried within. Sometimes an exhaustive search over discrete variables, although computationally inelegant, will attain a global maximum with the least expenditure of computer plus engineering costs. For example, in a spring design with the wire size d as the sole decision variable, marching through the discrete preferred (or available) wire diameters (Ref. [5-1], p. 20) will solve the problem efficiently:

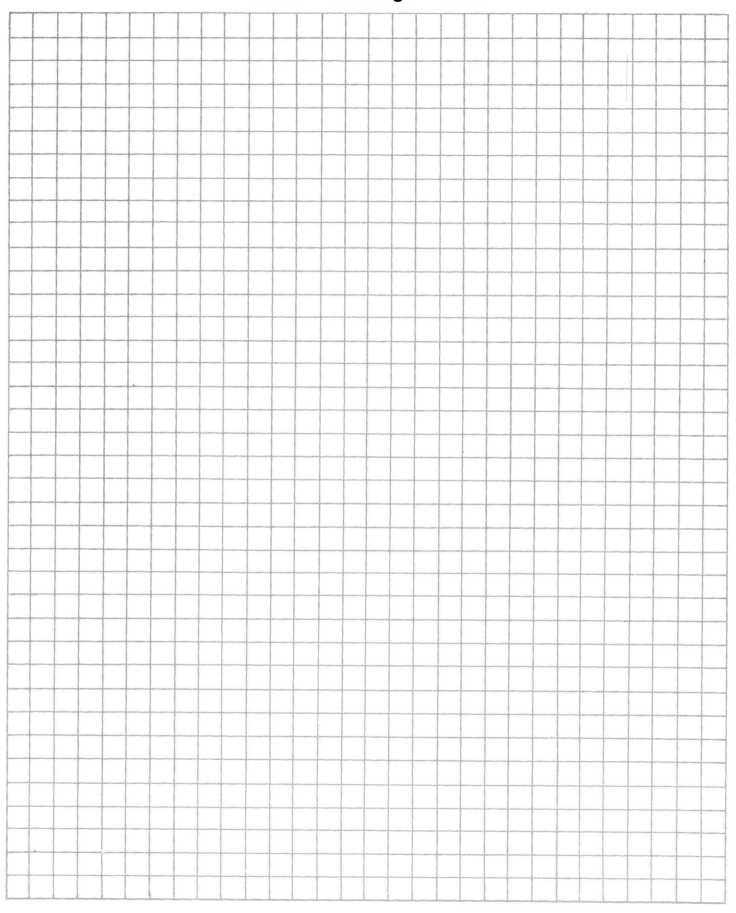

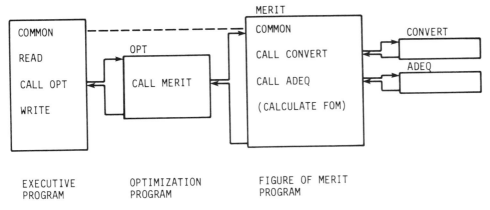

FIG. 5-4 Organization and subordination of programs for the helical-coil compression spring example.

Washburn and Moen gage: No. 40, 39, 38, 37, . . .

Decimal inch preferred: 0.004, 0.005, 0.006, 0.008, . . .

Decimal millimeter preferred: 0.1, 0.12, 0.16, 0.20, 0.25, . . .

Suppose two decision variables remain after four a priori decisions, and these are wire diameter d and free length ℓ_f (d is discrete and ℓ_f is continuous). The steps might be

1. Enter d and bounds on ℓ_f.
2. For an available wire size d, use a do-loop to show 11 springs of different lengths, displaying d, ℓ_f, FOM, and NG.
3. If there exists a feasible range, enter the ℓ_f bounds which define the range.
4. Use a golden-section search strategy [5-4] on ℓ_f to find maximum figure of merit.
5. Display specification set and figure of merit.
6. Repeat for all possible wire sizes.
7. Select best of field as global optimum.

This procedure is best made interactive and can be presented to a user without requiring a knowledge of programming.

For the static-service helical-coil compression spring using one decision variable d and two decision variables d and ℓ_f, the specification sets are

	Case 1. One decision variable d	Case 2. Two decision variables d and ℓ_f
Material and condition	Cold-drawn spring wire 1066	Cold-drawn 1066
Wire size	W&M no. 11 (0.1205 in)	W&M no. 11 (0.1205 in)
End condition	Squared and ground	Squared and ground
Total turns	14.4	13.4
OD	1.091 in	1.091 in
Free length	3.25 in	3.19 in
(Wire volume)	(0.502 in³)	(0.467 in³)

Note that both springs are optimal for the conditions, but case 2 is a superior spring in that less material, and therefore less cost, is involved.

5-7 COMPUTER-AUGMENTED DESIGN ENGINEERING TECHNIQUE

A designer who

- Defines problems in quantitative terms
- Decides how to recognize a satisfactory solution
- Decides how to recognize solution merit so as to be able to distinguish between two satisfactory designs and chooses the better
- Generates alternatives
- Through analysis establishes alternative merit
- Discovers the solution with the highest merit using some search stratagem
- Makes design decisions and implements them

is naturally proceeding in a manner completely compatible with the capabilities of the digital computer.

One example, the *computer-augmented design engineering technique* (Iowa CADET), embodies these essential ideas:

- Meaningful competitive design is best accomplished when timely feedback is available from the marketplace. There are many situations in which the time available or the enormity of resources committed will not allow feedback from the marketplace to properly influence design decisions. Under these circumstances, the influence of the marketplace on design must be simulated. The vehicle of this simulation is the figure of merit.

- A *figure of merit* is simply a number whose magnitude changes monotonically with merit and constitutes an index to the merit or desirability of an alternative solution to a problem. Alternate names are *criterion function, utility function,* and *objective function.*

- The designer seeks to maximize the figure-of-merit function subject to the many constraints placed on the solution by nature; by law; by social, economic, and political factors; and by geometric and material considerations.

- If a designer proceeds as outlined above, then he or she is progressing in a manner completely compatible with the capabilities of the digital computer and the Iowa CADET algorithm.

- Computer time and the engineering and programming time associated with a problem must be charged to design costs. If programming is carried out in the usual fashion of solving only the specific problem at hand, the number of projects in which computer assistance can be economically justified will be few. However, if programming is carried out in such a way as to be useful in subsequent tasks, then the unit costs decline and the number of applications of computer assistance will increase.

- At the project-engineering level it will be generally fruitless to wait for proprietary programs to be developed by talented organizations (e.g., computer manufacturers) because the number of general problems that can be solved by canned proprietary programs is, at best, limited to a small fraction of existing problems. It will be necessary for the individual engineer or the engineering group to develop, in terms of their own knowledge of common or recurring problems, their own computer capabilities (programs).

- Documentation of any capability of substantial size to be used by many different persons must be carefully structured so as to *invite use*. Only in this way will the capability grow by local contribution toward greater utility, eventually becoming custom-made to the local needs (and no outsider is likely to do better).

The figure of merit is the means by which the designer compares two alternatives and with high precision chooses the better. This ability can be parlayed into an optimization stratagem. *Mathematical programming* optimization algorithms do precisely this. Simple attributes of systems are often candidates for figures of merit. Examples include design attributes such as design factor, cost, reliability, time interval, magnitude of displacement, and mass or weight. When multiple factors contribute to the decision, then the figure of merit is a function of the multiple factors, with the appropriate trade-offs quantitatively expressed. If you cannot do this, you cannot optimize, with or without the computer (see Ref. [5-11]).

5-7-1 Computer Requirements

The basic thrust in computer programming for engineering problems is to keep programming *general* by separating the strategy from the tactics. If one desires to use an algorithm such as variable secant, Newton's method, interval halving, etc. to find the zero place (root) of a function, then the technique is not to program the problem in one piece, but to separate the operator from the operand. Specifically, one can write a SUBROUTINE subprogram that will implement the method with *any function of the proper class* and write a FUNCTION subprogram to inform the subroutine exactly what mathematical function is to be operated on at this particular time. The programming of the strategy is the more difficult task, and this should be done only *once* and thereafter used by the engineer and others to find the zero place of other mathematical functions. The programming of the operand is often as simple as depicted below and in Fig. 5-5:

```
FUNCTION F(X)
F=(expression in x)
RETURN
END
```

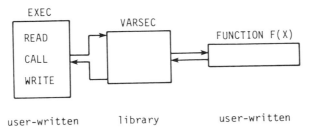

FIG. 5-5 Computer-program structure for a root-finding task showing how executive program and function subprogram interact with a library program implementing a variable-secant root-finding strategy.

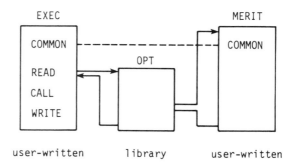

FIG. 5-6 Computer-program structure for an optimization task showing how executive program and merit subroutine interact with a library program implementing an optimization strategy.

This separation of the stratagem from details of a specific case is applicable to most mathematical operations and, indeed, to the optimization process itself. Figure 5-6 depicts the selected optimization stratagem program as OPT. The engineer writes the executive program which calls OPT. The program OPT in turn calls and manipulates user-written subroutine MERIT and reports back to the executive program the results of the maximization process.

We can see a structure emerging as a result of the posture of separating the strategic programming from the tactical detail. Figure 5-7 depicts an executive program whose purpose is to (1) READ in problem-specific information, (2) call SEARCH, and (3) WRITE the results of the search that happen to be problem-specific. SEARCH calls and manipulates another user-written problem-specific routine, MERIT. This routine is really an executive program at a lower level whose purpose is to generate the figure of merit. For this purpose it calls engineering-analysis routines which carry out the engineering-analysis rituals, but utilizing the specific information for the case at hand. MERIT also may have mathematical chores to accomplish and consequently it calls MATH, a mathematical-operation strategy (performed in this case on user-written EQUAT). The structural form is that of a

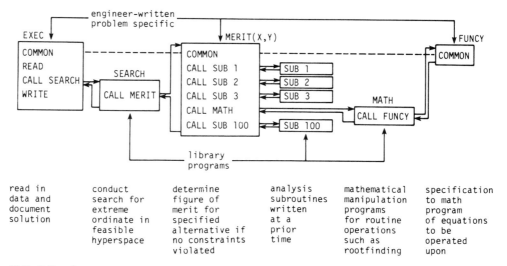

FIG. 5-7 Common program structure of a design problem showing the interrelationship of library and problem-specific programs.

multilayer laminate in which engineer-written problem-specific programs call and manipulate library programs the engineer has probably never seen. These in turn call and manipulate programs the engineer has written (which are problem-specific). The depth of the lamination stack is directly related to the complexity of the problem. The only way in which this structure can be expeditiously used is through the adoption of an *effective documentation scheme.*

5-7-2 Documentation

The following questions are foremost in the mind of the potential user of library routines and must be answered to user satisfaction in any effective documentation scheme (Ref. [5-4], Sec. 4.4):

1. What is the number of arguments in the call list?
2. What is the order of the arguments in the call list?
3. What is the mode of the arguments in the call list?
4. Which arguments are defined prior to the call, and which are defined as a result of the call?
5. Are additional subprograms required?
6. What is the definition of the arguments in the call list?
7. What declarations are required in the calling program?
8. Where can the user find the analysis upon which the subroutine or function subprogram is based, including diagrams and additional information?
9. What are the units of measurement of the call-list arguments?
10. Who wrote the subprograms and has test results?
11. Have any subprogram names or COMMON labels been preempted?
12. How much memory is utilized by the subprogram in core?

The conventions adopted for documentation in the Iowa CADET algorithm are a response to the user need as expressed by the preceding 12 questions.

All subprogram arguments are presented in a form similar to

$$\text{ME0000 (A1,A2,A3,A4,B1,B2,B3)}$$

wherein the arguments defined in the calling program are denoted A1, A2, A3, and A4 and the call-list arguments defined as a result of the call (and consequently returned to the calling program) are denoted B1, B2, and B3. If arguments in the list are of integer mode, then the call-list arguments displayed in the documentation are

$$\text{ME0000 (A1,I2,A3,A4,B1,B2,J3)}$$

wherein the second argument is a variable in integer mode and defined in the calling program prior to the call and the last argument in the call list is a variable in integer mode and defined in the calling program as a result of the call. Thus the symbol I2 is used for an integer variable which must be defined as the calling program prior to the call, and J3 is used for the third variable defined as a result of the call. If the subprogram is considered to be a function in the mathematical sense, independent variables are documented as A's (real) and I's (integer) and dependent variables are documented as B's (real) and J's (integer).

In general, subroutines will print out information in the case of (1) an erroneous call, (2) if a convergence monitor is requested by the user, and (3) if the objective of the subprogram is to create tabular information. An erroneous call will trigger error messages of the following form, indicating a *logic error* on the part of the user:

```
*****ERROR MESSAGE SUBROUTINE ME0000*****
     VALUE OF I2, 51, OUTSIDE ALLOWABLE RANGE
     1 THRU 50.
```

The message identifies the offended subprogram, the documentation name of the offending variable, the numerical value of the offending variable, and some indication of the nature of the offense so that the user need not refer to the documentation. Some subroutines will return an error variable, commonly at the end of the call list.

Subroutine documentation is purposely in the form that encourages users to *select their own meaningful names for the variables.* The format of the documentation page is the subject of Fig. 5-8.

5-7-3 Error Messages

The Fortran compilers (particularly WATFOR and WATFIV) have excellent diagnostics of a grammatical and syntactical nature. They cannot detect logical errors because there is very little problem structure imposed on the Fortran user. However, the laminar structure imposed on the engineer faced with a design (optimization) problem allows the detection of symptoms of logic error on the part of the user, and enough information can be given users to point them toward their errors (and away from the library subprogram).

Subprograms should WRITE in only two circumstances, since the user loses control over what is written and where it is displayed. These circumstances are

1. Usage error by user (written on next available line of output)
2. Convergence or display monitor (written on separate page so user can detect and discard at his or her pleasure)

The error-message warning to the user of logic error performs most of the following duties:

*   Declares the offended subprogram by *name.*
*   Declares which argument is offending by giving *documentation name.*
*   Declares the *numerical value* of the offending argument.
*   Declares *why* the value is offensive.
*   Declares circumstances leading to a subsequent abort or suspension of subprogram operation.
*   Declares circumstances of subprogram frustration.

Most important, the error message points *away* from the subprogram and *toward* the user's logical error. For example,

```
*****ERROR MESSAGE SUBROUTINE ME0001*****
     VALUE OF A1, 0.130241E02, IS GREATER THAN
     UNITY
```

```
                                                    Page 0000

Descriptive short-title of subprogram
MEOOOO(A1,A2,I3,A4,B1,J2)                            Author

    ⌈ Sentence or paragraph describing what the subprogram  ⌉
      does.
    ⌊                                                        ⌋

    ⌈ Paragraph, which is more specific than that above,     ⌉
      identifying the independent and dependent information.
    ⌊                                                        ⌋

    ⌈ Paragraph reference to source of the theory.           ⌉

    ⌊                                                        ⌋

    ⌈ Paragraph noting special features or warnings.         ⌉

    ⌊                                                        ⌋


CALLING PROGRAM REQUIREMENTS:

    ⌈ Listing of declarations necessary in the calling program.  ⌉

    ⌊                                                            ⌋

    ⌈ Listing of names and arguments of any subprograms that must ⌉
      be user-written and are necessary for the use of the subprogram.
      Names of other documented subprograms called in turn by this
      subprogram.
    ⌊                                                            ⌋

CALL LIST ARGUMENTS:

    List of all dummy variables, meaning, units of measurement.


PREEMPTED NAMES:

    Listing of SUBROUTINE and FUNCTION names or COMMON labels used by
    the subprogram and consequently not available to the user.


SIZE:

    Memory utilization citing compiler(s).
```

FIG. 5-8 Structural organization of a library-program documentation page. *(After Iowa CADET.)*

5-7-4 Monitors

There are many processes in which the engineer desires to see evidence of the fulfillment of the evolution, e.g., attainment of a maximum or a minimum, the vanishing of a residual, an approach to a signal matrix, etc. This purpose is served as a monitor (or convergence monitor) displayed on a separate page (or not) at the user's discretion. A monitor from a successful run will usually be discarded. It builds confidence in the solution integrity but has no place in formal output or in its interpretation.

In statistical work, when a maximum-likelihood-parameter estimate for a parent distribution is determined by a maximization process, the user may be interested in inspecting (or plotting) the hazard function, the cumulative-density function, the density function, or the reliability. A library routine which accepts the likelihood estimates and return points on all these curves can use a monitor with a tabular display so that the graph from the plotter can be compared with data the user would otherwise never use.

5-7-5 Test Program

When a program must be written by the engineer to fill a gap in the library, it is important that a test be carried out by a program that

- Exercises *every path* in the logic flowchart with correct answers
- Exercises *every error message* single and in multiple
- Verifies the return arguments now defined in the calling program as a result of the call

This test program is filed in the library capability. If the program just written is to be lightly used, it may be left as is, awkward programming and all, for subsequent use. If the program has a high usage potential, it may be given to a professional technical programmer together with the test deck and a valid output. The programmer may be permitted to change programming to conserve storage, expedite execution, and improve numerical accuracy, rates of convergence, etc., as long as the improvements do not alter the test-deck results. The engineer wrote the program for personal use (and use by others), and confidence is largely in himself or herself, his or her knowledge, and the confirmation resulting from the test-deck runs. After surrendering the program to a professional or technical programmer, the engineer may see the methodology changed beyond his or her confident comprehension. Such an engineer now relies on the test program to confirm confidence in the modified program. If the answers are the same (or numerically superior), then the engineer can be reasonably confident that the technical programmer has made only tactical changes and left the strategy intact. The engineer can now use the modified program with the same confidence with which the original was used, and enjoy the benefits of reduced memory, faster execution, and perhaps improved numerical precision.

If a suggestion is later made that the subprogram could be made more useful with some modification, this can be done by the technical programmer by adding data cards to the test deck which exercise the new, additional capability, and both the programmer and the engineer can see from the old data card results that the former capability has not been compromised.

This procedure allows a useful and effective division of labor between the engineer and the programmer. Each does what he or she knows best, and the responsible engineer has the test deck as a final check against any esoteric methodology practiced by the programmer in the interests of economy of execution time or storage and in the pursuit of numerical accuracy. Figure 5-9 depicts the steps necessary to add a program to an existing design library.

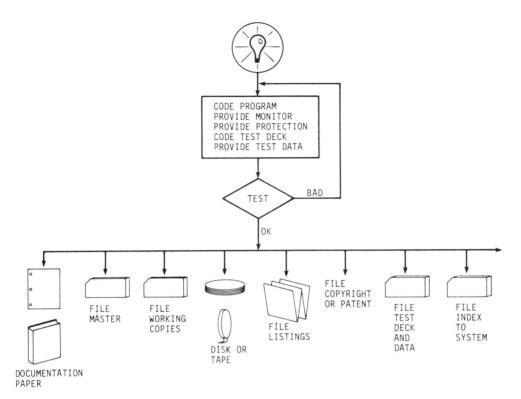

FIG. 5-9 Flowchart of events incidental to adding a program to a library.

5-8 SIMULATION

The computer is useful to the designer for those elements of computation which arise and have a statistical basis but for which no closed-form theory exists. The fundamental building block is supplied by the computer vendor and provides the user with a set of random numbers (actually psuedorandom) which come from a uniform random distribution in the interval 0,1. The list can have enormous length without repetition, and numbers of lists can be created using one or more "seed" integers. This enables the user to impose the same sequence of random events on multiple situations. A common Fortran name for such a subroutine is RANDU (I1,I2,R), in whose argument list are the two seed integers $I1$ and $I2$, and the returned random number R is uniformly distributed in the interval 0,1.

Random numbers from other distributions are created by user programming. From the central limit theorem of statistics it is known that the sum of variates of any distribution approaches a Gaussian (normal) distribution as the number of additions increases. In the brief coding that follows, 12 uniform random numbers are summed and the desired means and standard deviations are accommodated.

```
SUBROUTINE GAUSS (I1,I2,XMEAN,SIGMA,G)
REAL NORMAL
SUM=0.
DO 10 I=1,12
```

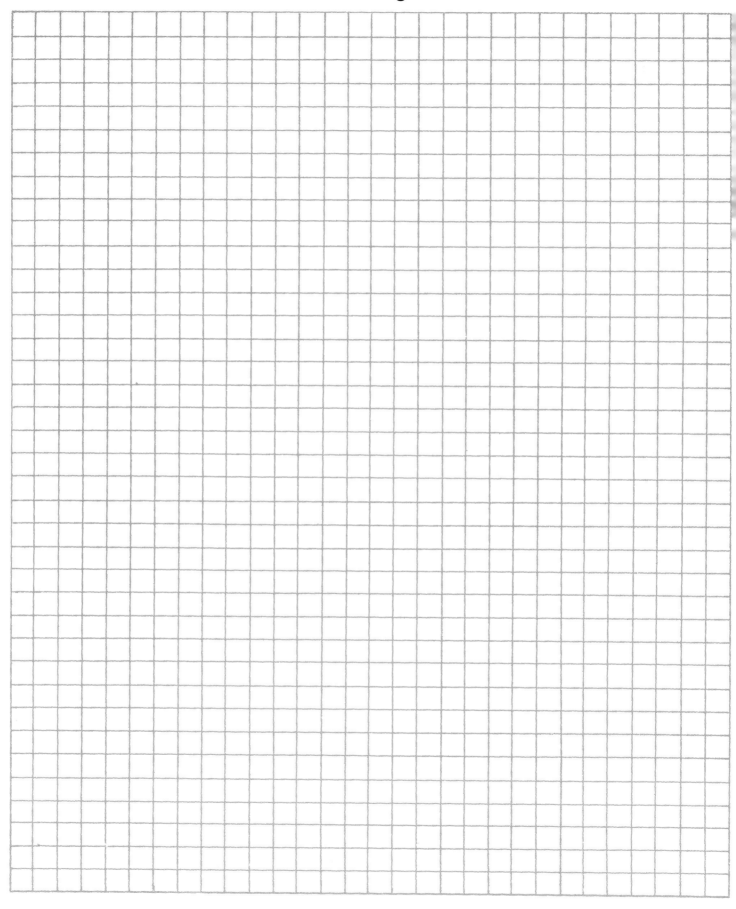

```
        CALL RANDU(I1,I2,R)
 10     SUM=SUM+R
        NORMAL=SUM -6.
        G=NORMAL*SIGMA+XMEAN
        RETURN
        END
```

For a distribution for which the cumulative density function CDF or reliability function R can be written explicitly, substitute a uniform random variable z for the reliability and solve the relation for the desired variate. For example, if y has a Weibull distribution, the reliability is given by

$$R(y) = \exp\left[-\left(\frac{y - y_o}{\theta - y_o}\right)^b\right] = z$$

from which

$$y = y_o + (\theta - y_o)\left(\ln\frac{1}{z}\right)^{1/b}$$

where y_o, θ, and b are parameters of the desired Weibull distribution. By substituting uniform random numbers in the interval 0,1 for z, the sequence of y's will be Weibullian.

One kind of problem that can confront a designer is estimating the distribution in a parameter that is a function of others with manufacturing tolerances assigned and material property variability involved. For example, the spring rate in a helical-coil spring is given by

$$k = \frac{d^4 G}{8 D^3 N}$$

Each of the elements on the right side of the equation is a random variable. If the distribution of d is Gaussian, surely the distribution of d^4 is not. If

$$d \sim N(0.063, 0.00017) \text{ in toleranced } 0.0625 \pm 0.001 \text{ in}$$

$$D \sim N(2.000, 0.014) \text{ in toleranced } 2.000 \pm 0.030 \text{ in}$$

$$G \sim W(11.5 \times 10^6, 1.73 \times 10^5) \text{ psi untoleranced}$$

$$N \sim N(10, 0.12) \text{ turns toleranced } 10 \pm 0.5 \text{ turns}$$

what is the distribution of k and its parameters? Can the distribution of k be approximated by a Gaussian or Weibull model? Such an investigation is easily conducted using the computer, generating hundreds of instances of k and examining the resulting data. This is but one example of a simulation technique.

Reference [5-12] is a periodical with many practical and detailed examples of the use of computers in mechanical engineering analysis and design.

REFERENCES

5-1 *Mechanical Engineering,* vol. 105, no. 8, Aug. 1983.

5-2 *Design Handbook,* Associated Spring-Barnes Group, Inc., 1981, p. 44.

5-3   J. E. Shigley and L. D. Mitchell, *Mechanical Engineering Design,* 4th ed., McGraw-Hill, 1983.

5-4   C. R. Mischke, *Mathematical Model Building,* 2d rev. ed., Iowa State University Press, 1980, Chap. 3.

5-5   D. J. Wilde and C. S. Beightler, *Foundations of Optimization,* Prentice-Hall, 1980.

5-6   G. S. Beveridge and R. S. Schechter, *Optimization Theory and Practice,* McGraw-Hill, 1970.

5-7   B. Carnahan, H. A. Luther, and J. O. Wilkes, *Applied Numerical Methods,* Wiley, 1969, p. 168.

5-8   R. C. Weast and S. M. Shelby (eds.), *Handbook of Tables for Mathematics,* 3d ed., The Chemical Rubber Company, 1967, p. 579.

5-9   J. E. Shigley and J. J. Uicker, *Theory of Machines and Mechanisms,* McGraw-Hill, 1980, p. 266.

5-10 W. H. Beyer, *Handbook of Tables for Probability and Statistics,* 2d ed., The Chemical Rubber Company, 1968, p. 414.

5-11 C. R. Mischke, "Organizing the Computer for Mechanical Design," in *Proceedings of the Design Engineering Technical Conference of ASME,* Oct. 1974, pp. 51–64.

5-12 *Computers in Mechanical Engineering,* vol. 1, no. 1, July 1982.

APPENDIX

Standard Prefixes for Metric Units

SI prefix*	Symbol	Multiple	
exa	E	1 000 000 000 000 000 000	= 10^{18}
peta	P	1 000 000 000 000 000	= 10^{15}
tera	T	1 000 000 000 000	= 10^{12}
giga	G	1 000 000 000	= 10^{9}
mega	M	1 000 000	= 10^{6}
kilo	k	1 000	= 10^{3}
hecto	h	100	= 10^{2}
deka	da	10	= 10^{1}
deci	d	0.1	= 10^{-1}
centi	c	0.01	= 10^{-2}
milli	m	0.001	= 10^{-3}
micro	μ	0.000 001	= 10^{-6}
nano	n	0.000 000 001	= 10^{-9}
pico	p	0.000 000 000 001	= 10^{-12}
femto	f	0.000 000 000 000 001	= 10^{-15}
atto	a	0.000 000 000 000 000 001	= 10^{-18}

*SI = International System of units.

Greek Letters

alpha	A	α, a	nu	N	ν	
beta	B	β	xi	Ξ	ξ	
gamma	Γ	γ	omicron	O	o	
delta	Δ	δ, ∂	pi	Π	π	
epsilon	E	ϵ, ε	rho	P	ρ	
zeta	Z	ζ	sigma	Σ	σ, ς	
eta	H	η	tau	T	τ	
theta	Θ, Θ	θ, ϑ	upsilon	Υ	υ	
iota	I	ι	phi	Φ	ϕ, φ	
kappa	K	κ	chi	X	χ	
lambda	Λ	λ	psi	Ψ	ψ	
mu	M	μ	omega	Ω	ω	

Conversion Factors A to Convert Input X to Output Y Using the Formula $Y = AX$*

Multiply input X	by factor A	to get output Y
British thermal unit, Btu	1055	joule, J
Btu/second, Btu/s	1.05	kilowatt, kW
calorie	4.19	joule, J
centimeter of mercury (0°C)	1.333	kilopascal, kPa
centipoise, cP	0.001	pascal-second, Pa·s
degree (angle)	0.0174	radian, rad
foot, ft	0.305	meter, m
foot², ft²	0.0929	meter², m²
foot/minute, ft/min (fpm)	0.0051	meter/second, m/s
foot-pound, ft·lb	1.35	joule, J
foot-pound/second, ft·lb/s	1.35	watt, W
foot/second, ft/s	0.305	meter/second, m/s
gallon (U.S.), gal	3.785	liter, l
horsepower, hp	0.746	kilowatt, kW
inch, in	25.4	meter, m
inch², in²	645	millimeter², mm²
inch of mercury (32°F)	3.386	kilopascal, kPa
kilopound, kip	4.45	kilonewton, kN
kilopound/inch², kpsi (ksi)	6.89	megapascal, MPa (N/mm²)
mass, lb·s²/in	175	kilogram, kg
mile, mi	1.610	kilometer, km
mile/hour, mi/h	1.61	kilometer/hour, km/h
mile/hour, mi/h	0.447	meter/second, m/s

Multiply input X	by factor A	to get output Y
moment of inertia, lbm·ft²	0.0421	kilogram-meter², kg·m²
moment of inertia, lbm·in²	293	kilogram-millimeter², kg·mm²
moment of section (second moment of area), in⁴	41.6	centimeter⁴, cm⁴
ounce-force, oz	0.278	newton, N
ounce-mass	0.0311	kilogram, kg
pound, lb*	4.45	newton, N
pound-foot, lb·ft	1.36	newton-meter, N·m
pound/foot², lb/ft²	47.9	pascal, Pa
pound-inch, lb·in	0.113	joule, J
pound-inch, lb·in	0.113	newton-meter, N·m
pound/inch, lb/in·	175	newton/meter, N/m
pound/inch², psi (lb/in²)	6.89	kilopascal, kPa
pound-mass, lbm	0.454	kilogram, kg
pound-mass/second, lbm/s	0.454	kilogram/second, kg/s
quart (U.S. liquid), qt	946	milliliters, ml
section modulus, in³	16.4	centimeter³, cm³
slug	14.6	kilogram, kg
ton (short 2000 lbm)	907	kilogram, kg
yard, yd	0.914	meter, m

*The U.S. Customary System unit of the pound-force is often abbreviated as lbf to distinguish it from the pound-mass, which is abbreviated as lbm. In most places in this book the pound force is usually written simply as the pound and abbreviated as lb.

List of Symbols in General Use in Machine Design

A	Area; constant
a, a	Acceleration
a	Constant; dimension; addendum
b	Weibull exponent; dedendum; section width; dimension; constant; fatigue-strength exponent
C	Coefficient; spring index; bearing-load rating; column end-condition constant; gear factor; center distance; specific heat; diametral clearance
c	Clearance; radial clearance; distance from neutral axis in beam; fatigue ductility exponent; coefficient of viscosity
D, d	Diameter
E	Modulus of elasticity; kinetic energy
$\mathbf{F}, F$	Force
F	Face width
f	Frequency; coefficient of friction
G	Shear modulus of elasticity
g	Acceleration due to gravity
H	Hardness number; heat gained or lost; power
h	Section depth; bearing clearance
I	Moment of inertia; second area moment; geometry factor
i	Integer
J	Polar moment of inertia; second polar area moment; geometry factor; mechanical equivalent of heat
j	Integer
K	Stress-concentration factor; wear factor; Wahl correction factor; gear factor; bearing-rating ratio; strength coefficient; stress-intensity factor; bolt-torque coefficient
k	Spring rate; endurance-limit modification factor; radius of gyration
L	Length; life; lead
l	Length
$\mathbf{M}, M$	Moment
m	Mass, margin of safety; slope; contact ratio; module
n	Design factor; strain-hardening exponent; speed in rpm
$\mathbf{P}, P$	Force
P	Diametral pitch; bearing pressure
p	Pressure; linear or circular pitch
Q	First moment of area; flow volume
q	Load intensity; notch sensitivity; arc length
R	Reliability; reduction in area
r	Radius; radial direction indicator; correlation coefficient
S	Strength; bearing characteristic number; scale
s	Sample standard deviation; distance
T	Torque; temperature
t	Thickness; tangential direction; time
U	Energy; velocity; coefficient
V	Shear force; velocity; rotation factor for bearings
W	Weight; load; cold-work factor
X	Radial factor for bearings
x	Rectangular coordinate; distance
Y	Thrust factor for bearings
y	Rectangular coordinate; distance
Z	Section modulus; viscosity
z	Rectangular coordinate; distance; standard statistical variable
α	Coefficient of thermal expansion; thread angle; axial fatigue-stress correction factor; angle
β	Partial bearing angle
Γ	Gamma function
γ	Pitch angle; shear strain; pitch angle; articulation angle
Δ	Increment or change
δ	Total deformation or elongation
ϵ	Unit engineering strain
ε	True strain; eccentricity ratio
η	Efficiency
η	Factor of safety (distinguished from design factor n)
θ	Twist angle; slope; a Weibull parameter
λ	Lead angle
μ	Population mean; absolute viscosity
ν	Poisson's ratio
ρ	Radius of curvature; density
Σ	Summation sign
σ	Normal stress (engineering or nominal)
$\bar{\sigma}$	True stress
σ	Population standard deviation
τ	Shear stress
ϕ	Pressure angle; angle
ψ	Helix angle
ω	Angular velocity

INDEX

ABOUT THE EDITORS

Joseph E. Shigley, Professor Emeritus, The University of Michigan, is a Fellow of the American Society of Mechanical Engineers. He received the ASME Mechanisms Committee Award in 1974, the Worcester Reed Warner Medal in 1977, and the ASME Machine Design Award in 1985. He is the author or coauthor of eight books, including *Mechanical Engineering Design, Theory of Machines and Mechanisms* (with J. J. Uicker, Jr.), and *Applied Mechanics of Materials* (all McGraw-Hill).

Charles R. Mischke is Professor of Mechanical Engineering, Iowa State University, and a consultant to industry. He received the Ralph Teeter Award of the Society of Automotive Engineers in 1977 and the University's Outstanding Teacher Award in 1980. He is the author of *Elements of Mechanical Analysis, Introduction to Computer-Aided Design, Mathematical Model Building,* as well as many technical papers. He serves on the Reliability, Stress Analysis, and Failure Prevention Executive Committee of the American Society of Mechanical Engineers.